by the same author

Brickwork 1
Brickwork 3
Brickwork Bonding Problems and Solutions

Brickwork 2

Revised Third Edition

W. G. Nash, MCIOB

Hutchinson
London Sydney Auckland Johannesburg

Hutchinson Education

An imprint of Century Hutchinson Ltd
62-65 Chandos Place, London WC2N 4NW

Century Hutchinson Australia (Pty) Ltd
89-91 Albion Street, Surry Hills
New South Wales 2010, Australia

Century Hutchinson (NZ) Ltd
PO Box 40-086, Glenfield, Auckland 10, New Zealand

Century Hutchinson South Africa (Pty) Ltd
PO Box 337, Bergvlei 2012, South Africa

First edition 1969
Second edition 1976
Third edition 1983
Revised third edition 1988
Reprinted 1989

© W. G. Nash 1969, 1983, 1988

Printed in Great Britain by
Anchor Press Ltd, Tiptree, Essex

British Library Cataloguing in Publication Data
Nash, W. G.
 Brickwork.—3rd ed.
 2
 1. Bricklaying
 I. Title
 693'.23   TH5501

ISBN 0 09 182315 3

Contents

chapter 5
Wall construction

Definitions – Bonds – The Building Regulations requirements – Setting out
acute angles – Setting out obtuse angles or squint corners – Plinth courses –
Walls curved on plan – Reinforced brickwork – Composite walls – Self-
assessment questions

chapter 6
Decorative work

Coloured pointing – Contrasting coloured bricks – Bricks laid in special
patterns – Projecting patterns – Self-assessment questions

chapter 7
Door and window openings

Door openings: thresholds – Door frames – Door and window heads –
Concrete lintels – Arches – Camber arch – Three centre arch – Gothic
arches – Centring – Introduction to gauged and rubbed work – Procedure
for cutting a semi-circular arch in gauged and rubbed work – Self-
assessment questions

chapter 8
Stairways

Building Regulations requirements – Precast concrete stairs – Open riser
stairways – The spiral or circular stairway – Slate stair surfacing – Balustrades – Self-assessment questions

chapter 9
Chimneys and flues

Definitions – Structural requirements for chimneys – Construction of
hearths – Fireplace recesses for Class I appliances – Flues and chimneys –
Chimneys for Class I appliances – Flue linings – Chimney construction –
Proximity of combustible material – Bonding for chimney stacks – Outlets
of flues – Chimney pots – Damp prevention in chimney stacks – Self-
assessment questions

chapter 10
Fire appliances

Open fires – Installing the fireback – Fixing the surround – Fixing an inset
open fire or all-night burner – Inset fire with underfloor primary air supply –
Open fire with boiler – Fixing the convector open fire – Free-standing
convector open fires – The independent boiler – Self-assessment questions

Workability – The water/cement ratio – Types of cements – Cement/aggre-
gate ratio – Admixtures – Quality control – Concrete mixers – Batching –
Transporting the concrete – Compacting the concrete – Curing the concrete – The properties of concrete – Reinforcement – Fire resistance –
Self-assessment questions

Preface

This book progresses from *Brickwork 1* and is intended to increase knowledge of the bricklayer's craft. It aims to take readers up to, and slightly beyond, craft certificate standard, and to lead them into the advance stage, which will be dealt with in *Brickwork 3*.

The chapters have been set out especially to assist apprentice bricklayers with their studies, but this book should also be of definite reference value for students who are attending either a TEC certificate or building course in building studies.

Questions have been set at the end of each chapter to test the reader on the work covered, and to encourage research into further study of each chapter.

The author would like to record his sincere thanks to the following organizations for generously providing up-to-date information, and so kindly allowing their products to be described and illustrated:

Acrow (Engineers) Ltd, Paddington, London W2

Dorman Long & Co Ltd, Middlesbrough, Yorkshire

Francis W. Harris & Co Ltd, Burslem, Stoke-on-Trent

Harris and Edgar Ltd, East Greenwich, London SE10

Redland Pipes Ltd, Reigate, Surrey

The Delta Metal Co Ltd, East Greenwich, London SE10

The Hepworth Iron Company Ltd, Sheffield, Yorkshire

The Pitch Fibre Pipe Association, New Bridge Street, London EC4

William Selwood Ltd, Plant Engineers, Chandlersford, Hampshire

To Mr V. Pannell, lecturer in brickwork and associated subjects, Southampton Technical College, my sincere thanks for his help and guidance that he gave in the revision of this volume.

Finally, may readers find further pleasure and satisfaction in all their future studies and work.

W. G. Nash
1983

Metrication tables

Table 1   *Basic units*

Quantity	Unit	Symbol
length	metre	m
mass	kilogramme	kg
time	second	s
electrical current	ampere	A
temperature	degree Celsius, Kelvin	°C, K
luminous intensity	candela	cd

Table 2   *Derived* SI *units with special names*

Quantity	Unit	Symbol
force	newton	N
work, energy	joule	J
power	watt	W
electrical potential	volt	V
luminous flux	lumen	lm
illumination	lux	lx

Table 3   *Derived* SI *units with complex names*

Quantity	Unit	Symbol
area	square metre	m^2
volume	cubic metre	m^3
frequency	cycle per second, hertz	Hz
density	kilogramme per cubic metre	kg/m^3
velocity	metre per second	m/s
pressure, stress	newton per square metre	N/m^2
thermal conductivity	watt per metre kelvin	W/mK
luminance	candela per square metre	cd/m^2

Table 4   *Multiples and sub-multiples of* SI *units*

Multiplication factor		Prefix	Symbol
1000 000	10^6	mega	M
1000	10^3	kilo	k
100	10^2	hecto	h
10	10^1	deca	da
0.1	10^{-1}	deci	d
0.01	10^{-2}	centi	c
0.001	10^{-3}	milli	m
0.000 001	10^{-6}	micro	μ

Chapter 1

Excavations

After reading this chapter you should be able to:

1 Have a clear understanding of the necessity for site clearance.

2 Be able to set out building work.

3 Have a sound knowledge of timbering systems and trench sheeting for shallow excavations.

4 Be fully aware of the safety requirements for excavations under the Health and Safety at Work etc. Act.

5 Realize the pressures that may be imposed upon timbering in trenches.

6 Appreciate the precautions that must be taken when excavating adjacent to existing buildings.

7 Have a good understanding of the use of machinery for excavating trenches.

8 Have a good understanding of the types of pumps and their use in disposing of surface water.

Site clearance

Before building operations on a site can begin, it is necessary to clear the turf and vegetable soil from the land upon which the structure itself will stand. This type of soil is most unsuitable for building because of its instability and unreliable *bearing capacity*; that is, the load that the soil can carry without any appreciable settlement. For instance, if a soil has a bearing capacity of 200 kN/m^2, every square metre of the ground surface will carry 200 kN without any undue sinking. Vegetable soil, often referred to as *topsoil*, has a greatly variable bearing pressure depending upon the moisture content of the soil and also the amount of humus or decaying vegetable matter that it contains. At its best this pressure would be unlikely to exceed 55 kN/m^2. It is also unstable because it is very difficult to compact into a solid natural foundation. Therefore, when any heavy load is placed upon this soil, further compression

may take place, probably causing uneven settlement of the building which could result in cracks appearing in the walls. It is very important that a firm, natural, stable foundation is reached before building is commenced.

Vegetable soil also contains the organisms and chemicals necessary for the growth of plants. Another reason, therefore, for removing this type of soil is to prevent plants from growing underneath the ground floor of a building and thereby encouraging dry rot (see *Brickwork 1*, Chapter 6). For this reason the Building Regulations state that the part of a site to be covered by a building shall be effectively cleared of turf and other vegetable matter.

If gardens are to be laid out when the building is finished, the vegetable soil should be carefully stored in heaps in some convenient corner of the site so as to be completely clear of:

Any buildings which are to be erected

Hutments which are required on site
Plant, such as mixers and tower cranes
Storage areas for materials
Trenches for drains
Site roads

and not to impede the progress of the work on the site. If, for any reason, the soil has to be shifted to another storage spot because it is in the way of some other operation, this *double handling* creates an additional expense to the building costs, as each time a material is handled or moved its cost is increased. Therefore, careful planning before the work begins is very necessary to prevent these extra, and often unnecessary, costs. If there is insufficient room on the site to store the topsoil, it must be stored elsewhere until the building operations are completed, when it can be returned. A dumper suitable for this work is shown in Figure 1, and types of diesel dumpers are listed in Table 5. This may be quite costly owing to transport costs (depending on the distance to be travelled), loading costs and the cost of storing.

Some contracts do not require gardens to be laid out when the structure is finished, in which case the topsoil has to be removed from the site. If it is of a good quality and in sufficient quantity, it may well have a marketable value, particularly in urban areas, and it may be economical to skim off the vegetable soil and dispose of it and then carry on with the normal trench excavation. On the other hand, if the soil is of poor quality, or only in small quantities, it would be better to excavate it with the subsoil excavations. It therefore follows that the disposal of the topsoil would depend upon the results of the initial site survey and the requirements of the contract.

Table 5   *Types of diesel dumpers*

Payload	Description		
762 kg	Skip capacity (m³)	water level	0.34 m³
		struck level	0.424 m³
		heaped	0.51 m³
	Skip loading height		1 m
	Net mass		812 kg
	Overall length		2.34 m
	Overall width		1.37 m
	Takes full batch from mixers up to and including NT 0.283 m³ size		
1168 kg	Skip capacity (m³)	water level	0.51 m³
		struck level	0.616 m³
		heaped	0.756 m³
	Skip loading height		1 m
	Net mass		1016 kg
	Overall length		2.943 m
	Overall width		1.52 m
	Takes two batches from NT 0.196 m³ or one batch from NT 0.392 m³		
1524 kg	Skip capacity (m³)	water level	0.68 m³
		struck level	0.756 m³
		heaped	1.008 m³
	Skip loading height		1.12 m
	Net mass		1372 kg
	Overall length		3.15 m
	Overall width		1.698 m
	Takes two batches from NT 0.196 m³ or one batch from NT 0.34 m³ or NT 0.392 m³		

Setting out trenches

It is a good practice to stretch lines from the profiles so that each side of the trench is marked out (see *Brickwork 1*, Chapter 6). This is to ensure that the trench is dug at its correct width because if it is dug too wide, the digging operation will be more expensive. Extra concrete will be required at the bottom and more filling when the trench is being refilled. On the other hand, it is also

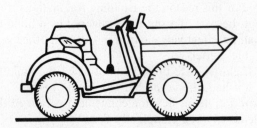

Figure 1   *A dumper*

uneconomical if the trench is not wide enough as the labourers who dug it will have to cut the sides back to adjust it to its correct width. As timbering will have been used to shore up the sides of the trench, this can create quite a lot of difficulty and again will cause a wastage of labour and money.

Systems for shoring up trench sides

Timbering (where all the members are of timber) This system has the advantage that it is flexible and can be adapted for use where awkward shapes are encountered. But, it is liable to shrink, can be wasteful, and unless carefully supervised, is not used enough to be economical. Timbering consists of the following members (see Figure 2).

Poling boards are the timber members in direct contact with the soil, generally placed in a vertical position, but sometimes horizontally.

Walings are the members placed in front of the poling boards to prevent them from being displaced.

Struts are the supports placed between the walings to keep them apart and form a rigid support.

Lipblocks or *strutlips* are small timber members fixed to the top of the struts and overlap on to the walings to prevent the struts from being easily displaced or falling down into the trench.

Wedges are tapering pieces of timber used in pairs and called folding wedges and are often used between the strut and waling to provide a means of tightening up the system should it become loose.

Pages are similar to wedges but have a much shallower taper and are used to provide a means of tightening a poling board to the waling where the irregularity of the earth makes this necessary.

Puncheons are timber members placed in a vertical position underneath a waling to prevent it from sliding down into the trench.

Corner blocks are small members fixed at the intersection of walings at angles and are to prevent the walings from any horizontal movement at that point.

Lacings are timbers fixed in a vertical position to prevent struts or walings from slipping down as the trench is being excavated below the timbering.

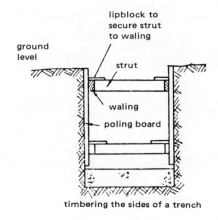

timbering the sides of a trench

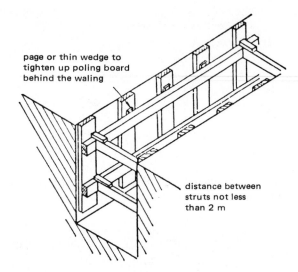

Figure 2 *Simple timbering for a shallow trench in a moderately compact soil*

Timber poling boards and walings with adjustable steel props

This system, illustrated in Figure 3, has the advantage of using the flexibility of timber in conjunction with the strength of steel in the struts. Timber struts are the most expensive item in the timbering of a trench owing to the amount of wastage and the size of the sections which are used. The capital cost of the trench props is high but the number of uses makes their actual cost per use an economical proposition. This system provides a ready means of tightening up any timbering which

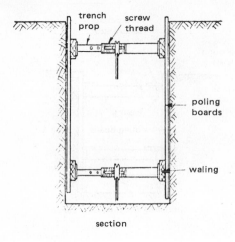

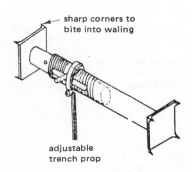

Figure 3 *Timbering with poling boards and trench props*

might have become loose through shrinkage of the timber or the surrounding earth.

Steel trench sheeting with timber walings and steel trench props

This system requires a minimum amount of timber with the use of steel. This equipment again has a high initial cost, but with reasonable care and use will give many years of service. The steel sheeting will stand being driven into the ground provided that a driving cap is used to protect it, therefore, excavating in a bad type of soil is much easier with this type of sheeting as the trench sides are constantly supported during excavation. The walings are supported by steel hangers to prevent them from slipping down the steel sheeting (Figure 4) or by puncheons. In all systems, the distance between the struts should not be less than 2

metres apart horizontally. This is to allow for sufficient working space in the trench.

Safety

The Health and Safety at Work etc. Act lays down rules for safe working on site but regulations, in themselves, do not ensure safety: if accidents are to be avoided then these regulations must be understood and obeyed by *everyone* who is employed on the site.

The Construction Regulations (No. 1580) include the following safety regulations for excavation work:

1   An adequate supply of suitable quality timber or other adequate support shall be provided where necessary. This should be used to prevent, so far as is reasonably practicable, danger to any employed person from a fall of earth, rock or any other material forming the side of, or adjacent to, an excavation. The exceptions to this rule are:
    (a)   an excavation where, due to the nature and slope of its sides and other circumstances, no fall or dislodgement of earth is liable to strike a person employed from a height of more than 1.22 metres, or bury or trap him;
    (b)   for the person who is actually engaged in timbering or other work provided that appropriate precautions are taken to ensure his safety.

2   Every part of an excavation shall be examined at least once a day while persons are employed there. The working end of every trench more than 2 metres deep shall be inspected by a competent person before the beginning of each shift.

3   All timbering must be erected by a competent person, and any alteration or dismantling of timbering must be done under the supervision of a competent person.

4   All timbering must be of good construction, sound material and of adequate strength.

5   All struts and braces shall be properly and adequately secured so as to prevent their accidental displacement or fall.

6   A suitable barrier must be provided to any

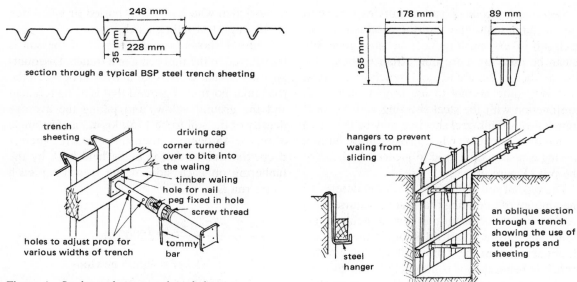

section through a typical BSP steel trench sheeting

Figure 4   *Steel trench prop and steel sheeting*

excavation which is more than 2 metres deep.

7   Material must not be placed or stacked near the edge of any excavation so as to endanger persons employed below.

8   No load, plant or equipment shall be placed or moved near the edge of any excavation where it is likely to cause a collapse.

Methods of ensuring safety when working in trenches

Battering the sides of the trench. The sides of the excavation are battered or sloped so that the batter is equal to the angle of repose of the soil which is being excavated. This method, while being completely safe, is rather expensive because time and labour are wasted in excavating much extra soil from the trench which has to be filled in and rammed when the work is finished. Also the trenches are much wider than those in which timbering is used and take up a lot of space. However, this method may well be considered useful on sites where space is plentiful (Figure 5).

Timbering. Timber is the material most often used to shore up the sides of trenches because it is easy to cut into suitable lengths and adaptable to varying shapes of trench. This, however, can be expensive and wasteful if the timber is not salvaged when the excavation is finished and used again in other trenches. The more uses that are obtained out of each piece of timber, the greater the reduction in cost for each operation. For example, if a piece of timber costs £1 and is only used once, the material for the operation has cost £1. If, on the other hand, it is used twice, the cost of material for each operation will be 50 pence; or four times only 25 pence, and so on. The only certain way to ensure the maximum use of this type of material, and thus reduce overall costs, is by good control on the site.

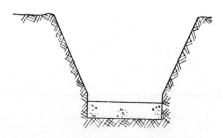

Figure 5   *Battering the sides of a trench*
This method needs no timber but requires more excavation and backfilling

Steel trench sheeting is rather more expensive to buy in the initial outlay, but the eventual cost to each job is very much reduced because generally it can be used far more times than timber. This also applies to the use of steel trench props. It is, however, quite normal to use timber walings in conjunction with the steel sheeting and the steel trench props. This steel sheeting may be driven in by hand or machine. When driving in by hand a driving cap should be used to protect the head of the pile (Figure 4).

The type of soil and its condition will determine the amount of timbering that will be required in a trench. For this reason it is very difficult to lay down any hard and fast rules, but if there is any doubt at all about the stability of a soil in which a trench is being dug, it is infinitely better to have too much timber than to take a chance by putting in too little. It should be a golden rule never to take unnecessary risks.

One of the characteristics of a soil which can never be taken for granted is its *angle of repose*, that is, the angle that the soil will make with a horizontal plane if left to adopt its own shape. Figure 6 illustrates the angle of repose of a soil. This angle of repose will vary according to the type of soil, its moisture content, and its density. This is one of the reasons why a trench which is being excavated into what appears to be a stable type of soil and for which no trench sheeting has been used, suddenly collapses without any warning because its angle of repose has changed perhaps due to drying out or becoming wet. Far too many accidents of this kind occur each year causing serious injuries and, in many cases, death

to workmen who have been buried or killed due to the impact of falling earth.

Figure 7 shows how the weight of the soil is transferred to the timbering in a trench. Discounting the fact that there is some friction between the triangular portion of ground that is being retained and the ground below, and taking the average density of the soil to be 1750 kg/m^3, and its angle of repose 45 degrees, then for a trench 2 metres deep, the weight that is being held back by the timbering on each side of the trench for each metre run is:

$$\frac{2 \times 2 \times 1750 \text{ kg}}{2} = 3500 \text{ kgf}$$

$$1 \text{ kgf} = 9.806 \text{ newtons}$$

Therefore, 3500 kgf = 34,251 N

say, 35 kN

As this force will be exerted on each side of the trench the timbering will have to retain twice this amount.

The 35 kN would be acting in the direction of the arrow shown in Figure 7, that is, in the direction of the angle of repose of the soil. This may exert a direct horizontal thrust of up to 24.2 kN, say, 25 kN, on each side of the trench, as shown in the force diagram Figure 7. The space diagram shows both the angle at which the force is exerted and the horizontal and vertical thrusts. These can be measured by drawing a force diagram to a suitable scale. Although the figure of 25 kN would be the maximum for the conditions stated, it would be far safer for the timbering to be capable of resisting this force than to assume a lower one and thereby risk a collapse. If the sides of the trench are to be kept secure, additional factors, such as the weight of machinery, materials, the spoil and adjacent buildings should also be taken into account.

Timbering to trenches is normally necessary since it is important to realize that all soils and even some types of rock are suspect and should not be regarded as quite safe. Remember that it is the trenches in soils which have been regarded as 'safe' that cause the accidents. Soils which are

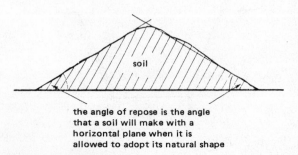

the angle of repose is the angle
that a soil will make with a
horizontal plane when it is
allowed to adopt its natural shape

Figure 6   *The angle of repose of a soil*

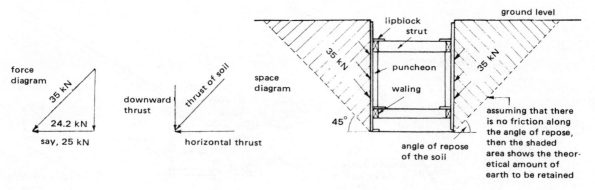

Figure 7 *The typical thrust that has to be resisted by timbering in a trench*

obviously bad are automatically timbered without question.

When a soil is exposed to the atmosphere it begins to dry out and then shrink. When this happens the timber is likely to become loosened, so that if a man steps on to the struts when getting into a trench they are liable to give way and cause a nasty accident. Therefore, provision must be made for tightening up the timbering to take up this shrinkage. This can be done with wedges or pages, or by using the steel trench props which are tightened by the screw thread. Clay soils are very prone to this shrinkage and great care must be taken to ensure the safety of everybody working in trenches which are being dug in these types of soil.

Causes of collapse of trench sides

The following are typical causes of failure in the sides of trenches:

1 Variation in the bearing pressure on the timbering and the angle of repose of the soil due to the moisture content varying.
2 The effects of frost and thawing upon soils. The formation of ice cracks in the soil causes expansion and then lifts. This is called *frost heave* and can seriously damage the stability of the soil. When a thaw sets in, the moisture content of the soil is greatly increased. Any soil which was lifted by frost heave may now slide down into the trench, particularly as the water will act as a lubricant.
3 Failure due to heavy loads being placed near to the edge of the trench. These loads may be materials which are being stacked nearby or lorries, dumpers or powered barrows being allowed to run too near the edge. In this case, vibration may cause a sudden collapse of the sides.
4 Variation in the types of soil, unsuspected pockets of weak soil or the presence of made-up ground which may be hidden just behind the sides of the trench. What may be thought to be a firm soil may well turn out to be an accident hazard.
5 Timber is often an indeterminate material and, if overloaded, can fail quite unexpectedly. It is quite usual to use oversized members to offset this and safeguard the safety of men working in the excavation.

Excavating on sloping sites

When trenches are excavated on sloping sites there are two ways in which the sides of the excavation may be safeguarded against collapse:

1 By sloping the sides (Figure 8); or
2 By using rakers (Figure 9).

The former method is generally the better of the two as it provides a clear working space, but if it involves too much extra excavation it is wiser to use rakers. These should be kept about 2.5–3 metres apart as they tend to impede the construction work inside the excavation. The rakers should also be kept at a shallow angle to the horizontal to provide the greatest resistance to the

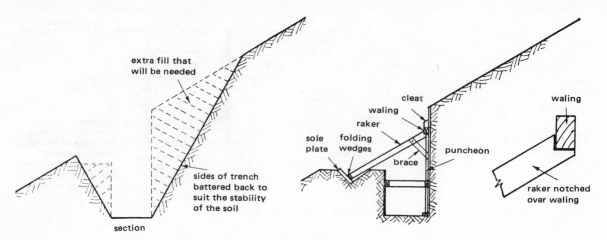

Figure 8   *Cutting a trench on a sloping site*

Figure 9   *Excavating a trench on a sloping site showing the use of timbering*

pressure of the earth and prevent the rakers from sliding upwards. They must also be well-supported on a secure base to prevent them from being forced into the ground and thereby allowing the sides to give way.

Return, fill and ram

This is the general term for filling in an excavation after the construction work has been completed. If the ground above the trench is to be subjected to any heavy loading, the earth being filled into the trench should be similar to that in which the trench was dug. It should also have a similar water content and be well-rammed in layers not exceeding 225 mm in depth if compacting by mechanical rammer, such as a vibrating tamper compactor (Figure 10), a portable impact compactor (Figure 11), or a portable power rammer (Figure 12); or 150 mm if compacted with a hand punner.

A trench should never be refilled while a hose pipe is pouring water into it. This is a bad practice because:

1   When the earth becomes saturated it will have a poor bearing capacity.
2   When it dries out it will most likely shrink and cause cracks to appear.
3   When the water has evaporated it will leave voids in the soil making it weak. In all these cases the stability of the soil will be greatly affected.

for compacting soil, sand, gravel, crushed stone, hardcore and dry concrete, etc.

baseplate contact area 900 x 450 mm

Figure 10   *Vibrating tamper compactor*

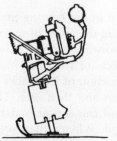

approximate output: deep fill work 30 m³ per hour in 150—600 mm lifts

275 mm wide x 395 mm tamper shoe

Figure 11   *Portable impact compactor*

260 mm diameter foot

Figure 12   *Portable power rammer*

Excavating near to an existing building

When trenches are to be dug near to an adjacent building care must be taken to ensure that no damage is caused to that building by undermining its foundations. If necessary, the building should be supported as a temporary measure by raking shores (Figure 13) and the structure safeguarded against movement. The timbering in the trench should also be strong enough to resist the extra pressure created by the weight of the structure.

When the work inside the trench is completed, the refilling must be done with great care. If the trench is within 914 mm of the existing building, the trench must be filled in with concrete up to the level of the underside of the foundation of that building, and then the rest of the trench may be filled in with earth and well-rammed. If the trench is more than 914 mm away, the depth of the concrete filling below the foundations need only be 150 mm less than the amount of space measured between the trench and the building. For example, if the trench is 1.2 m away from the building, the concrete filling in the trench need only be taken up to within 1.05 m below the level of the underside of the existing foundations (Figure 14).

Methods of excavating trenches

Trenches may be excavated by hand or by machine. If the work is being done by hand the labourer may require a shovel, pick, graft, fork and a bucket for water depending upon the type

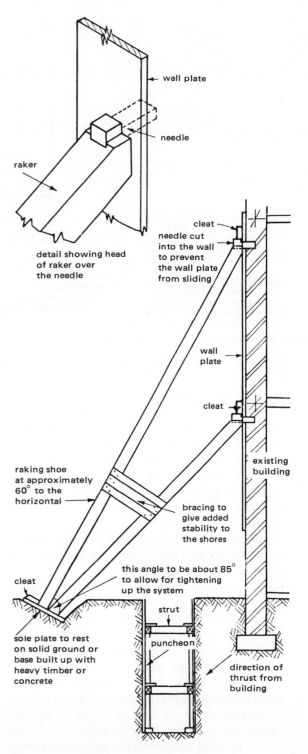

Figure 13   *Method of supporting a structure when excavating near its foundations*

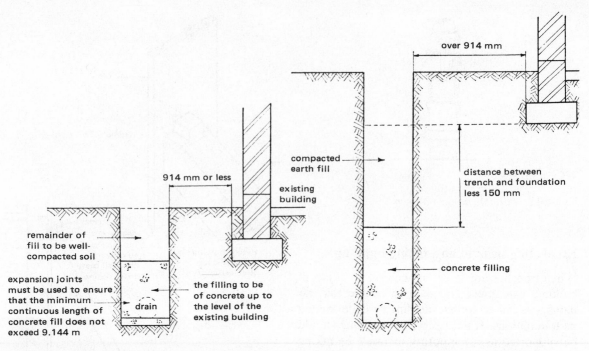

Figure 14   *Filling in trenches which are adjacent to existing buildings*

of soil he is digging. In clay, a fork or graft will be most useful, and a bucket of water to keep the graft wet, whereas in more granular soils the pick and shovel would be more effective.

When excavating machinery is required a trenching machine may be used. This type of machine is available in a range of sizes from quite a small machine for domestic buildings up to the larger type for deep and wide excavation. A series of buckets are driven round and round at the face of the trench and the excavated earth is thrown out from the side of the machine. A trencher has the advantage of allowing men to work quite close to the machine when timbering the sides of the trench (Figure 15). Another type of machine which can be used is an excavator with a single bucket on an arm. There is a wide variety of these machines and some types are shown in Figures 16, 17 and 18. The trench is excavated by the machine which lowers the arm into the trench and draws the bucket up the face of the trench and throws the excavated material either into lorries or within a safe distance of the side of the trench. Again, there is a wide range of excavating machines of this type, each with its own special

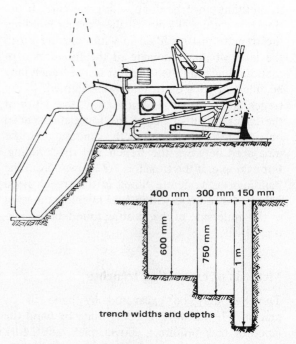

Figure 15   *A Davis T66 trencher*

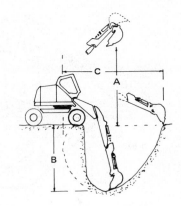

back actor

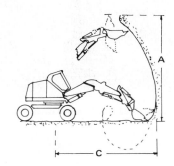

face shovel

advantage for particular jobs. If timbering has to be done in the trench, the men who are shoring up its sides cannot work too close to the excavator, and in a deep trench in a poor type of soil special precaution must be taken to ensure the safety of the workmen. A cage can be lowered into the trench to protect them from being buried by falling earth should the sides of the trench collapse. Visits to plant and building exhibitions or the

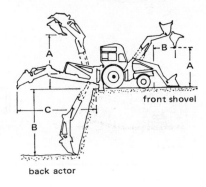

front shovel

back actor

buckets

1   375–450 mm wide fitted with 3 teeth

2   525–600 mm wide fitted with 4 teeth

3   675–750 mm wide fitted with 5 teeth

4   825–900 mm wide fitted with 6 teeth

5   1140–1220 mm wide fitted with 8 teeth

6   ditch cleaning bucket 1.83 m wide

7   taper bucket with ejector
     150 x 450 x 1220 mm

hydraulic grab

stump saw

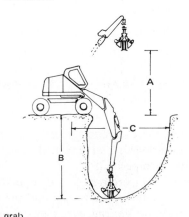

grab

Maximum working dimensions:

	back actor	face shovel	grab
A	4.7 m	3.05 m	3.1 m
B	4.175 m	–	4.7–5.68 m
C	6.525 m	5.405 m	3–4 m

Figure 16   *An Atlas 1200 excavator*
Four-wheel drive, all-hydraulic excavator, fitted with either back actor, face shovel, or hydraulic powered rotating grab

Maximum working dimensions:

	back actor	grab	front shovel
A	3.8 m	2.6 m	2.5 m
B	4.27 m	4.88 m	1.32 m
C	5.5 m	5.65 m	–

Figure 17   *A Whitlock Dinkum Digger excavator*
Hydraulic trencher with front end loading shovel

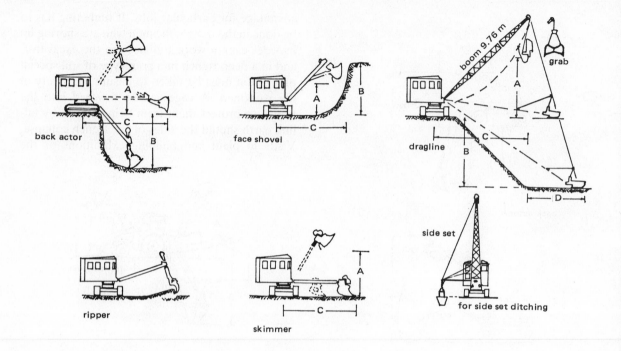

Maximum working dimensions:

	back actor	face shovel	dragline	skimmer
A	2.89 m	3.59 m	4.88 m	3.74 m
B	4.42 m	5.18 m	4.57 m	–
C	7.17 m	5.18 m	7.92 m	5.88 m
D	–	–	3.66 m	–

Figure 18   *A Ransomes and Rapier 414 excavator*
Tracked excavator fitted with either back actor, face shovel, dragline, grab attachment, skimmer or ripper attachment

obtaining of literature from plant firms will give readers a good idea of the types of available excavating machinery and also keep them up to date with modern ideas, trends and techniques.

Disposal of surface water

Water may be found at various depths below the surface. This is called *surface water* and the level at which it is found is called the *table level*. If the table level of the surface water is near to the ground level the trench can become very quickly filled with water and create difficulty for the workmen. It may also wash out the earth from behind the poling boards and loosen the timbering and even cause the sides of the trench to col-

lapse. Under these circumstances, the trench should be close-boarded, or trench sheeting used, and the water pumped out.

The type of pump required will depend upon the amount of water in the trench and the depth of the excavation. Various types are shown in Figures 19 and 20. For shallow trenches with only a small quantity of water a hand-operated lift pump may be quite adequate, but where there is more water either a centrifugal or a diaphragm pump would be more suitable. Both types can be driven by petrol or diesel engines. The centrifugal pump has normally a higher output than the diaphragm and Table 6 shows a typical range of outputs for various sizes of pump, though this will vary with different makes.

(a)   diesel 150 mm
maximum output 272,760 litres/hour
maximum total head 22.86 metres
maximum suction lift 7.62 metres

(a)   diesel trench pump (simplite) 100 mm
maximum output 45,460 litres/hour
maximum total head 12.19 metres
maximum suction lift 8.53 metres
self-priming to 6.7 metres

(b)   diesel 100 mm
maximum output 129,000 litres/hour
maximum total head 28.95 metres
maximum suction lift 7.62 metres

(b)   diesel 75 mm
maximum output 18, 200 litres/hour
maximum total head 18.9 metres
maximum suction lift 6.1 metres

(c)   diesel 75 mm
maximum output 81,830 litres/hour
maximum total head 22.86 metres
maximum suction lift 7.62 metres

(c)   petrol (simplite) 50/75 mm trench pump
maximum output 11,350 litres/hour
maximum total head 18.29 metres
maximum suction lift 8.84 metres
self-priming to 6.7 metres

(d)   diesel 50 mm
maximum output 38,740 litres/hour
maximum total head 30.48 metres
maximum suction lift 7.62 metres

(d)   hand-operated 50/75 mm

Figure 19   *Types of centrifugal pumps*

Figure 20   *Types of diaphragm pumps*

The pumps may be of the self-priming type or they may have to be primed before they start lifting water. Even most self-priming pumps are only self-priming up to a maximum lift of about 6.1–6.4 m. To prime a pump, the pump chamber should be filled with water before the machine is started. This will assist it in pulling the water from the excavation. A foot valve (sometimes called a clack valve) is fitted at the foot of the suction hose to save priming every time that the pump is started. This will retain the water in the suction hose and will allow the pump to pull water as soon as it is started. It is also a good practice to fit a strainer at the foot of the suction hose to prevent the pump from sucking up mud and silt which can cause excessive wear. The foot valve and strainer can be contained in one unit.

In the winter, pumps should be well drained at the end of the day, so that the water in the pump chamber does not freeze and split it by expanding. If the machine is started up without cleaning out the ice in the chamber, the pump may be seriously damaged.

Pumps are usually very efficient machines and will give many years of useful life, provided that a little care is taken when they are in use. They

Table 6

Type	Size	Maximum output	Maximum suction	Maximum total head
Centrifugal	50 mm	38,740 litres/hour	lift 7.62 m	30.48 m
Centrifugal	75 mm	81,830 litres/hour	lift 7.62 m	22.86 m
Centrifugal	100 mm	129,100 litres/hour	lift 7.62 m	28.95 m
Centrifugal	50 mm	11,350 litres/hour	lift 8.84 m	18.29 m
Centrifugal	75 mm	18,200 litres/hour	lift 6.10 m	18.90 m

should not be expected to operate at their maximum output at the maximum lift, and will work much more efficiently and give a longer working life if they are used with a short lift. It is, therefore, a better practice to place the pump as near to the water as is conveniently possible and force the water out of the excavation, rather than set the pump high up and suck up the water as this causes a lot of wear and tear on the pump.

Self-assessment questions

1   The site should be cleared before actual building operations begin in order to
    (a)   have a clean site to work on
    (b)   make it easy for the setting out of the building
    (c)   remove the vegetable soil

2   Puncheons are
    (a)   the horizontal timbers between the walings
    (b)   the vertical timbers between the walings
    (c)   the timbers between the soil and the walings

3   Every part of an excavation, while people are working in it, shall be examined
    (a)   at least once a day
    (b)   at least twice a day
    (c)   not always necessary to be examined

4   A suitable barrier must be provided to all excavations over
    (a)   1 metre deep
    (b)   1.5 metres deep
    (c)   2 metres deep

5   A piece of timber costs £6.00 and is used in four trenches at different times, then the cost of this material per use is
    (a)   £1.50
    (b)   £3.00
    (c)   £6.00

6   Steel sheeting may be driven by hand
    (a)   with the aid of a sledgehammer
    (b)   with a sledgehammer and a block of wood
    (c)   with a sledgehammer and a driving cap

7   The angle of repose of soil is the slope that it will adopt with the horizontal if it is
    (a)   in a dry state
    (b)   in a damp state
    (c)   in a wet state

8   When excavating a trench within 900 mm of an existing building, the refill must be in concrete up to
    (a)   the underside of the foundations of the existing building
    (b)   150 mm below the underside of the foundations of the existing building
    (c)   the top of the existing foundations

9   When refilling trenches the soil being replaced should
    (a)   be saturated with water
    (b)   have the same moisture content as the surrounding soil
    (c)   be completely dry

10   When using a pump to remove surface water from an excavation it should be placed
    (a)   at the bottom of the excavation
    (b)   half-way down
    (c)   at the top

Chapter 2

Setting out

After reading this chapter you should be able to:

1 Have a good knowledge of geometry for setting out buildings.

2 Understand the meaning of a 'building line' and the importance of correctly setting it out.

3 Be able to set out curved lines when the striking point is inaccessible.

4 Be able to set out a true ellipse and a false ellipse.

5 Appreciate the importance of accurate setting out, and the careful checking of the setting out before commencing building operations.

When the site clearance is completed or well under way, the setting out of the work may begin. It is very necessary to have a good knowledge of geometry to ensure that the work is set out correctly and accurately before building operations commence. Extra care at this stage of the contract is essential to prevent loss of time and money by having to carry out alterations because of inaccurate or slipshod setting-out.

Building line

The main building line on the site is generally the base line from which all the other setting-out will be taken. In most cases the building line will have been approved by the local authority and it will be clearly marked on the drawings. Usually it is measured from certain fixed points, such as an existing building, kerb line or centre line of a road. It is extremely important that this line is set out accurately to make certain there is no infringement of the local authority requirements.

Setting out of angles

Once the base line has been set out and checked for accuracy other lines may be taken from it. Therefore, angles have to be set out, the most common of which is the right angle, which may be set out by one of the following methods:

1 With the aid of a builder's square which may be 2 by 2 m, or 3 by 2 m in size.

2 With the aid of a tape, using the 3:4:5 rule, as described in *Brickwork 1*, Chapter 5. The measurements used in this method of setting out a right angle may be multiples of 3:4:5 such as 6:8:10; or 15:20:25, and so on.

3 With the aid of a tape from a fixed point, as shown in Figure 21, an equal distance is measured on each side of the fixed point, A, at points B and C. If a tape ring is held at point B and a known measurement held at peg C, point D can then be determined by pulling the tape taut at the half-way mark of the measurement. For example, if the distance on the tape was 10 m, the tape would be held at points B and C and pulled taut at 5 m and peg D driven in position. Line AD is perpendicular, that is, at right angles to line BC.

It is also possible to set out angles other than right angles, such as acute (having less than 90 degrees) or obtuse (having more than 90 degrees) with the aid of a tape. For example, a 45 degree angle may be set out as shown in Figure 22. A right angle is first set. An equal distance is measured along each side of the intersection or vertex

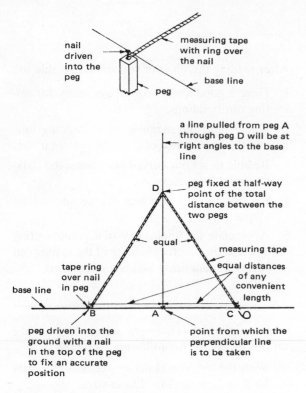

Figure 21   *To set out a right angle*

of the angle. Then, the distance between these two points is carefully measured and the half-way point determined. A line pulled from this point to the vertex forms an angle of 45 degrees to either of the lines forming the right angle. By using this

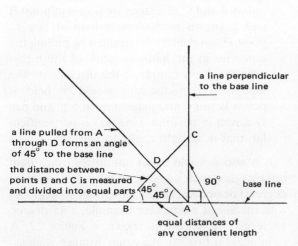

Figure 22   *To set out an angle of 45 degrees*

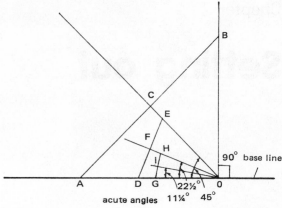

(a)   setting out angles of less than 90 degrees

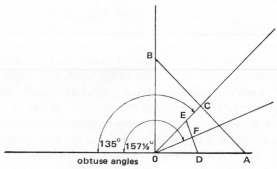

(b)   setting out angles greater than 90 degrees

Figure 23   *Setting out angles less than and greater than 90 degrees*

method an infinite number of angles can be calculated. Figure 23 shows angles of 11.25, 22.5, 67.5, 135 and 157.5 degrees set out by using this method.

An angle of 60 degrees may be set out by using the method illustrated in Figure 24. This is done by measuring any convenient distance between two points marked by pegs A and B. A third peg, C, is driven in at the same distance from both peg A and peg B. If lines are pulled from peg A through peg B and from peg A through peg C, the two lines will form an angle of 60 degrees. An angle of 30 degrees, 15 degrees and 7.5 degrees can be found by halving as shown in Figure 23.

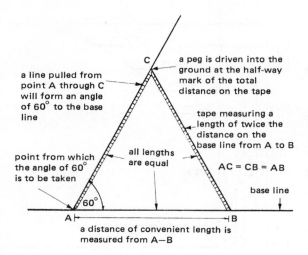

a peg is driven into the ground at the half-way mark of the total distance on the tape

a line pulled from point A through C will form an angle of 60° to the base line

tape measuring a length of twice the distance on the base line from A to B

point from which the angle of 60° is to be taken

all lengths are equal

AC = CB = AB

base line

60°

a distance of convenient length is measured from A—B

Figure 24   *To set out an angle of 60 degrees*

Setting out circular work

To set out a shape which is circular on plan, the easiest method is to determine first the centre or striking point. Then, with the use of either a measuring tape or a timber batten called a trammel, mark out the curve by securing the tape or trammel at the centre point and swinging round in an arc (Figure 25). If, however, the striking point is inaccessible because buildings or materials are in the way, it will then be impossible to use the methods previously described. The three following methods may be used without the aid of surveying instruments:

Method 1

Figure 26 shows a method of setting out an arc with the aid of battens if the radius of the curve is of a short length. The chord AB and rise CD are marked out, and, if possible, nails fixed at points A, B and C. Battens are then nailed together so that the first batten touches points A and C and the second batten touches points B and C. A

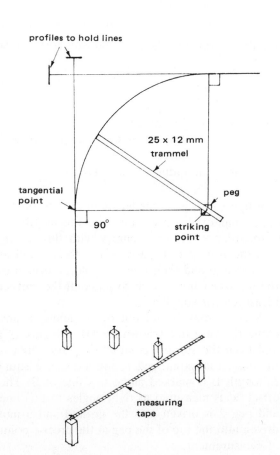

profiles to hold lines

25 x 12 mm trammel

tangential point

90°

peg

striking point

measuring tape

Figure 25   *Setting out a curve with a trammel or tape*

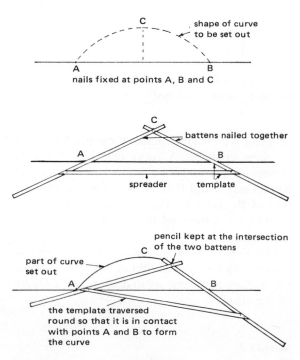

shape of curve to be set out

nails fixed at points A, B and C

battens nailed together

spreader   template

pencil kept at the intersection of the two battens

part of curve set out

the template traversed round so that it is in contact with points A and B to form the curve

Figure 26   *To set out a segmental curve with the aid of a template*

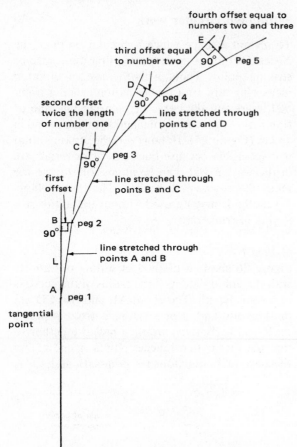

fourth offset equal to
numbers two and three

third offset equal
to number two

second offset
twice the length
of number one

line stretched through
points C and D

first
offset

line stretched through
points B and C

line stretched through
points A and B

tangential
point

Figure 27   *A method of setting a curve when the striking point cannot be reached*

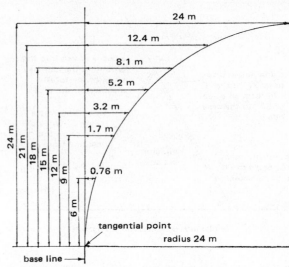

Figure 28   *Setting out a curve when the striking point cannot be reached*

spreader is then nailed across these two battens to fix them in shape. A curve may be set out by traversing this frame, so that it keeps in contact with points A and B and a pencil at the intersection of the battens. This method is particularly useful when setting out segmental curves particularly for arches.

Methods 2 and 3 are useful when setting out curves with longer radii, but in both cases simple calculations are necessary to determine the length of the offsets.

Method 2

The curve is set out by driving pegs in at regular intervals, as shown in Figure 27. To calculate the

lengths of the offsets the following formula is used:

$$x = \frac{L^2}{2R}$$

where x = the first offset
L = the distance between the pegs around the curve
R = the radius of the curve

This figure only gives the length of the first offset, because all other offsets are twice this length.

In order to ensure accuracy with this setting out, the pegs may be driven into the ground at each station and then a nail should be driven in the top of each peg so as to pinpoint the correct measurement and alignment.

A curve may be set out by stretching a line along the base line (shown as AB in Figure 27) and from the starting point of the curve, that is the tangential point, peg 1, and a distance equal to length L is marked along this line at B. The offset 'x' is measured at right angles to this line and peg 2 is driven into the ground and a nail driven into the top of the peg at the precise point of measurement.

The line is now stretched from peg 1 through

peg 2 and a distance equal to length L is marked from peg 2 to a point C. From this point a distance equal to *twice* the length of the first offset x (that is, 2x) is measured at right angles to the line, and peg 3 is driven into the ground and a nail driven into the peg as before.

The position of peg 4 is determined by stretching a line from peg 2 through peg 3 and a distance, again equal to length L, is measured from peg 3 to a point D. From D an offset equal to the second offset, that is 2x, is measured at right angles to the line and peg 4 is driven into the ground. This procedure is continued around the curve (using 2x as the length of all the offsets) until the required length of curve is obtained.

Example
Set out a curve with a radius of 30 m. The pegs are to be fixed at intervals of 3 m around the curve. The striking point of the curve is not accessible.

The first offset $x = \dfrac{L^2}{2R}$

$$= \dfrac{3 \times 3}{2 \times 30}$$

$$= \dfrac{3}{20}$$

$$= 0.15 \text{ m}$$

All of the remainder of the offsets will be twice this. Thus:

$2 \times 0.15 \text{ m} = 0.30 \text{ m}$

Method 3
A curve can also be set out from a base line using the theorem of Pythagoras: the square of the hypotenuse of a right-angled triangle is equal to the sum of the squares of the other two sides. Figure 28 shows the application of this method (commonly called Baker's method) and the formula for calculating the offsets is as follows:

$$y = R - \sqrt{R^2 - x^2}$$
where y = the offset
R = the radius
x = the distance from the tangential point to the offset

Each offset will have to be calculated separately.

Example
If a curve having a radius of 24 m is to be set out, calculate the lengths of the offsets at 6 m, 9 m, 12 m, 15 m, 20 m and 21 m along the base line.

First offset at 6 m $y = R - \sqrt{R^2 - x^2}\text{m}$

$$= 24 - \sqrt{24^2 - 6^2}$$

$$= 24 - \sqrt{576 - 36}$$

$$= 24 - \sqrt{540}$$
$$= 24 - 23.24$$
$$= 0.76 \text{ m}$$

Second offset at 9 m $= 24 - \sqrt{24^2 - 9^2}$

$$= 24 - \sqrt{576 - 81}$$

$$= 24 - \sqrt{495}$$
$$= 24 - 22.3$$
$$= 1.7 \text{ m}$$

Third offset at 12 m $= 24 - \sqrt{24^2 - 12^2}$

$$= 24 - \sqrt{576 - 144}$$

$$= 24 - \sqrt{432}$$
$$= 24 - 20.8$$
$$= 3.2 \text{ m}$$

Fourth offset at 15 m $= 24 - \sqrt{24^2 - 15^2}$

$$= 24 - \sqrt{576 - 225}$$

$$= 24 - \sqrt{351}$$
$$= 24 - 18.8$$
$$= 5.2 \text{ m}$$

Fifth offset at 18 m $= 24 - \sqrt{24^2 - 18^2}$

$$= 24 - \sqrt{576 - 324}$$

$$= 24 - \sqrt{252}$$
$$= 24 - 15.9$$
$$= 8.1 \text{ m}$$

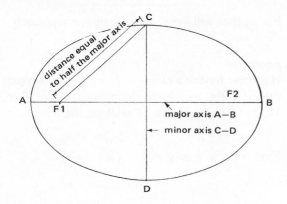

Figure 29   *Setting out a curve with the aid of offsets*

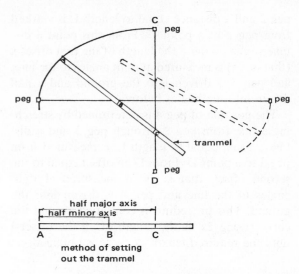

Figure 30   *Method of setting out a true ellipse with the aid of a trammel*

Sixth offset at 21 m $= 24 - \sqrt{24^2 - 21^2}$

$$= 24 - \sqrt{576 - 441}$$

$$= 24 - \sqrt{135}$$

$$= 24 - 11.6$$

$$= 12.4 \text{ m}$$

Setting out an ellipse

An ellipse has two axes which pass through the centre point and are perpendicular to each other. The longer line is called the major axis and the shorter line the minor axis. An ellipse also has two foci (plural of focus) which are determined by measuring a distance from the end of the minor axis equal to half the length of the major axis, and cutting the major axis each side of the centre point (Figure 29). These two points are the foci of that ellipse.

There are quite a number of different geometrical methods which can be used to set out an ellipse but there are two particularly useful methods which may be adopted for setting out this shape on the site.

The trammel method

This is useful when the length of the major axis does not exceed about 2–3 m. The major and minor axes are first marked out either with pegs and lines, or, if on a hard surface, with pencil or chalk. A length of batten (37 by 25 mm would be very suitable) is then marked with two distances, one equal to the length of half the major axis and the other equal to half the length of the minor axis. Both distances are measured from the same point on the batten. Thus, there are now three marks on the batten shown as A, B and C in Figure 30. If the trammel is now traversed so that mark B is kept in line with the major axis and mark C is kept in line with the minor axis, a true elliptical curve can be obtained by setting pegs or marking out with pencil or chalk at point A. This is very useful when, for example, setting out arches or bay windows.

Peg and line method

This may be used when the lengths of the axes of the ellipse are too long for the trammel method to be used. Pegs are driven firmly into the ground at each end of the minor and major axes which have been carefully set out perpendicular to each other. A building line is stretched between the two pegs marking the length of the major axis. From one end of the minor axis, stretch a measuring tape and drive a peg into the ground where the tape measures a distance equal to half the length of the major axis and meets the building line stretched between the pegs indicating the major

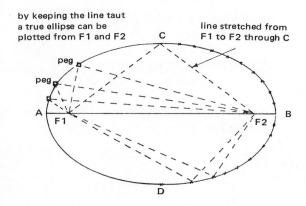

Figure 31   *To set out a true ellipse from its foci with the aid of a line*

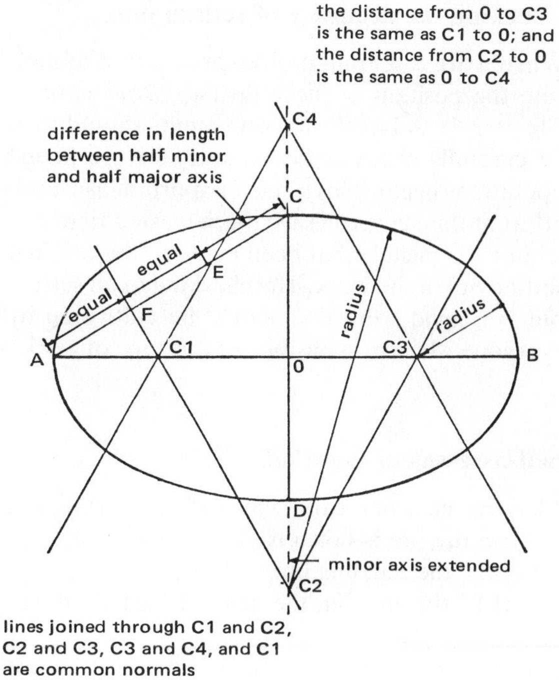

Figure 32   *To set out a four-centred ellipse*

axis; and repeat this operation with a peg on the other side of the minor axis. These two pegs shown as F1 and F2 in Figure 31 represent the two foci of that ellipse. Nails are then driven into these pegs and a strong building line is stretched from F1 round either of the pegs which are fixed at each end of the minor axis and then secured at the other focus. The line is now detached from the end of the minor axis, and by keeping the line taut it can be traversed and pegs driven in at convenient intervals to mark out the ellipse. An ellipse with a major axis of more than 30 m may be set out with the aid of this method provided that a great deal of care is taken to ensure:

The pegs are stout enough to take the strain and driven firmly into the ground;

The nails in the pegs are stout and well-driven into the pegs;

The line is not too thick but capable of taking quite a strong pull without excessive stretching; and

The line is kept at the same strain when marking out the positions of the pegs as it was when setting out from the focal points to the end of the minor axis.

A false ellipse

This type of ellipse has the advantage over a true one because it is comprised of a series of arcs which can be set out from their striking points. Figure 32 shows the method of setting out a false

ellipse which is comprised of four arcs which are scribed from four centres. The major and minor axes are determined and marked out AB and CD. A line is then pulled from one end of the major axis to one end of the minor axis from A to C. A distance equal to the difference in length between half the major axis and half the minor axis is measured along this line from the end of the minor axis at E. The distance between A and E is now measured and this distance divided into two equal parts, and from the centre point F a line is stretched at right angles to the line AC. If this line is now extended so that it cuts the major axis at C1 and the extension of the minor axis at C2, these two points are two of the striking points of the arcs forming the ellipse. The other two points are determined by measuring equal distances from the centre point O on the major and minor axes at C3 and C4. The arcs are marked out with the aid of a measuring tape, and the points at which each arc starts and finishes are determined by the common normals which are lines pulled through the striking points C1, C2, C3, and C4.

Checking the accuracy of setting out

When work is set out, profiles are erected to indicate the position of the walls (see *Brickwork 1*, Chapter 6). All of the measurements should then be carefully checked for accuracy before actual operations begin. This is most important as a little effort at this stage can save much wasted time and labour if a mistake has been made in the original setting out of the work. The checking of all setting out is a good habit that should be cultivated by everyone who is responsible for this type of work.

Self-assessment questions

1 The base line from which all the setting out on the site is taken is
   (a) the building line
   (b) the line at the extreme edge of the foundations
   (c) a line at the front of the furthermost projection from the main walling, such as a porch or bay window

2 A right angle may be set out with the aid of a measuring tape by measuring three sides of a triangle using the following ratios
   (a) $2:3:4$
   (b) $3:4:5$
   (c) $4:5:6$

3 An angle of $22\frac{1}{2}$ degrees may be obtained by dividing a right angle
   (a) into two equal parts
   (b) into three equal parts
   (c) into four equal parts

4 An angle of 60 degrees can be obtained by setting out
   (a) a triangle having all sides equal in length
   (b) a triangle with two sides of equal length
   (c) a triangle having the lengths of its sides in the ratio of $3:4:5$

5 A striking point is the point
   (a) from which the curve starts from the straight
   (b) at the end of a trammel
   (c) from which the curve is set out

6 The formula for calculating an offset, x, for a curved line is
   (a) $\dfrac{2L}{2R}$
   (b) $\dfrac{L^2}{2R}$
   (c) $\dfrac{L^2}{R^2}$

7 A curve having a radius of 20 m is to be set out using the formula
   $$y = R - \sqrt{R^2 - x^2}\, m.$$
   If x equals 4 m, then the offset, y, is
   (a) 0.3 m
   (b) 0.4 m
   (c) 0.5 m

8 Using the peg and line method for setting out a true ellipse, the line is secured at
   (a) the two ends of the major axis and one end of the minor axis
   (b) the foci and one end of the major axis
   (c) the foci and one end of the minor axis

9 With the aid of a diagram, show how to set out a four-centred false ellipse.

10 What advantages has a false ellipse over a true ellipse?

Chapter 3

Foundations

After reading this chapter you should be able to:

1 Have a clear knowledge of natural foundations and the types of soil which are suitable for building on.

2 Understand why foundations are necessary under structures.

3 Have a knowledge of the Building Regulations concerning foundations.

4 Have a good understanding of the various types of foundations and the situations for which they are best suited.

5 Have an understanding of stepped foundations and their construction.

Natural or sub-foundations

Once the excavations are finished, the foundations should be laid as soon as possible to prevent the ground from drying out and causing movement by shrinking. The ground immediately below the foundation concrete is called the *ground bearing* and should be levelled off and well-rammed to receive the base. This is to ensure that there is no loose earth beneath the concrete base which could fail to hold the loading and thus cause a fracture. The foundations of a structure have to carry loads which may be divided into two categories:

1 *Dead load*, that of all floors, walls, partitions and permanent construction.
2 *Imposed loads*, all loads other than those of the permanent structure such as contents of the premises, or intermittent ones such as wind, snow and rain.

Types of soil

There are many different types of soil suitable for building on. Each type has its own particular characteristics and properties. These may be broadly classified into one of the following groups:

1 Rocks
2 Granular soils
3 Cohesive soils (see Table 7)

There are also two other types of ground which are quite common:

1 *Peat*, made up of decomposed vegetation, is not a very stable type of ground on which to build and usually requires specially designed foundations.
2 *Made ground*, a ground artificially formed by filling in a depression or raising the level of a site. Again, special care must be taken when building on this type of ground.

The purpose of foundations

All foundations built on compressible soils are liable to settle to some extent and they should, therefore, be designed to allow the structure to settle evenly and to a minimum extent. This means that they must carry the dead and imposed loads and also resist soil movement caused by alternate wetting and drying or by freezing. Cohesive soils are liable to shrink when drying out and to expand upon becoming wet. This can create a great deal of movement underneath foundations particularly when they are not very deep and quite near to the surface of the ground. There-fore, to resist this movement, foundations should normally be not less than 0.6 m deep and in heavy clay soils, even deeper.

Frost can also have an effect on some types of soils, especially silts and chalks. These are liable to severe expansion owing to the freezing of water which they may contain. When soils are affected by expansion in this way they are said to be sub-ject to *frost heave*. Foundations which are built on these types of soils should be at least 0.9 m deep, or at least 1.25 m in hilly areas which may have very severe frosts, in order to give adequate pro-tection to the foundations against possible dam-age by frost heave.

Soils underneath the foundation may contain chemicals such as sodium sulphate and mag-nesium sulphate which may be harmful to the foundation concrete (see *Brickwork 1*, Chapter 6). In these soils the foundations must be con-structed of materials that will resist this chemical action.

It is, therefore, unwise to generalize too widely on the types of soils below foundations. Expert advice should always be sought and special tests carried out if there is any doubt at all about the stability of the soil upon which a building, even if a comparatively light structure, is to be erected.

The bearing capacity of a soil

This is the load that a soil can safely carry without any appreciable settlement and is commonly given in tonnes force per square metre or newtons per square metre. In this book, the latter method of measurement will be used as in the calculation of the minimum width or area of foundation suit-able for a wall or pier.

Example

A brick pier 0.45 m² exerts a force of 200 kN, including the mass of the pier.

Calculate (1) the pressure in kN/m² on the brick pier and (2) the minimum area of foundations required if the soil has a bearing capacity of 150 kN/m².

Force exerted by the pier	$= 200 \text{ kN/m}^2$
Area of pier	$= 0.45 \text{ m} \times 0.45 \text{ m}$
	$= 0.2025 \text{ m}^2$
Pressure on pier	$= \dfrac{\text{force}}{\text{area}}$
	$= \dfrac{200 \text{ kN}}{0.2025 \text{ m}^2}$
	$= 987.65 \text{ kN/m}^2$
Bearing capacity of soil	$= 150 \text{ kN/m}^2$
Total force to be resisted by the foundations	$= 200 \text{ kN}$

Table 7

Group	Types of soil suitable for building on	Bearing capacity
Rock	Granite Limestone Sandstone Slate Shales Hard solid chalk	650 kN/m² and upwards
Non-cohesive or granular soils	Compact well-graded sands. Gravel-sand. Mixtures. Loose well-graded sands. Compact uniform sands. Loose uniform sands	From 100 kN/m² to 650 kN/m² in their *dry* state (Dry in this case means that the ground water level is at a depth not less than the foundation width below the base of the foundation) From 50 kN/m² to 300 kN/m² in a *wet* state
Cohesive soils	Stiff boulder clays. Stiff clays. Sandy clays. Firm clays. Soft clays. Sandy silts. Very soft clays and silts	From 50 kN/m² to 650 kN/m²

Therefore, the minimum area of foundations required

$$= \frac{200 \text{ kN}}{150 \text{ kN/m}^2}$$
$$= 1.333 \text{ m}^2$$

If the foundations are to be square then the minimum size will be

$$\sqrt{1.333 \text{ m}^2} = 1.155 \text{ m}$$

Building Regulations

These state that the foundations of a building shall:

1 Safely sustain and transmit to the ground the combined dead load and imposed load. This shall be done without causing any settlement or other movement which would impair the stability of, or cause damage to, the whole or any part of the building or of any adjoining building or works.

2 These foundations shall be taken down to such a depth, or be so constructed, as to

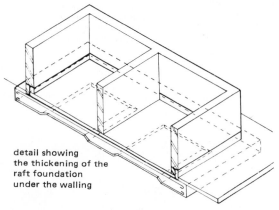

detail showing
the thickening of the
raft foundation
under the walling

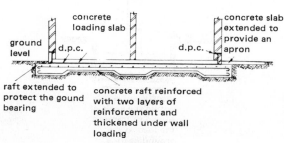

Figure 33 *Raft foundations*

safeguard the building against damage by swelling, shrinking or freezing of the subsoil.

3 They shall be capable of adequately resisting any attack by sulphates or any other deleterious matter present in the soil.

Types of foundations

The most suitable types of foundations for structures not exceeding four storeys in height are:

Raft foundations
Pad foundations
Strip foundations
Wide strip foundations
Stepped foundations
Short bored piled foundations

Raft foundations

These may either be used where the building is on soft natural ground or fill, or on harder ground in preference to strip foundations because they are quicker to place, provided adequate machinery is available for the excavation and the concreting operations. The level of the base of the raft foundation will usually be near the surface of the ground. It is advisable to extend the raft or provide a protective apron beyond the effective ground-bearing area, so that extensive movement of the soil, which may have shrunk through drying and swelling due to moisture absorption, can be prevented (Figure 33). Holes for pipes and services should not be cut into the raft as they may cause its strength to be reduced. Provision of deep chases and holes should be made when the raft is being concreted and the design should make allowances for them.

Pad foundations

These are isolated foundations which may be of unreinforced concrete, brick or masonry, provided that the angle of the spread of the load from the pier to the outer edge of the ground-bearing is not more than a quarter of a brick per course (56–75 mm) for brick, or one-to-one for concrete or masonry. The minimum thickness of the foundation at the edge should not be less than 150 mm (Figure 34). These foundations are very suitable

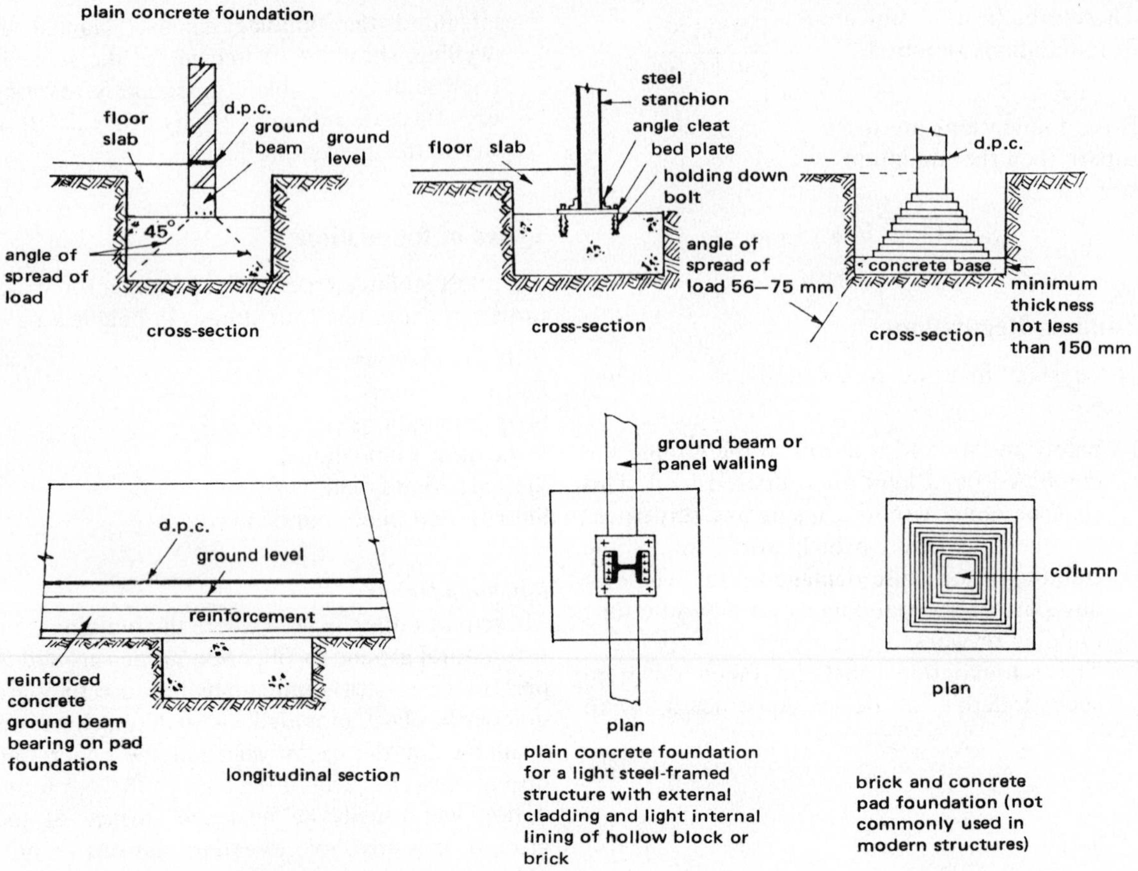

plain concrete foundation

floor slab | d.p.c. | ground beam | ground level

angle of spread of load

45°

cross-section

steel stanchion
angle cleat
bed plate
holding down bolt

floor slab

angle of spread of load 56—75 mm

cross-section

d.p.c.

concrete base

cross-section

minimum thickness not less than 150 mm

d.p.c.
ground level
reinforcement

reinforced concrete ground beam bearing on pad foundations

longitudinal section

ground beam or panel walling

plan

plain concrete foundation for a light steel-framed structure with external cladding and light internal lining of hollow block or brick

column

plan

brick and concrete pad foundation (not commonly used in modern structures)

Figure 34   *Pad foundations*

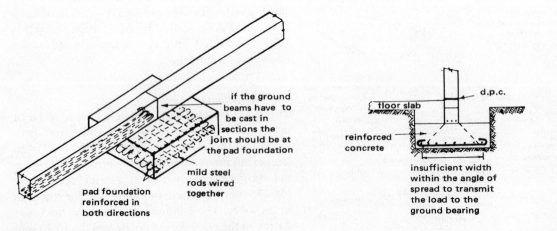

if the ground beams have to be cast in sections the joint should be at the pad foundation

mild steel rods wired together

pad foundation reinforced in both directions

d.p.c.

floor slab

reinforced concrete

insufficient width within the angle of spread to transmit the load to the ground bearing

Figure 35   *Reinforced concrete pad foundation*

for structures which are framed with steel members or where the weight is carried by columns, and the walls are built as panel walls or cladding. Such walls may be carried by ground beams which rest on the pad foundations. Where there is insufficient depth to transfer the load to the ground which is within the permissible angle of spread, the foundation should be of reinforced concrete (Figure 35).

Strip foundations

These are generally the most suitable for low-rise buildings on most types of soils and if constructed of plain concrete should be placed centrally under the walls. When deciding upon the foundations for building some investigation must take place. Solid rock requires only to be levelled with the cavities and fissures being filled with concrete. If the rock surface is very uneven then the surface of the rock may be levelled with a thin layer of concrete.

When excavating trenches in chalk the surface of the chalk should be protected against the action of water or frost by putting a protective layer of concrete as soon as the trench is bottomed up. Gravel is a good sub-foundation but care must be taken to ensure that there is no danger of fine particles being washed out with surface water. In such cases good land drainage should be provided. Similarly with sandy soils, these also make good foundations but good drainage must be provided to prevent any scouring or loss of fine particles.

Soils such as silts and clays tend to retain water and therefore must be excavated deeply enough

Table 8 *Minimum width of strip foundation*

Type of subsoil	Condition of subsoil	Field test applicable	Minimum width in millimetres for total load in kilonewtons per lineal metre of load-bearing walling of not more than:					
			20 kN/m	30 kN/m	40 kN/m	50 kN/m	60 kN/m	70 kN/m
Rock	Not inferior to sandstone, limestone or firm chalk	Requires at least a pneumatic or other mechanically-operated pick for excavation	In each case equal to the width of wall					
Gravel sand	Compact	Requires pick for excavation. Wooden peg 50 mm square in cross-section hard to drive beyond 150 mm	250	300	400	500	600	650
Clay Sandy clay	Stiff	Cannot be moulded with the fingers and requires a pick or pneumatic or other mechanically-operated spade for its removal	250	300	400	500	600	650
Clay Sandy clay	Firm	Can be moulded by substantial pressure with the fingers and can be excavated with a graft or spade	300	350	450	600	750	850
Sand Silty sand Clayey sand	Loose	Can be excavated with a spade. Wooden peg 50 mm square in cross-section can be easily driven	400	600	*Note:* Foundations do not fall within the provisions of the regulations if the total load exceeds 30 kN/m			
Silt Clay Sandy clay Silty clay	Soft	Fairly easily moulded in the fingers and readily excavated	450	650				
Silt Clay Sandy clay Silty clay	Very soft	Natural sample in winter conditions exudes between fingers when squeezed in fist	600	850				

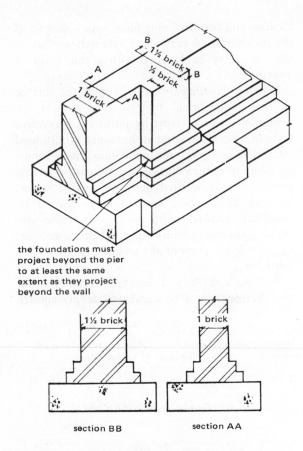

the foundations must
project beyond the pier
to at least the same
extent as they project
beyond the wall

Figure 36   *Foundations for piers and buttresses*

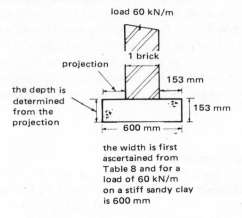

(a)   foundations suitable for a 1-brick wall
carrying a load of 60 kN/m

load 60 kN/m

1 brick

projection

153 mm

the depth is
determined
from the
projection

153 mm

600 mm

the width is first
ascertained from
Table 8 and for a
load of 60 kN/m
on a stiff sandy clay
is 600 mm

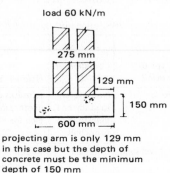

(b)   foundations for a 275 mm cavity wall
carrying a load of 60 kN/m

load 60 kN/m

275 mm

129 mm

150 mm

600 mm

projecting arm is only 129 mm
in this case but the depth of
concrete must be the minimum
depth of 150 mm

Figure 37   *Suitable foundations for walling built on a
stiff sandy clay*

to avoid the action of frost; in such cases it is usual
for the foundations to be at least 600 mm below
ground level. The recommended widths for various soils and loadings are shown in Table 8.

The concrete is composed of cement and fine
and coarse aggregate conforming to BS 882, in
the proportion of 50 kg of cement to not more
than 0.1 m³ of fine aggregate and 0.2 m³ of coarse
aggregate.

The thickness of the concrete is not less than its
projection from the base of the wall or footing
and in no case is it less than 150 mm. Where the
foundations are laid at more than one level, at
each level the higher foundations extend over and
join the lower foundations for a distance of not
less than the thickness of the foundations – in no
case less than 300 mm. Where a pier, buttress or
chimney forms part of a wall, the foundations
must project beyond the pier, buttress or chimney
on all sides to at least the same extent as they

project beyond the wall (Figure 36).

Examples of foundations suitable for different
conditions:

1   If a structure is transmitting a total load of 60
kN/m load-bearing wall on a stiff sandy clay,
the foundations suitable for a 1-brick wall and
a 275 mm cavity wall are shown in Figure 37.

2   Show the foundations that would satisfy the
Building Regulations and would be suitable
for a 1-brick wall and to carry a load of
30 kN/m on a soft silty clay. The alternative
answers are shown in Figure 38.

3   Figure 39 shows a foundation that would
satisfy the Building Regulations and be suitable for a 275 mm cavity wall carrying a total
load of 40 kN/m on a compact sand.

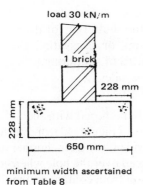

minimum width ascertained
from Table 8

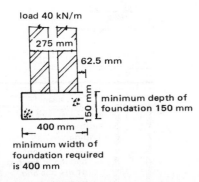

alternative methods that both satisfy the minimum requirements of the Building Regulations for the conditions stated

Figure 38   *Foundations suitable for a 1-brick wall*
carrying a load of 30 kN/m on a soft silty clay

load 40 kN/m

275 mm

62.5 mm

minimum depth of
foundation 150 mm

400 mm

minimum width of
foundation required
is 400 mm

(would normally be made a
little wider to allow standing
room for the bricklayer)

Figure 39   *Foundation for a 275 mm cavity wall carry-*
ing a load of 40 kN/m on a compact sand

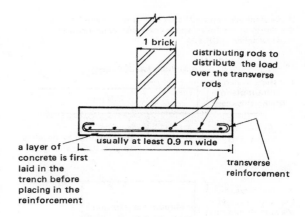

distributing rods to
distribute the load
over the transverse
rods

a layer of
concrete is first
laid in the
trench before
placing in the
reinforcement

usually at least 0.9 m wide

transverse
reinforcement

the reinforcement may be wired
together to form a mat, or b.r.c.
welded fabric may be used

Figure 40   *Wide strip foundation*

Wide strip foundations

These foundations are of such width that transverse reinforcement is necessary. They are used
where ordinary strip foundations become so wide
that tension is induced in the concrete and failure
might occur. The reinforcement should be lapped
at the corners of the wall and at junctions. The
depth of these foundations should be the same as
for strip foundations. Figure 40 shows a typical
wide strip foundation.

Stepped foundations

These are used when a structure is built on a sloping site and are intended to save the excessive
amount of excavating and materials that would be
necessary if the foundations were kept at one
level. As stated earlier in this chapter, the
minimum lap of one layer of concrete over the
lower one must be equal to the thickness of the
concrete or 300 mm, whichever is the greater.
The steps should not be of greater height than the
thickness of the foundation unless special precautions are taken and should be in multiples of brick
thickness so that the brickwork will bond without
being cut at each of the steps. It is quite a common practice to bevel the underside of the concrete to give added strength at the steps (Figure
41).

if the steps are required to be of a greater height than the depth of the foundations then special precautions must be taken — CP 101

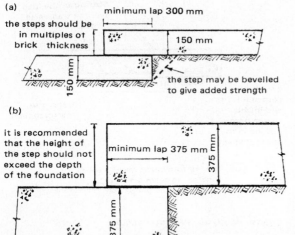

(a)

the steps should be in multiples of brick thickness

minimum lap **300** mm

150 mm

150 mm

the step may be bevelled to give added strength

(b)

it is recommended that the height of the step should not exceed the depth of the foundation

minimum lap 375 mm

375 mm

375 mm

Figure 41 *Stepped foundations*

Short bored piled foundations

Shrinkable clays can increase greatly in volume on becoming wet and will shrink if they are allowed to dry out. Such movement may have a harmful effect upon the stability of foundations. This expansion and contraction may be accelerated if trees are situated adjacent to such foundations. In cases where buildings are to be erected on shrinkable clay soils and where the foundations need not be more than 900 mm deep then short bored piled foundations may be introduced. This system consists of a series of short concrete piles cast in holes bored in the ground and spanned by light beams of reinforced concrete which are cast in trenches dug between the bored piles (Figure 42). This system has the following advantages over deep strip foundations:

1 Cleaner site owing to the reduced amount of spoil which is excavated.
2 Greater speed of construction especially if the holes are bored by mechanical means.
3 Work can proceed when the weather makes it difficult for normal excavating of trenches.

This system, however, is not so suitable on clay sites where there is stoney clay or many tree roots. Four main operations are involved:

1 Boring the holes for piles.
2 Forming the shuttering for the reinforced concrete beams or excavating the trenches to serve instead of shuttering.
3 Casting the piles.
4 Casting the beams.

The holes may be bored with the aid of an auger either by hand (Figure 43) or mechanically. A metal or wooden concrete hopper (Figure 44) should be placed over the hole when concreting to prevent any soil from contaminating the concrete. The diameter of the piles may be 250, 300 or 350 mm and the depth usually about 2.4 m, but this may be extended to about 4.2 m. Any water in the bore-hole should be pumped out first and then a dry mix poured into it and punned until a dry *bottom* is achieved. Then, the ordinary mix may be poured and tamped. Reinforcing rods of

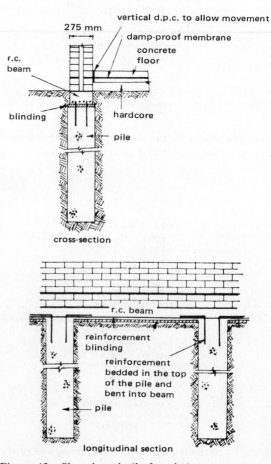

275 mm

vertical d.p.c. to allow movement

damp-proof membrane

concrete floor

r.c. beam

blinding

hardcore

pile

cross-section

r.c. beam

reinforcement

blinding

reinforcement bedded in the top of the pile and bent into beam

pile

longitudinal section

Figure 42 *Short bored pile foundation*

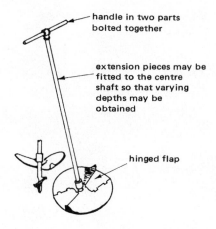

Figure 43 *Earth auger for boring holes for short bored piles by hand*

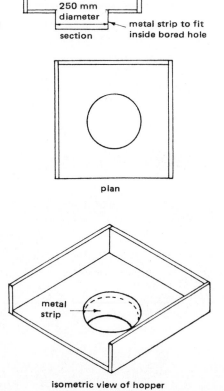

Figure 44 *Wooden hooper for placing over the bored hole to pour the concrete into the hole without dragging in loose soil which would contaminate the concrete*

9 mm diameter and about 1.2 m long should be inserted into the top of the piles to a depth of 600 mm and bent over to be incorporated into the beam. The bottom of the trenches for the beams should be blinded with well-burnt ashes, clinker or a layer of sand. Figure 42 shows a typical cross-section and longitudinal section through a short bored pile foundation.

Self-assessment questions

1 'Dead load' is the
   (a) amount of load that can be carried by the soil
   (b) load of all floors, walls and partitions
   (c) load of contents of premises, snow and rain

2 The general bearing capacity of a non-cohesive or granular soil is
   (a) above 650 kN/m^2
   (b) 100–650 kN/m^2
   (c) 50–650 kN/m^2

3 A brick pier exerts a force of 240 kN and the bearing capacity of the soil 120 kN/m^2, then the minimum area of the foundations would be
   (a) 2.0 m^2
   (b) 1.8 m^2
   (c) 2.4 m^2

4 For 50 kg of cement, the amount of coarse and fine aggregates should not exceed
   (a) 0.075 m^3 of fine aggregate and 0.15 m^3 coarse aggregate
   (b) 0.1 m^3 fine aggregate and 0.2 m^3 coarse aggregate
   (c) 0.125 m^3 fine aggregate and 0.25 m^3 coarse aggregate

5 If a structure transmits a load of 50 kN/m run of wall on a compact gravel sand, the minimum width of foundation shall be
   (a) 500 mm
   (b) 600 mm
   (c) 700 mm

6 If a structure transmits a load of 30 kN/m run of walling on a firm clay, then the minimum width of foundation shall be
   (a) 300 mm
   (b) 350 mm
   (c) 400 mm

7 Make neat sketches showing sections through the two foundations outlined in questions 5 and 6.

8 When using stepped foundations which are 350 mm thick on a sloping site, the minimum lap should be
   (a) 300 mm
   (b) 350 mm
   (c) 375 mm

9 Why is it necessary to ram the bottom of foundation trenches?

10 Describe a short bored pile foundation and list the site operations for constructing such a foundation.

Chapter 4

Ground floor construction

After reading this chapter you should be able to:

1 Have a good knowledge of the Building Regulations concerning ground floor construction.

2 Understand how to prevent dampness penetrating ground floors.

3 Know what types of bricks are suitable for brickwork below ground level.

4 Have a sound knowledge of the construction of floors which are situated below ground level.

5 Understand how to construct ground floors on sloping sites.

6 Have a good knowledge of the thermal insulation of buildings.

7 Have a sound understanding of the methods for laying floor screeds.

Building Regulations

Protection of floors next to the ground

1 Any part of a building which is next to the ground shall have a floor which is so constructed as to prevent the passage of moisture from the ground to the surface of the floor.

2 Any floor which is next to the ground shall be so constructed as to prevent any part of the floor being adversely affected by moisture or water vapour from the ground.

3 No hard core laid under such a floor shall contain water-soluble sulphates or other harmful matter in sufficient quantities so as to be liable to cause damage to any part of the floor.

Suspended timber floors

1 The ground surface should be covered with a layer of concrete not less than 100 mm thick, consisting of cement and fine and coarse aggregate in the proportions of 50 kg of cement to not more than 0.1 m^3 of fine aggregate and 0.2 m^3 of coarse aggregate. This should be properly laid on a bed of hardcore consisting of clean clinker, broken brick or some similar inert material, free from water-soluble sulphates or other deleterious matter liable to cause damage to the concrete.

2 The concrete is finished with a trowel or spade finish and so laid that its top surface is not below the highest level of the surface of the ground or paving adjoining any wall of the building.

3 There must be space above the upper surface of the concrete of not less than 75 mm to the underside of any wall plate, and of not less than 125 mm to the underside of the suspended timbers, and this space must be clear of debris and have adequate ventilation.

4 There must be damp-proof courses in such a position as to ensure that moisture from the ground cannot reach any timber or other material which would be adversely affected by it.

Solid ground floors

1 The ground surface is to be covered with a

layer of concrete not less than 100 mm thick in the same manner as for suspended floors. In addition, it must have one of the following:

(a)   a damp-proof sandwich membrane either consisting of a continuous layer of hot-applied, soft bitumen or coal-tar pitch not less than 3 mm thick, or consisting of bitumen solution, bitumen/rubber emulsion or tar/rubber emulsion; or

(b)   the timber laid or bedded directly upon a damp-proof course of asphalt or pitchmastic not less than 12 mm thick; or

(c)   in cases where the floor incorporates wood blocks not less than 16 mm thick, these are dipped in an adhesive of hot, soft bitumen or coal-tar pitch and so laid upon the concrete that the adhesive forms a continuous layer.

2   Such membrane, damp-proof course or layer of adhesive must be situated at a level not less than 150 mm above the highest level of the surface of the ground or paving adjoining any external wall of the building.

3   It shall be carried up the walls adjoining the floor to the level of the upper surface of the floor.

4   It shall be continuous with, or joined and sealed to, any damp-proof course inserted in any wall, pier, buttress, column or chimney adjoining the floor.

5   Where the timber is fixed to wooden fillets embedded in the concrete they should be impregnated under pressure with an aqueous solution of copper-chrome-arsenate. Any surfaces which are exposed by cutting the timber should be thoroughly treated by dipping, spraying or brushing them with an aqueous solution of not less than 10 per cent of copper-chrome-arsenate.

The structure of any building above the foundations has to be strong enough to carry the combined dead and imposed loads and transmit them to the foundations without such deflection or deformation that will impair the stability of the structure or cause damage to the whole or any part of the building. It is, therefore, most important that the quality of the materials and work-

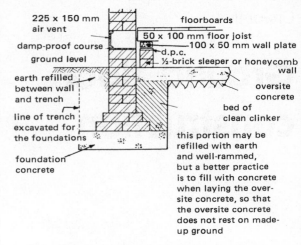

(a)   section through a 1-brick external wall showing a hollow floor construction

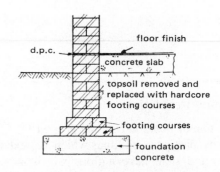

(b)   section through a 1-brick external wall showing a solid floor construction

Figure 45   *Sections through a 1-brick external wall showing hollow and solid floor construction*

manship must be of a good standard, particularly in the work which is below ground level.

Bricks

These may be of clays, and lime or calcium silicate, or concrete. On well-drained sites, bricks that are suitable for other external faces of the building will normally be satisfactory below ground level. Where, however, there is a possibility of the brickwork being constantly wet any clay bricks used should be capable of resisting sulphate attack and frost, both of which can have a harmful effect. A high proportion of clay bricks contain water-soluble sulphates. If the brickwork remains wet for long periods of time, these sulphates may react with certain components in Portland cement used in the mortar and form compounds which can cause disintegration of the cement mortar. Another form of disintegration is caused by the crystallization of soluble salts in the pores of the bricks. This may result in the flaking or spalling of the brick surfaces.

Low temperatures have no effect on bricks which are kept dry, but if the brickwork is wet and becomes frozen, disintegration may be caused by the water freezing and expanding within the pores of the bricks. This again causes flaking or spalling of the surfaces which are exposed. For this reason, both sand lime and concrete bricks should be of *special purposes* quality (see *Brickwork 1*, Chapter 1).

The mortar

Where there is a risk of deep frost, mortars rich in cement should be used, either one part cement to three parts of sand, or one part cement, quarter part lime to three parts sand, the lime giving extra workability. If a high early strength or resistance to sulphate attack is required, a high alumina cement mortar may be used in the ratio of one part high alumina cement to three parts sand. On no account should lime be added to this type of cement as this will cause a *flash set* to take place. That is, the mortar will set hard almost immediately after mixing, and cannot be used for laying bricks. The same effect will be produced if Portland cement is mixed with high alumina cement.

Footings

A brick wall may be built directly off the foundations without the need of footings. However, if the foundations are so wide that a failure may occur in them by shear or bending, footings

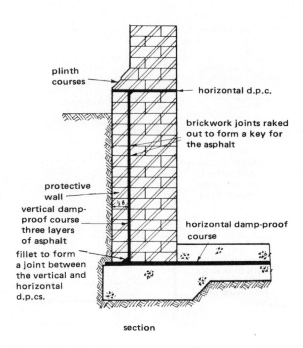

plinth courses

horizontal d.p.c.

brickwork joints raked out to form a key for the asphalt

protective wall

vertical damp-proof course three layers of asphalt

horizontal damp-proof course

fillet to form a joint between the vertical and horizontal d.p.cs.

section

Figure 46 *Section showing how moisture may be prevented from entering a floor below ground level*

should be provided so that the load is spread evenly over the foundations (Figure 45). When footings are used they should increase in width downwards by regular quarter brick offsets on one or both sides of the wall. As far as possible, the bricks should be laid as headers.

Damp-proof courses

The purpose of damp-proof courses is to provide a barrier to the passage of water from the ground into the structure. They may be horizontal or vertical and placed either below ground level or just above ground level to prevent water rising up the wall. Those below ground level are provided where the lowest floor in a building is below ground level and will consist of both horizontal and vertical damp-proof courses. The lower damp-proof course must be placed below the floor level, the upper damp-proof course must be placed at least 150 mm above the ground level and the vertical damp-proof course must connect the two damp-proof courses, forming a complete barrier to moisture (Figures 46 and 47). Every

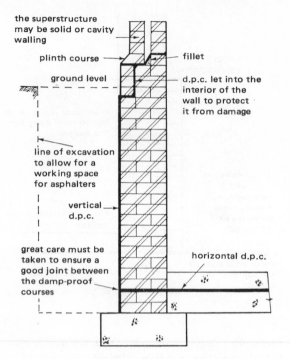

the superstructure may be solid or cavity walling

plinth course

fillet

ground level

d.p.c. let into the interior of the wall to protect it from damage

line of excavation to allow for a working space for asphalters

vertical d.p.c.

great care must be taken to ensure a good joint between the damp-proof courses

horizontal d.p.c.

Figure 47   *A section showing an alternative method of damp-proofing a sub-basement*

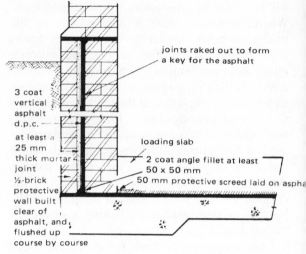

joints raked out to form a key for the asphalt

3 coat vertical asphalt d.p.c.

at least a 25 mm thick mortar joint

½-brick protective wall built clear of asphalt, and flushed up course by course

loading slab

2 coat angle fillet at least 50 x 50 mm

50 mm protective screed laid on aspha

Figure 48   *Detail showing the method of building a protective wall against an asphalt damp-proof course*

wall in a building should have a damp-proof course which is:

At least 150 mm above ground level;
Above the surface of any oversite concrete;
Below the lowest member of a timber floor.

Figure 48 shows a detail of the method of building up the protective walling to the tanking. The wall should be kept about 25 mm away from the asphalt and each course flushed up solidly. The asphalt which is laid on the floor slab should also have a protective screed on top to prevent any damage by people walking over it, reinforcement being placed on it, or petrol and oil being spilt from machinery.

Important points to note when laying damp-proof courses

1 Keep the mortar bed even and ensure that there are no stones or other projections which may cause a puncture in the d.p.c.
2 Unroll bitumen materials carefully, especially in cold weather, as coldness tends to make them brittle and liable to crack badly.
3 Bed slates and bricks carefully to ensure that there are no air pockets beneath them.
4 Take care to ensure a good bonding between slates or bricks and the mortar.
5 Paint lead damp-proof courses on both sides with bitumen to prevent corrosion of the lead through being in contact with the cement mortar.
6 Sheet damp-proof courses should always be lapped at least 100 mm and preferably sealed with bitumen. In the case of lead or copper, welted joints may be preferred.
7 Ensure that the ground floor damp-proof course has a sound waterproof joint with the d.p.c. in the walls so that a continuous layer is formed.

Air ducts

Where hollow floors are constructed it is most important that they are well ventilated and Figure 49 shows how a duct may be laid under a solid floor to provide ventilation to an adjacent hollow timber floor. Either glazed ware or pitch fibre pipes may be used for this purpose and the ends of the pipes should be built solidly into the brick-

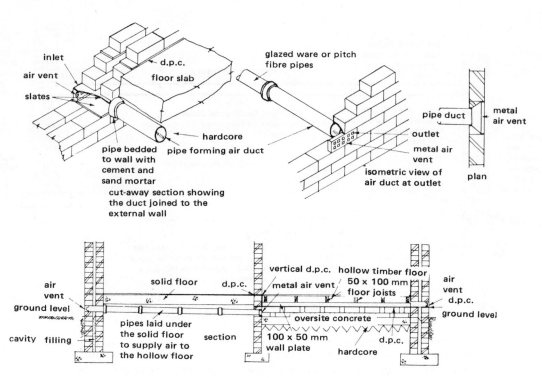

Figure 49 *A method of ventilating a hollow floor by means of a pipe duct*

work. An air brick should be built in front of the air duct and a metal vent at the outlet of the duct. Another air vent should be built into the external wall opposite the duct to induce a current of air to pass under the floor.

Air ducts may also be formed in a brick wall to provide a means of ventilating a basement floor or room and Figure 50 shows how this may be done without affecting the efficiency of the damp-proof courses.

Treatment on sloping sites

When buildings are erected on sloping sites their foundations may be constructed either:

1 By using stepped foundations, as described in Chapter 2; or
2 Excavating the site so that the foundations are all at one level.

Solid or hollow floors may be used with both methods.

When solid floors are used with stepped found-

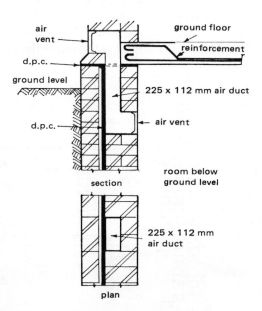

Figure 50 *A method of ventilating a room which is situated below ground level*

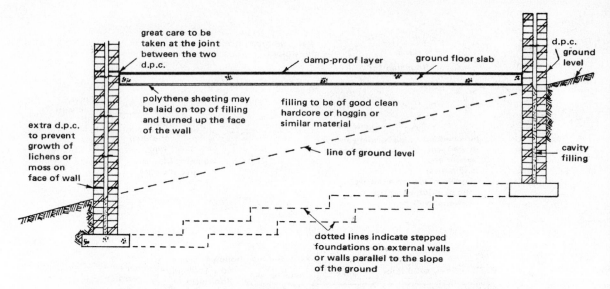

Figure 51   *Section showing the construction of a ground floor in conjunction with stepped foundations*

ations, the space underneath the floor should be filled with a good-quality filling, such as hoggin, compacted hardcore or a suitable granular soil, and well-compacted before laying the floor slab. A layer of heavy-quality polythene sheeting may be laid immediately above the filling and underneath the floor slab to prevent the passage of moisture through the floor. Alternatively, a bituminous damp-proof course may be laid either in the middle of the slab or at the top of the floor immediately below the floor finish. Care must be taken to ensure a sound joint between the floor d.p.c. and the wall d.p.c. (Figure 51).

If a hollow or suspended floor is used with a stepped foundation, the site concrete may be stepped down in convenient steps (Figure 52). In this case the wall d.p.c. should be kept level all round the building immediately below the floor timbers. This means that at the lower side of the incline much of the brickwork will show between

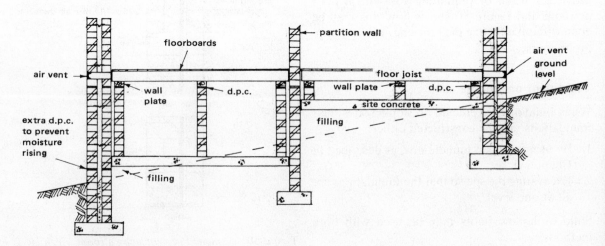

Figure 52   *Section showing the construction of a hollow timber floor in conjunction with a sloping site*

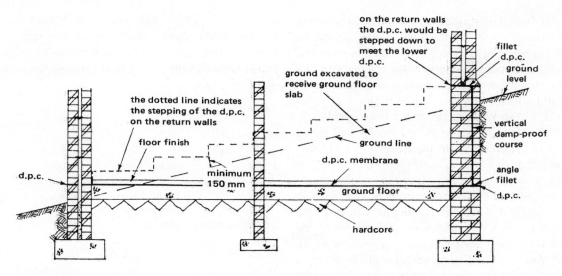

Figure 53 *Section showing a method of constructing a ground floor by excavating the soil and using asphalt damp-proofing*

ground and d.p.c. level. If it tends to be damp, there may also be a possibility of the growth of lichens or moss on the face of the wall, which would be unsightly. To prevent this happening an additional d.p.c. may be placed at the base of the wall to stop the moisture rising from the ground (Figures 51 and 52). This will prevent the lichens from spreading as they need moisture.

At the upper end of the incline, the moisture may be prevented from entering the building by providing two horizontal d.p.c. and a vertical d.p.c. connecting them (Figure 53) or by building an open area or dry area beyond the external wall (Figure 54).

Heat insulation

Increasing attention is now being paid to keeping a building warm and preventing an excessive amount of heat being lost through walls, floors

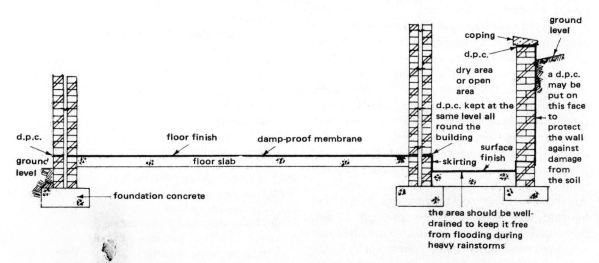

Figure 54 *Section showing the construction of a ground floor on a sloping site, using a dry area*

and ceilings. Good insulation results in a saving in fuel costs, more comfortable living standards, quicker warming from cold, less condensation and cooler conditions in summer. Air is a bad conductor of heat. Therefore, a good insulating material should contain a void or large number of voids which will trap air and prevent it from circulating. For example, an unventilated cavity wall has a greater insulating value than one which is well-ventilated.

In a ventilated cavity, the air will circulate freely and will rise when warmed by contact with the inner leaf. Therefore, cooler air will enter the cavity through the air bricks at the base of the wall. This movement will create a draught which will absorb heat. The same principle is demonstrated if you blow across your hand. The breath feels cool because the draught or air is extracting heat from your hand. You can produce the same effect when you blow across your tea to cool it down. The air extracts heat from the liquid.

In an unventilated cavity, the air is contained, and, therefore, there are no draughts. Consequently, the wall is kept warmer which has the effect of reducing heat losses. A cavity wall which has its inner skin or leaf built with lightweight blocks such as clinker, fly ash, breeze, pumice, foamed concrete or any other similar material will have better insulation against heat losses than a cavity wall which is built with hard bricks on the inner skin. Even greater insulation may be obtained by building insulating slabs within the cavity as the work proceeds. These slabs must not allow the passage of water across the cavity and supplier's instructions must be carefully observed if the external walls of the building are to remain dry. Good insulation may also be achieved by filling the cavity with a foamed plastic called ureaformaldehyde, which traps the air into very small voids and prevents any circulation in the cavity itself. The constituents of the foamed plastic are a plastic fluid and a hardener in water solution. These are stored in separate containers. As soon as these constituents are mixed and injected with pressurized air through 18 mm holes at 900 mm centres into the cavity, the foam is formed immediately and adheres rapidly to the walls. It fills every part of the cavity and its density is 8 kg/m^3. With this application, the 'U'

value of a cavity wall constructed with two 112 mm brick skins and 18 mm plaster may be reduced from 1.98 to 0.57, which means a considerable saving in the loss of heat through the walls of a building.

Table 9

Good insulators (poor conductors of heat)	Fair insulators	Poor insulators (good conductors of heat)
Air	Concrete	All metals such as:
Glass wool	Stone	steel
Exfoliated mica	Bricks	copper
Cork	Glass	brass
Slag wool	Roofing tiles	lead
Wood		aluminium
Aerated concrete		
Insulating board		
Plaster board		
Carpets		

Table 10

Material	'U' value W/m^2 deg C
Brickwork:	
225 mm solid, one side plastered	2.44
275 mm ventilated cavity wall, plastered on one side	1.98
275 mm unventilated cavity wall, brick outer leaf, and inner leaf and plastered	1.70
275 mm unventilated cavity wall, brick outer leaf, clinker block, inner leaf and plastered	1.30
Windows:	
single-glazing	5.67
double-glazing	2.84
Ground floors:	
wood block on concrete	0.85
thermoplastic tiles on concrete	1.13
wood floor on joists	1.70
Pitched roofs – above plaster ceiling:	
tiles on battens	3.18
tiles on boards and felt	1.70
tiles on boards and felt, but ceiling overlaid with 25 mm mineral wool or 50 mm loose insulation	0.85
wood, 25 mm thick	2.84

The 'U' value is the thermal transmittance in the overall air to air coefficient of heat which is transmitted through a structure and the surface film. The lower the 'U' value, the better the degree of heat insulation, and this is given in watts/metre^2/degree Celsius or joules/second/metre^2/degree Celsius.

Table 9 lists some materials which are good or poor heat insulators, and Table 10 lists approximate values for some typical kinds of construction.

The 'Q' value is the heat loss from a building per square metre of structure. This is the 'U' value, as shown above, multiplied by the temperature rise (the temperature inside the room minus the temperature outside).

$$Q = U \times A(t_i - t_o)$$
where U = the 'U' value of the wall
  t_i = the internal temperature
  t_o = the outside temperature
  A = the surface area of the room or building in metres squared

Heat transmittance coefficients (approximations)

The following are recommended maximum values of thermal transmittance to maintain a suitable degree of comfort without excessive loss of heat. 'U' value not to exceed:

External walls	1.13
Ground floor	0.85
Roof and top floor ceiling	1.13

In the case of floors, all soft coverings such as plastic tiles, linoleum, carpets and wood finishes provide good heat insulation. This may be increased with hollow floors by supporting felt, mineral, wool, cork slab or other similar materials on light platforms or between the floor joists (Figures 55–58). These all have the effect of creating still air pockets below the floorboards and thereby increasing the insulating value of the floor.

With solid floors the heat losses are generally lower than is the case with hollow floors which have no insulating material below them. Their insulating value, however, may be increased by laying a floor finish of wood blocks, cork or plas-

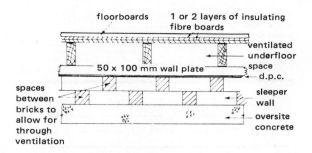

Figure 55 *Section showing how the heat insulation value of a suspended timber floor may be increased by using insulating fibre boards*

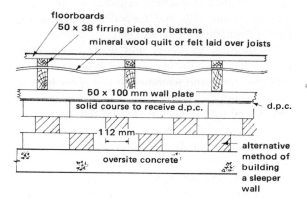

Figure 56 *Increasing the heat insulating value or reducing the 'U' value of a suspended timber floor by means of an insulating quilt*

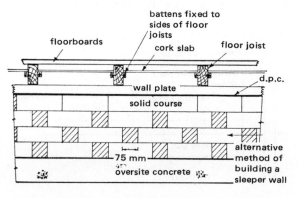

Figure 57 *Method of insulating a floor against heat losses with the use of cork slabs*

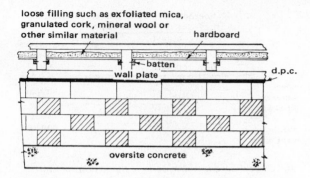

Figure 58   *Insulating a floor against heat losses with the use of a loose filling underneath the floorboards*

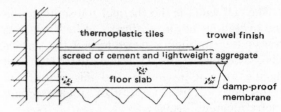

Figure 59   *Insulating a solid ground floor against heat losses*

tic tiles or by laying a lightweight concrete screed on top of the slab and immediately below the floor finish (Figures 59 and 60).

In addition to floors and walls being well-insulated against the loss of heat, it is also important that roofs and windows do not allow heat to pass through them too easily. The roof space may be covered with a layer of mineral felt, glass wool or exfoliated mica. The ceiling of the room below the roof space may be composed of plaster board, and this should preferably have a thin layer of tin foil on the back which has the effect of reflecting heat downwards into the room. There should also be a layer of sarking felt underneath the roof tiles (Figure 61).

Glass is only a fair conductor of heat, but, because of its thinness, allows heat to escape very quickly. Therefore, windows should be double-glazed. That is, they should have two frames with a layer of air between the outer and inner panes

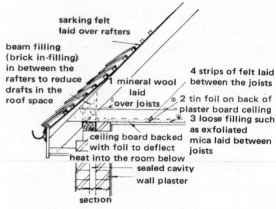

Figure 61   *Methods that may be used to prevent heat being lost through the roof space*

of glass. This will prevent draughts and keep the room warmer.

Laying screeds

Points to remember when laying screeds:

1   They should have sufficient thickness to withstand the loading they are expected to take.
2   Have good adhesion to the concrete floor slab.
3   Be sufficiently strong to resist cracking or deformation.
4   Be laid to the correct levels.
5   Be laid with a fairly dry mix.
6   After wetting the slabs, have any surplus water carefully brushed off so that the slab is left merely damp.

The surface of the sub-floor must be thoroughly

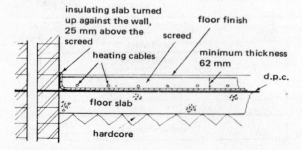

Figure 60   *Heat insulation for a solid ground floor with electric underfloor heating*

roughened and cleaned to form a key. The slab should then be saturated and left for some time to allow all the surplus water to evaporate. (It can even be left overnight if necessary.) Immediately before laying the screed the sub-floor should be brushed with neat cement grout. The floor should be divided into bays of about 10–12 m², or alternatively at expansion joints (Figure 62). The second method has the advantage of not having four bays meeting at one point. The screed should be laid with a sufficiently *dry* mix, that is, only just wet enough to allow for tamping and thorough compaction.

Figures 63 and 64 show two methods that are used to compact screeds.

1 A rotary float which is a large disc, driven by petrol engine or electric motor. This machine is guided by the operator and produces a float finish. To achieve this, it is essential that the mix should be of a dry consistency (Figure 63).

2 A typical tamper which has been fitted with a vibrator. The vibrator will give better compaction to the screed than if the tamper is used on its own without any mechanical aid. After a screed has been compacted with this equipment, it is usually trowelled over to give a smooth finish (Figure 64).

The surface finish of the screed will depend upon the type of floor finish to be laid and may be float or steel trowel finish. The surface should not be trowelled too soon after laying as this will cause the cement and water to rise to the surface, thus creating a scum called *laitance*, which is not desirable in a screed as it has little strength and can come away from the surface as dust.

area of each bay about 11.16 square metres

1	6	3	8
5	2	7	4

4 bays meet at one point

(a)   method of laying alternate bays for screeding — the numbers indicate the sequence of operations

Figure 63   *A power-operated rotary float*
Driven by petrol engine. For compaction and screed finish to concrete floor, etc. Available with disc type float or trowel type float

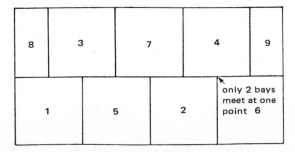

8	3	7	4	9
1	5	2	6	

only 2 bays meet at one point 6

(b)   an alternative method of laying alternate bays so that any four bays do not meet at a point

Figure 62   *Methods of laying alternate bays*

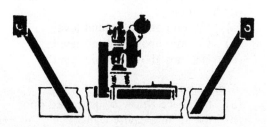

Figure 64   *A vibrating tamper (screed)*
Driven by petrol engine. Vibrating unit and vibration-free handles

Typical floor coverings requiring screeds:

Float finish	*Trowel finish*
Asphalt tiles	Cork carpet and tiles
Clay tiles	Linoleum
Composition blocks	Rubber
Concrete tiles	Thermoplastic tiles
Hardwood blocks	
Terrazzo	

The screed should be properly protected during the drying-out period, and properly cured, as described in *Brickwork 1*. If the screed is to be laid on a bituminous damp-proof course, the d.p.c. should have sand thrown on to it when it has been laid to provide a key for the screed. The minimum thickness for a screed in this case should be 50 mm. If a heating coil is to be laid in the screed, great care must be taken to ensure that the heating coil is not damaged when laying the screed, either by treading on the coil or by damaging with a shovel or trowel.

Self-assessment questions

1   The ground surface should be covered with a layer of concrete not less than
   (a)   100 mm thick
   (b)   125 mm thick
   (c)   150 mm thick

2   The space above the upper surface of the concrete to the underside of the wall plate must not be less than
   (a)   75 mm
   (b)   100 mm
   (c)   125 mm

3   The damp-proof course in a wall should be not less than
   (a)   100 mm above ground level
   (b)   150 mm above ground level
   (c)   200 mm above ground level

4   A dry area is
   (a)   the space below a suspended floor
   (b)   the air in a cavity wall
   (c)   an open space provided in front of a building which is situated below ground level

5   When laying heating cables in a solid floor, the minimum thickness of the screed should be
   (a)   45 mm
   (b)   50 mm
   (c)   62 mm

6   Sarking is a layer of felt which is
   (a)   laid under the floor joists
   (b)   laid over the roof rafters
   (c)   laid over the ceiling joists

7   When laying floor screeds, the mixture should be laid
   (a)   very wet to allow easy compaction
   (b)   just wet enough to be compacted
   (c)   very dry

8   By means of neat sketches show how a floor below ground level may be provided with ventilation.

9   What are the advantages of having good heat insulation in a building?

10   Explain why it is better to avoid ventilating a cavity and to completely seal a cavity wall.

Chapter 5

Wall construction

After reading the following chapter the reader should be able to:

1 Understand the definitions relating to walling.

2 Have a good knowledge of the regulations regarding cavity walling.

3 Understand the requirements for external walls for certain small buildings, parapets, and the cutting of chases in walling.

4 Be able to set out acute and obtuse angles, plinth courses, and walls curved on plan.

5 Understand the methods of reinforcing brickwork and its application to walling.

6 Appreciate the construction of composite walling and their uses.

Definitions

The Building Regulations state the following definitions:

Base in relation to a wall means the underside of that part of the wall which immediately rests upon the footings or foundation or other structure by which the wall is carried.

Separating wall means a wall or part of a wall which is common to two adjoining buildings (previously known as a *party wall*).

Buttressing wall means a wall which is so designed and constructed as to afford lateral support to another wall from the base to the top of the wall. Such a buttressing wall shall be bonded at one end to the supported wall and no opening shall be situated nearer to the point of junction with the supported wall than 550 mm and measure in length not less than one-sixth of the height of the supported wall. Its thickness shall be not less than 75 mm if it forms part of a house and the supported wall does not exceed 6 m in height and 10 m in length, otherwise it must not be less than 90 mm. See Figure 65.

A buttressing pier may project from one or both sides of a supported wall and shall extend from the base of the wall to the top and have a dimen-

sion measured at right angles to the length of the supported wall of not less than three times the thickness of the wall (including the thickness of the wall) and be not less than 190 mm in width.

Supported wall is a wall which receives support from a buttressing wall or pier.

Bonds

The choice of bond will have an effect on strength, appearance and economy. In a normal construction, the type of bond has little effect on the strength of the wall because usually the principal bonds give more than the strength required. It is, however, essential that efficient bonding is used in walling to distribute the loading evenly and also to tie in the junction or buttressing walls and the quoins (see *Brickwork 1*, Chapter 4). For carrying the total dead and superimposed loads it is usually more important to consider the combined strength of the bricks and mortar.

Principal bonds in brickwork

These are shown in Figure 66 and include elevations of English, Flemish, garden-wall, Dutch and stretcher bonds. (For further details see *Brickwork 1*, Chapter 4.)

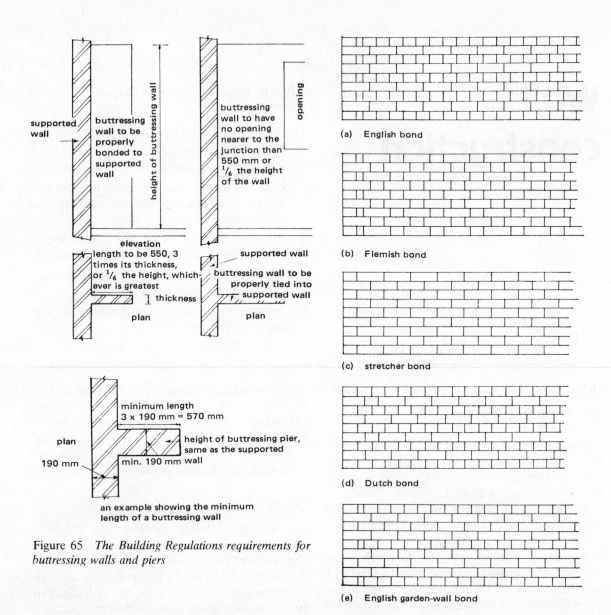

Figure 65   *The Building Regulations requirements for buttressing walls and piers*

Figure 66   *The principal bonds used in brickwork*

The Building Regulations requirements

Strength of bricks

The Building Regulations requirements include the following: where the wall is a wall of a house of one or two-storeys or of a building of one or two-storeys which is divided into flats, the bricks or blocks shall have a crushing strength of not less than 2.8 N/mm². Where the wall is a wall of any other building, the bricks or blocks shall have a resistance to crushing of not less than 7.0 N/mm² if the bricks or blocks are solid; or 5.0 N/mm² of gross horizontal area if the bricks or blocks are hollow.

For the purpose of this rule a brick or block shall be deemed solid if the solid material is not less than 50 per cent of the total volume of the brick or block, calculated from the overall dimensions. Similarly it shall be deemed hollow if the solid material is less than 50 per cent of the total volume of the brick or block.

Cavity walls

The Building Regulations include the following requirements:

1. These rules apply to any wall constructed as a cavity wall of two leaves, each leaf being constructed of bricks or blocks and properly bonded and solidly put together with mortar.
2. The leaves shall be securely tied together with ties being placed at distances apart not exceeding 900 mm horizontally and 450 mm vertically and as near as practicable to any opening. A tie should be placed to each 300 mm of height if the leaves are not connected by a bonded jamb (Figure 67).
3. The cavity shall be not less than 50 mm nor more than 75 mm in width at any level.
4. The leaves shall be not less than 100 mm in thickness at any level.
5. The overall thickness shall be not less than 190 mm or the thickness that would be required for a solid wall plus the width of the cavity, whichever is the greater, and the wall does not exceed 3.5 m in height and 12 m in length, or not exceeding 9 m in height and 9 m in length.

If the wall exceeds 9 m in height but does not exceed 12 m in length then the thickness shall be 290 mm for the height of the first storey and 190 mm for the rest of the height. Where a wall does not exceed 12 m in height and 12 m in length, the wall shall be 290 mm for the height of two storeys and 190 mm for the rest of the height.

6. The mortar for cavity walls shall be cement-lime mortar composed of Portland cement, calcium lime and fine aggregate in the proportion by volume of one part cement, one part lime and six parts fine aggregate, or any other type of mortar of equivalent strength or greater strength if appropriate.

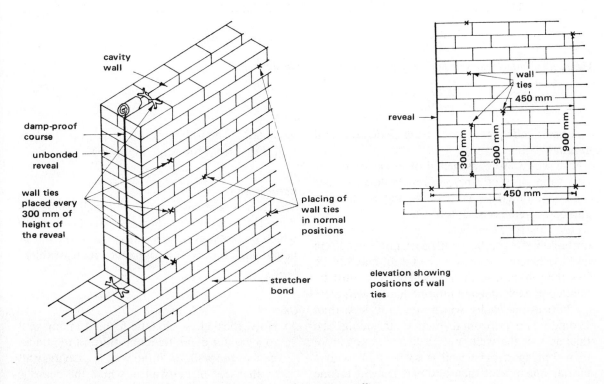

Figure 67 *Placing of wall ties at an unbonded reveal in cavity walling*

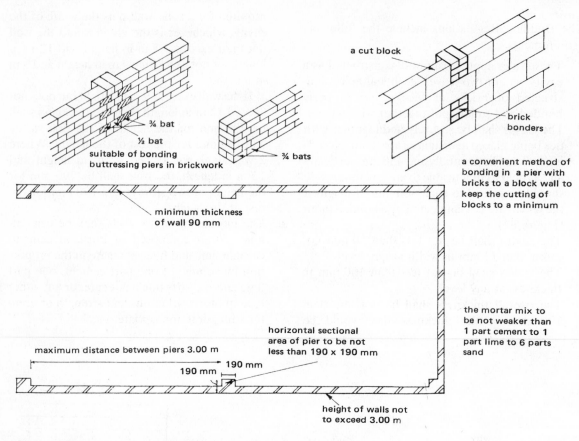

Figure 68 *Suitable construction for a small building such as a garage*

External walls of certain small buildings and annexes

Those which are constructed of bricks or blocks and form part of single-storey buildings other than a house (these include: verandahs, loggias, garages, greenhouses, tool sheds, fuel stores, water closets, lavatories, wash-houses or other outbuildings), and the width does not exceed 9 m and the height does not exceed 3 m, may not be less than 90 mm in thickness. The wall must be bonded at each end and intermediately with piers or buttressing walls which are not less than 190 mm² in horizontal section including the thickness of the wall, and at distances not more than 3 m apart. The wall is to be built with a mortar not weaker than one part cement to one part lime and not more than six parts of sand (fine

aggregate). The wall must not be subjected to any side thrust from the roof (Figure 68).

Parapet walls

The thickness of any parapet wall shall not be less than 190 mm or the thickness of the wall on which it is carried (whichever is the *least*) and its height shall not exceed four times its least thickness.

Chases

1   No vertical chase shall be formed in any wall to a greater depth than one-third of the thickness of the wall, or, if the wall is a cavity, wall of that leaf of the wall in which the chase is formed (Figure 69).

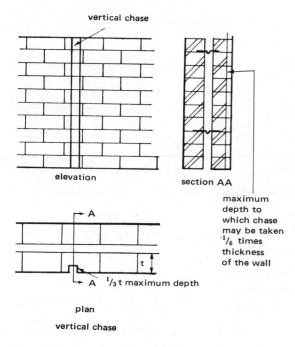

Figure 69   *Forming chases in cavity walling*

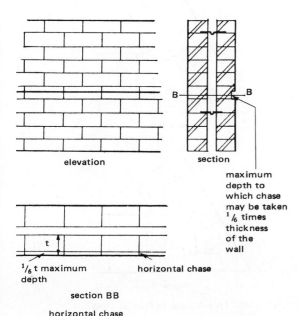

Figure 70   *Forming chases in cavity walling*

2   No horizontal chase shall be formed in any wall to a greater depth than one-sixth of the thickness of the wall or the thickness of the leaf of a cavity wall (Figure 70).

3   The number, size or position of chases in a wall shall not be such as to impair the stability of the wall or any part of the wall.

Setting out acute angles

Not all sites are square on plan particularly in town or city areas and, therefore, it is often necessary for walls to be built out of square with each other. Walls which are set out at an angle of less than 90 degrees, or a right angle, form an acute angle. Figures 71 and 72 show typical examples of this type of wall construction and their bonding arrangements. There will be little difficulty in cutting the shapes of the bricks at the angle if a mechanical brick-cutting saw is available. It is unlikely that this work would be cut by hand nowadays because of the extra expense.

If an acute angle is formed in an exposed position, it is liable to become damaged. In such cases, it is quite usual to cut the angle short (Figure 73) and to form two obtuse angles.

Setting out obtuse angles or squint corners

Purpose-made bricks may be purchased for this work (see *Brickwork 1*), and are generally used for standard angles such as 135 degrees or 120 degrees. For other angles the bricks would have to be purpose-made if a sufficient number were required. If only a small number were needed they would be cut on a mechanical brick-cutting saw.

It is important to remember that *a closer should always be placed next to a squint brick* to form the bond in the brickwork (Figures 74 and 76).

An alternative method of building an obtuse angle is to overlap ordinary square bricks at the angle. Figure 75 shows this method being used in English bond. Figure 78 shows the same method in Flemish bond. The use of this technique for forming an obtuse angle saves the cost of the squint bricks, but great care is required to ensure accuracy in plumbing.

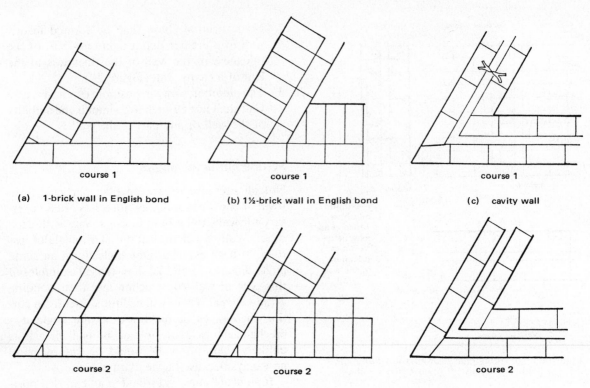

(a)   1-brick wall in English bond   (b) 1½-brick wall in English bond   (c)   cavity wall

Figure 71   *Bonding acute angles*

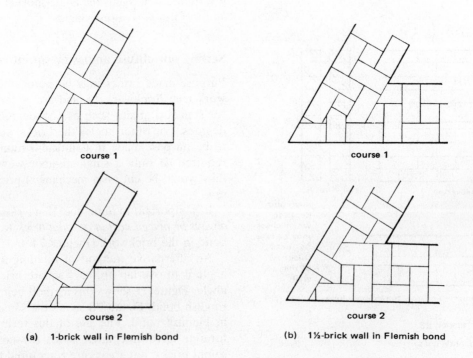

(a)   1-brick wall in Flemish bond   (b) 1½-brick wall in Flemish bond

Figure 72   *Bonding acute angles*

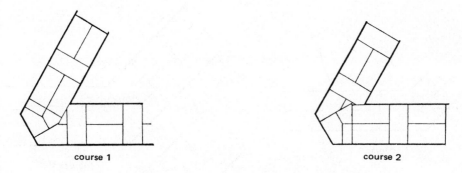

course 1 course 2

Figure 73 *An alternative method of bonding an acute angle in Flemish bond*

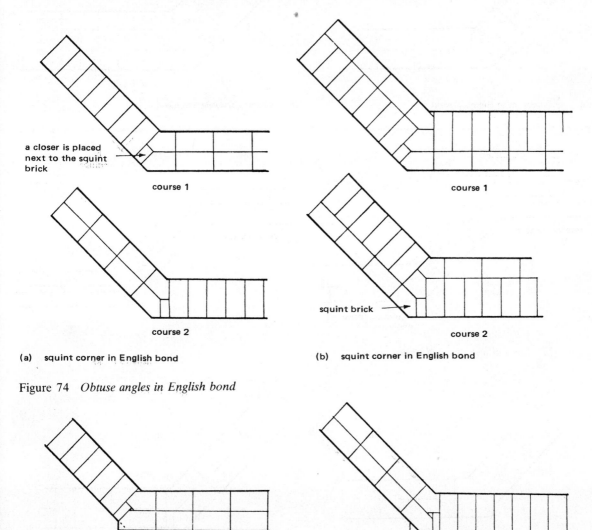

a closer is placed
next to the squint
brick

course 1 course 1

course 2 squint brick

course 2

(a) squint corner in English bond

(b) squint corner in English bond

Figure 74 *Obtuse angles in English bond*

course 1 course 2

Figure 75 *An alternative method of building an obtuse angle in English bond without using squint bricks*

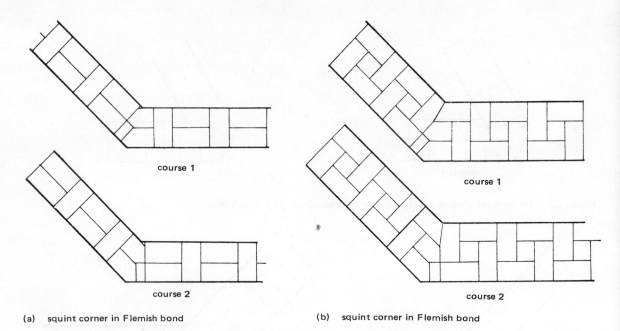

(a)   squint corner in Flemish bond   (b)   squint corner in Flemish bond

Figure 76   *Obtuse angles in Flemish bond*

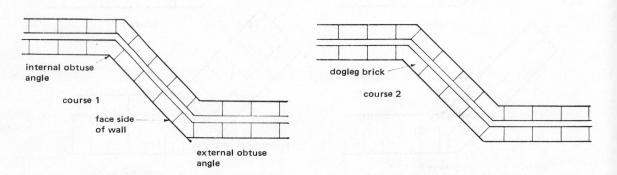

Figure 77   *Internal and external obtuse angles*

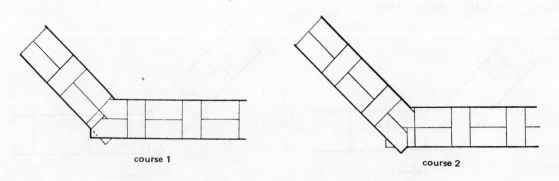

Figure 78   *An alternative method of building an obtuse angle in Flemish bond without using squint bricks*

Internal obtuse angles

When the walling is built to form an internal obtuse angle, dogleg bricks are generally used to form the bonding at the angle (Figures 78 and 79). This method is much stronger than with ordinary square bricks cut at the angle to form the bond (Figure 80), as it is then very difficult to ensure an adequate lap. This poor lapping is likely to create a weakness and allow cracking to take place in the angle should there be any slight movement in the structure.

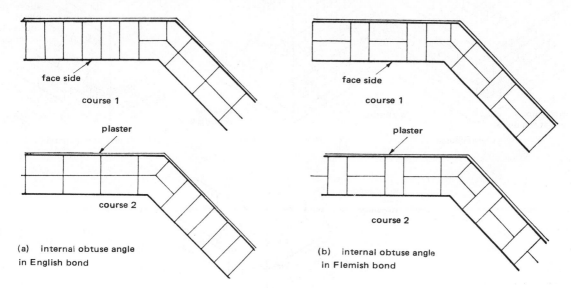

Figure 79 *Internal obtuse angles in English and Flemish bond*

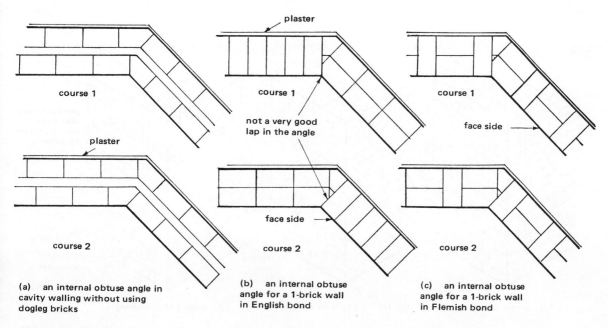

Figure 80 *Internal obtuse angles*

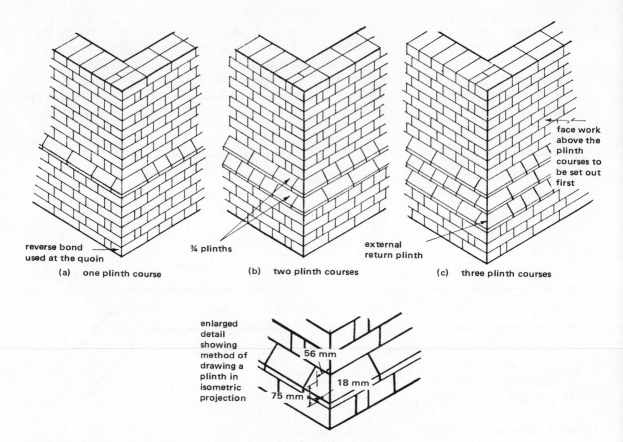

reverse bond
used at the quoin

¾ plinths

external
return plinth

face work
above the
plinth
courses to
be set out
first

(a)   one plinth course

(b)   two plinth courses

(c)   three plinth courses

enlarged
detail
showing
method of
drawing a
plinth in
isometric
projection

56 mm

18 mm

75 mm

Figure 81   *Quoins in English bond showing the bonding for plinth courses*

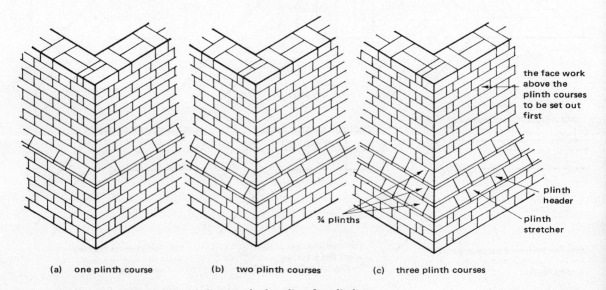

the face work
above the
plinth courses
to be set out
first

¾ plinths

plinth
header

plinth
stretcher

(a)   one plinth course

(b)   two plinth courses

(c)   three plinth courses

Figure 82   *Quoins in Flemish bond showing the bonding for plinth courses*

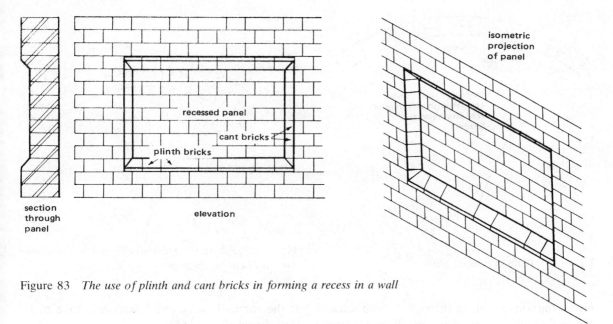

Figure 83   *The use of plinth and cant bricks in forming a recess in a wall*

Plinth courses

These are commonly used to reduce the thickness of a wall (see Chapter 4). The golden rule to remember when setting out the bonding for plinth courses and the walling below is to set out the neat work immediately above the plinth course first and let the bonding below the plinth be bonded to suit the neat work. In other words, always bond downwards from the face work and *not* upwards from the work below the plinth courses.

There will always be a broken bond introduced when plinth courses are used, so it is better for this to be placed in the walling under the plinths than in the face work above. Figures 81 and 82 show suitable methods of bonding angles in English and Flemish bond when one, two and three courses of plinths are used. Plinth bricks are occasionally used to form decorative panels in boundary walls (Figure 83). Cant bricks are used to form the recess on the vertical sides of the panel.

Walls curves on plan

When the radius of the curved work is large enough, the bricks may be laid around the curve

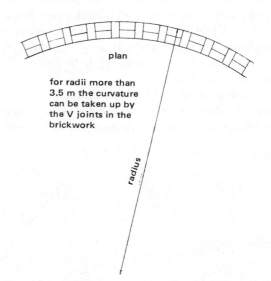

Figure 84   *Building a curved wall using 'V' joints*

with vee joints between them so that no cutting is necessary on the front 112 mm of the wall. A certain amount of cutting will, however, be required on the inside of the curve because of the reduced radius (Figure 84). The face work may be built using any of the principal bonds.

If the face work is on the concave face (Figure 85), some difficulty may be found with the bond-

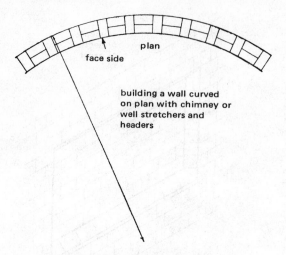

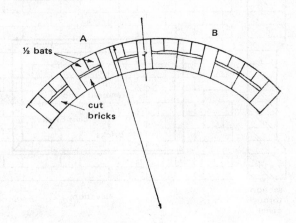

Figure 85   *Walls curved on plan*

Figure 86   *Alternative methods of using heading bond for a wall curved on plan*

ing on the convex side of the wall. If both sides of the wall should be neat work, much care is essential and it is normally better to use purpose-made bricks called chimney or well bricks (see *Brickwork 1*, Chapter 1). These may be supplied as headers or stretchers and will allow a good face to be obtained, for example, on both sides of a 225 mm thick wall.

Another method of building curved work, particularly when the radius is on the small side, is to use all heading bond on the face side of the wall.

If the radius is very small, bats will have to be introduced (Figure 86).

Serpentine walling

This type of walling curves in and out along its length (Figure 87). Its use is normally confined to boundary walling and gives a pleasant unmonotonous effect. It also may be seen on some large housing estates where the roads are deliberately

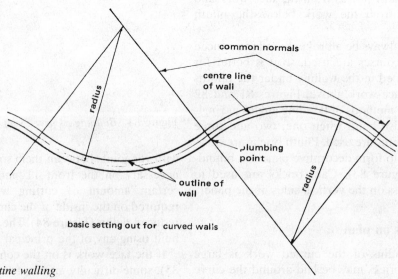

Figure 87   *Serpentine walling*

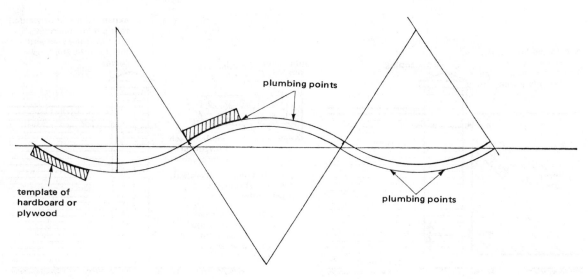

Figure 88 *Plan showing a method of maintaining the true alignment of a serpentine wall throughout its height*

constructed with curves in them to control the speed of the traffic. Low serpentine boundary walls are then constructed parallel to these roads.

When building walls which are curved on plan, it is most important to set out the plumbing points at the base and to maintain these points all the way up the wall. The work in between the plumbing points should be checked by the use of a template cut to the shape of the curve, out of plywood or hardboard (Figure 88).

Another method for checking the accuracy of curved work with a small radius is to use a radius rod. First, a piece of steel rod or conduit is fixed into position and plumbed; a batten is then drilled so that it fits easily over the rod and is cut to the length of the radius. The batten is threaded over the rod and the wall can now be built to the batten (Figure 89). This method is particularly useful in

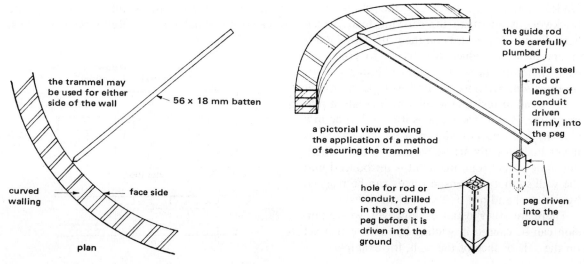

Figure 89 *The use of a trammel for the building of a concave curve*

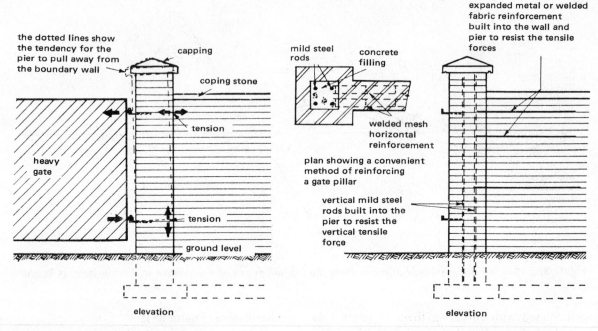

Figure 90   *Reinforced brickwork for a gate pillar*

the construction of walls for spiral staircases and other similar types of work which may be carried out in rather confined spaces.

Reinforced brickwork

Under normal circumstances the strength of brickwork is adequate for carrying loads which bear directly downwards on the wall. These loads create pressures which are trying to crush the wall; therefore the wall is said to be in a *state of compression*. Brickwork, however, is comparatively weak in resisting loads which create a pulling force. When this happens it is said to be in a *state of tension*. For this reason, brickwork is never built directly across window or door openings unless steel reinforcement is introduced into the wall so that the tensile forces can be resisted by the steel and not by the brickwork itself.

There are other instances, however, where tension can be caused in walling by loads which act on the side or face of the wall, for example:

1   Wind on a long exposed wall.

2   A boundary or garden wall with earth piled up behind it.

3   A pillar supporting a heavy gate (Figure 90).

The longer and higher an exposed wall is built, the more difficult it will be to resist the side thrusts of the forces acting upon it. Unless some form of reinforcement is introduced into the brickwork it is liable to fail. Reinforcement, thus,

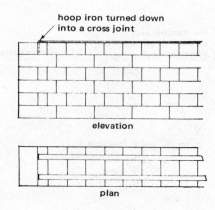

Figure 91   *Anchoring hoop iron reinforcement*

increases the lateral strength of walling and helps to prevent failures through tensile loading.

Reinforcement may also be used to great advantage where a decorative panel is introduced into a wall and a series of straight joints have to be used. In this case, reinforcement may be built into the joints to bond the wall together and to prevent failure in the decorative panel.

Types of reinforcement

The following are some of the types of reinforcement which are commonly used for the strengthening of brickwork:

Hoop iron. This is usually 30 by 2 mm and supplied in coils. It is not very much used now as it is difficult to obtain a good bond between the mortar and the hoop iron. This is because the bed joint between the bricks is so thin that it does not form a sufficiently large enough *body* around the steel to hold it in position. Therefore, there is a tendency for the steel to slide through the joint. This can, however, be largely overcome by bending the steel down at the ends into a convenient cross-joint (Figure 91) or by lapping or welding the ends at junctions or quoins (Figures 92).

Expanded metal. This is a metal strip which has been perforated and pulled out to form an excellent type of reinforcement which is very suitable for brickwork. This is because the holes thus formed will provide a good key between the reinforcement and the mortar. There is, therefore, little chance of its sliding through the joint. This is also supplied in coils 23–82 m long in various widths to suit different sizes of walling.

Welded fabric. This type of reinforcement usually consists of two 3 mm diameter rods with connecting rods welded at intervals. It, too, provides an excellent type of reinforcement because of the key which is formed between the mortar and the steel. Thus, there is little likelihood of any slipping by the reinforcement through the joint. Welded fabric is usually supplied in 23 m rolls. It is excellent for building into walls which are to be carried over openings.

Mild steel rods. These provide a good method of reinforcing brickwork where vertical reinforcement is required. They are particularly used for the reinforcing of brick lintels (or soldier arches, see *Brickwork 1*, Chapter 9), or gate pillars (Figure 90), or in the use of quetta bond (Figure 93).

Reinforced walling may also be constructed with hollow concrete blocks which are laid half-bond and the reinforcement being placed in the hollows, and the hollows filled with concrete as the wall is built (Figure 94).

Placing of the reinforcement

The spacing of the reinforcement will depend on the amount of pressure on the wall and the actual position where the maximum tensile force will occur.

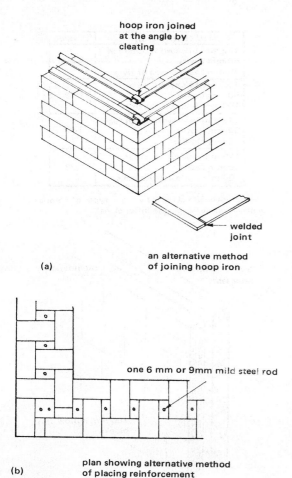

hoop iron joined at the angle by cleating

welded joint

(a) an alternative method of joining hoop iron

one 6 mm or 9mm mild steel rod

(b) plan showing alternative method of placing reinforcement

Figure 92   *Reinforced brickwork*

Composite walls

These are built of a combination of materials. The external walls have the advantage of being constructed in traditional brick (or stone) to blend with local surroundings, while the inside of the wall may be of a lightweight type of block. This would be made of any one of the following mater-

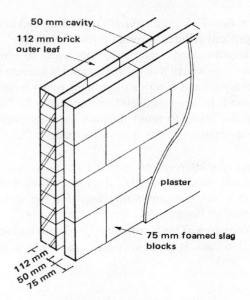

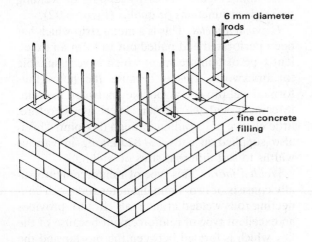

Figure 93 *Quetta bond*

Type of construction:	'U' value
112 mm brickwork outerleaf 50 mm cavity 75 mm foamed slag or fly ash	1.30
11·2 mm brickwork outer leaf 50 mm cavity 100 mm foamed slag or fly ash	1.13
112 mm brickwork outer leaf 50 mm cavity 75 mm clinker	1.42
112 mm brickwork outerleaf 50 mm cavity 100 mm hollowclay blocks	1.36

comparative 'U' values for various types of composite walls all plastered on the internal leaf

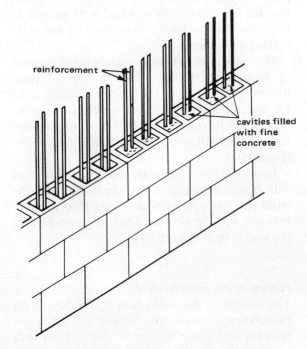

Figure 94 *Reinforced concrete block walling*

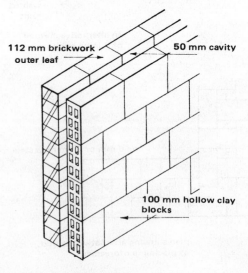

Figure 95 *Composite walls*

ials: breeze, clinker, foamed slag, hollow clay or fly ash (Figure 95). This type of construction reduces the cost of building, speeds up production and reduces the 'U' value of the wall, thereby minimizing heat losses. Composite walls may also be constructed with bricks of different sizes. For example, 50 mm thick bricks might be used on the face side of the wall and the common 65 mm thick bricks on the inside of the wall. In this case the wall should be bonded as frequently as possible and where the courses correspond in height (Figure 96).

Dry linings. These may also be classified as types of composite walls. They are constructed with normal solid or cavity walling. Battens are

then fixed to the wall either by plugging or, more usually, by a power gun or by masonry nails. Plaster board or some other type of wall board is then fixed to the battens (Figure 97). This type of wal-

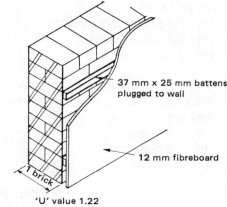

'U' value 1.22

1-brick solid wall with fibreboard fixed on battens

brick solid wall with plasterboard on battens 'U' value 1.65

as above, but plasterboard backed with aluminium 'U' value 1.30

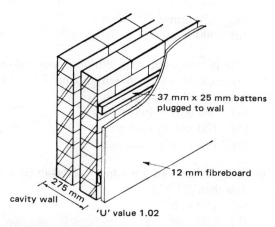

'U' value 1.02

275 mm cavity wall with 12 mm fibreboard fixed on battens

275 mm cavity wall with plaster-board fixed on battens 'U' value 1.45

as above, but plasterboard backed with aluminium 'U' value 1.08

Figure 96   *Composite walls using different thickness bricks*

Figure 97   *Dry linings*

ling has two advantages. It further reduces the 'U' value of the wall and also the amount of water used in its construction with the result that less time is required for drying out the structure.

Self-assessment questions

1 A 'supported wall' is a wall which receives support from
   (a) the foundation concrete
   (b) the footing courses
   (c) a buttressing wall

2 The minimum crushing strength of solid bricks or blocks for a one or two-storey building should be
   (a) 2.5 N/mm^2
   (b) 2.8 N/mm^2
   (c) 3.3 N/mm^2

3 If the blocks or bricks are hollow then the minimum crushing strength should be
   (a) 4.0 N/mm^2
   (b) 4.5 N/mm^2
   (c) 5.0 N/mm^2

4 The maximum distance apart that cavity wall ties should be placed is
   (a) 800 mm
   (b) 850 mm
   (c) 900 mm

5 The external wall of a building which does not exceed 9.0 m in length and 3.0 m in height shall be not less than
   (a)   90 mm in thickness
   (b) 100 mm in thickness
   (c) 110 mm in thickness

6 The thickness of a parapet wall shall be not less than
   (a) 180 mm
   (b) 190 mm
   (c) 200 mm

7 The height of a parapet wall shall not exceed
   (a) four times its thickness
   (b) five times its thickness
   (c) six times its thickness

8 The maximum depth to which a horizontal chase may be taken in a wall is
   (a) one-third of its thickness
   (b) one-quarter of its thickness
   (c) one-sixth of its thickness

9 The maximum depth to which a vertical chase may be taken in a wall is
   (a) one-third of its thickness
   (b) one-quarter of its thickness
   (c) one-sixth of its thickness

10 A squint brick is used
    (a) at the internal angle of an acute-angled quoin
    (b) at the external angle of an acute-angled quoin
    (c) at the external angle of an obtuse-angled quoin

11 With the aid of neat sketches show the bonding arrangement for an obtuse-angled (135 degrees) quoin in a 1-brick wall in
    (a) English bond
    (b) Flemish bond

12 Show the bonding arrangement for a quoin built in Flemish bond and having three plinth courses.

13 Describe the method of setting out and building a wall which is curved on plan.

14 What advantages has reinforced brickwork over normal walling?

Chapter 6

Decorative work

After reading this chapter you should be able to:

1 Have a good knowledge of the formation of decorative brickwork.
2 Understand the uses of coloured mortars for pointing.
3 Appreciate the use of contrasting coloured bricks.
4 Have a sound knowledge of the use and the setting out of special patterns in brickwork.
5 Know how to introduce tumbling-in to brick piers.
6 Have a sound knowledge of the construction of gable shoulders and cutting to gables.
7 Know how to use projecting patterns to their best advantage.
8 Understand how to set out and build various types of string courses.

Although the main purpose of bonding is to stabilize and strengthen brickwork, some types of bond are intended for decorative purposes only. The use of these is to introduce a feature into walling which might have only a plain surface.

Decorative work provides some relief and depth in appearance by creating shadow lines and forms a design in which might otherwise be merely a mass of brickwork. Although all this type of work must add extra cost to mass walling it is possible to introduce simple features at an economic cost.

The following are some of the economical methods which may be used for decorative work:

1 Use of contrasting coloured pointing mortars.
2 Introduction of different coloured bricks into the walling.
3 Laying of bricks in special patterns.
4 Laying of bricks which project from the face work and thereby form shadow lines on the face of the walling.

Coloured pointing

Interesting patterns can be formed in face work by using coloured mortars for pointing. One method is to *blind out* all of the perpends with a mortar that matches the colour of the face bricks, and then point the bed joints with a light or contrasting coloured mortar. This gives the effect of the wall being built with long thin slabs.

Another method is to use a *flying Flemish bond* and blind out the joint between each pair of stretchers with a mortar matching the colour of the bricks, and point the remainder with a contrasting coloured mortar. The stretchers in each case appear to be elongated (Figure 98).

A third method is to have two colours, one for the perpends and the other for the bed joints. This can cause a particularly pleasing effect, especially for internal face work, and greatly enhance the colour in the bricks. Great care must, however, be taken in selecting the colours as it is easy to *kill* the colour in the walling by the use of wrongly coloured mortars.

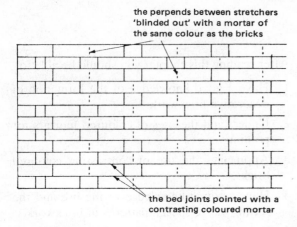

the perpends between stretchers 'blinded out' with a mortar of the same colour as the bricks

the bed joints pointed with a contrasting coloured mortar

Figure 98   *An elevation showing a use of coloured mortars for pointing*

There are many colouring agents that are available for use in mortars, but it is most important to remember when mixing such mortars that:

1   The mix is carefully gauged and the same gauge used for each mix.
2   The same class and type of sand is used for each mix.

Contrasting coloured bricks

In multi-storeyed buildings it is common practice to introduce large panels of contrasting coloured bricks in the external walls. These are very often of black or dark blue bricks and give a *shadow effect* in the walls, as they create an impression of depth. Sometimes these panels are pointed with a mortar of the same colour as the bricks to create an even better effect of depth in the elevation of the structure.

Another use of contrasting coloured bricks is to build block-bonded corners (Figures 99–101) which create a very pleasing effect at the external angles of a building.

Bricks laid in special patterns

Diaper bond
On large areas of plain walling, diamond patterns may be formed by using coloured bricks which are in contrast to the general walling. This method of forming a feature in brickwork has always been popular and there are many very good examples of this work to be seen in both old and modern buildings (Figures 102 and 103).

Basket weave bond
This is mainly used in panels. It consists of sets of three bricks laid alternately horizontally and vertically. Sets of four bricks may also be used provided that the thickness of four bricks plus four bed joints are equal to the length of a brick (Figures 104 and 105). The important points to watch when building panels with this bond are first to keep the vertical bricks truly plumb and the horizontal courses level, secondly to select the bricks carefully for consistency in length so that the patterns are of even shape and thirdly to keep the main horizontal and vertical joints which pass

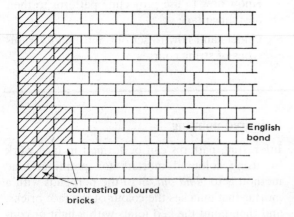

English bond

contrasting coloured bricks

Figure 99   *Block bonded quoins*

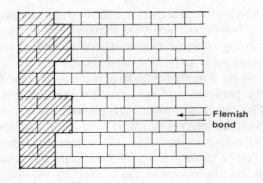

Flemish bond

Figure 100   *Block bonded quoin*

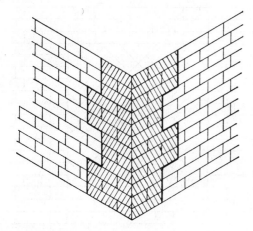

Figure 101   *Block bonded quoin*

Figure 102   *Diaper bond*

Figure 103   *Diaper bond*

right through the panel in straight lines. Although this appears to be quite a straightforward type of bond, much skill and care are essential for a first-class job.

A variation of this bond may be made by building the basket pattern at an angle of 45 degrees to the horizontal. This can produce a very effective panel, but involves a great deal of extra cutting at the edges (Figures 106 and 107).

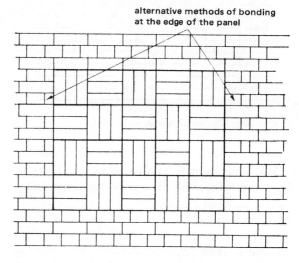

Figure 104   *Basket weave bond using three courses to 225 mm*

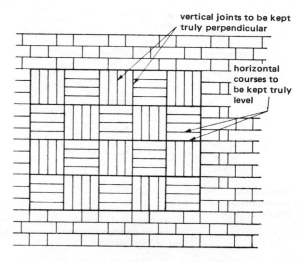

Figure 105   *Basket weave bond using four courses to 225 mm*

Figure 106   *Diagonal basket weave bond*

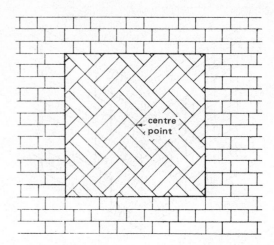

Figure 107   *Diagonal basket weave bond*

Whenever panels in diagonal basket weave bond are being built, it is a good practice to set out the panel first on a suitable flat surface such as hardboard, plywood or even a concrete floor or slab. The bricks are then carefully marked out and cut to their required shapes before building into the panel. Another economical way to set out

such panels is to lay the bricks dry on a convenient flat surface, allowing the correct width of joint between the bricks. Then, with the aid of a straightedge, the outline of the panel is marked out on the top of these bricks (Figure 108). The bricks which are on the edge of the panel are now marked ready for cutting which can be done with the aid of a mechanical saw or by hammer and bolster as required.

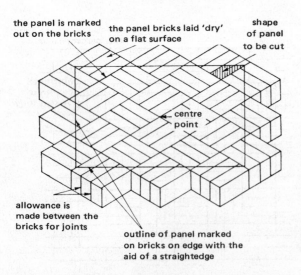

Figure 108   *A method of setting out a panel in diagonal basket weave bond*

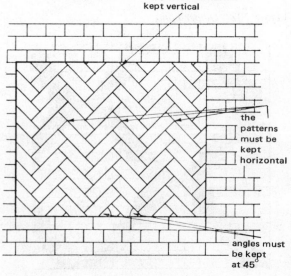

Figure 109   *Vertical herring-bone bond*

Figure 110   *Horizontal herring-bone bond*

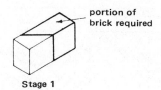

Stage 1

the brick is marked out
for a cut in a herring-bone
pattern

portion of
brick required

Stage 2

the brick is cut with a
hammer and bolster at right
angles to its face

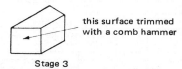

this surface trimmed
with a comb hammer

Stage 3

the brick is cut along
the splayed line and the face
of the cut trimmed to an even
surface

Figure 111   *Cutting bricks with a bolster and hammer*

Herring-bone bond

This consists of a series of patterns of bricks which are laid at 90 degrees to each other, but at 45 degrees to the horizontal plane. Such patterns may be laid vertically or horizontally (Figures 109 and 110).

This work should be carried out by either of the methods described for the diagonal basket weave bond. When panels are being built with herring-bone bond, great care should be taken to ensure that each pattern is kept truly vertical or horizontal as the case may be, by ensuring that all of the angles in the pattern are maintained in a straight line.

When cutting the bricks with a hammer and bolster, do not attempt to cut the brick directly along the slanting line as it is liable to break off at the acute angle. First, cut the brick at right angles across its thickness from the point where the slanting line meets the edge of the brick. Then, cut along its slanting line. This method will ensure a clean-cut brick (Figure 111).

Diagonal herring-bone bond

This may be formed by travelling the herring-bone patterns at 45 degrees to the horizontal. It is a very pleasant-looking pattern and one which requires much less cutting than either the vertical or horizontal herring-bone bonds (Figure 112).

Figure 112   *Diagonal herring-bone bond*

Figure 113   *Double herring-bone bond*

Figure 114   *Diagonal double herring-bone bond*

Double herring-bone bond

This is similar in every respect to herring-bone bond except that double stretchers are used to form the patterns instead of single bricks (Figures 113 and 114).

All the foregoing bonds are suitable for the building of decorative panels, the in-filling of tympanums – the walling between the lintel over an opening and the relieving arch over the lintel (Figure 115), in building up a pediment over an opening and forming a gable.

Tumbling-in courses

These are used where buttresses or walls have to be reduced in size. They allow the face sides of the bricks to form the sloping side of the work and thereby provide a good surface to resist the action of rain and frost. This may be done in one of two ways:

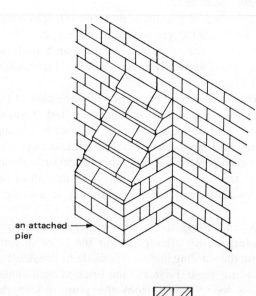

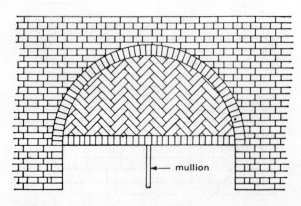

Figure 115   *Filling in a tympanum with herring-bone bond*

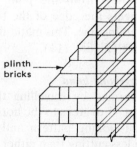

Figure 116   *Tumbling-in with the aid of plinth bricks*

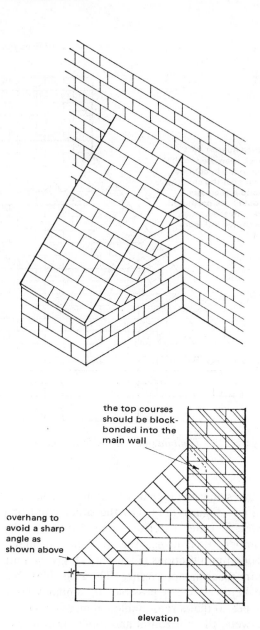

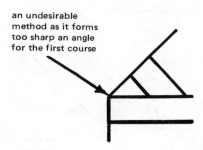

Figure 118 *Undesirable method of cutting the first course of tumbling-in*

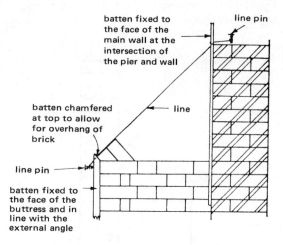

Figure 119 *Method of lining-in tumbling-in*

the top courses should be block-bonded into the main wall

overhang to avoid a sharp angle as shown above

elevation

Figure 117 *Tumbling-in courses*

1 By using plinth bricks (Figure 116), or
2 By laying the bricks at an angle with their beds being cut to suit the angle of the slope of the tumbling-in (Figure 117).

It is usual to overhang the first course of the tumbling-in to prevent the first bricks from having to be cut at a sharp angle and leaving a small area of brick to resist the action of the weather (Figure 118).

The following methods are used to ensure the accuracy of the work when building tumbling-in courses:

1 One batten is fixed to the wall so that it cuts the point where the apex of the tumbling-in will occur and another at the springing of the tumbling-in. This enables the bricklayer to fix a line from the apex to the first course of the work and the tumbling-in courses may now be built in to the line (Figure 119).
2 A gun or a template is cut from hardboard or plywood.
3 Two pieces of batten are fixed together to form a gun to suit the angle of the slope of the

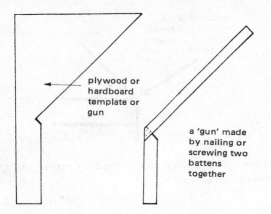

Figure 120   *Templates or 'guns' for lining-in tumbling-in courses*

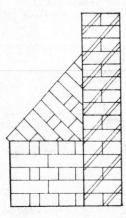

Figure 121   *A typical method of bonding for a small tumbling-in*

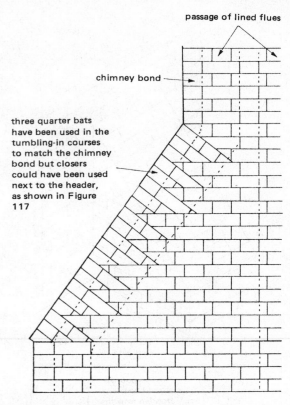

Figure 122   *Tumbling-in courses for a chimney stack*

tumbling-in courses (Figure 120). These may be used to check the accuracy of the work by placing the template or gun at the right height and against the work immediately below the tumbling-in. It is, therefore, most important that this work is kept truly plumb. Before beginning to build the tumbling-in courses, the work should be carefully set out on a board or other suitable flat surface. The distance from the springing to the apex of the tumbling-in should be gauged to prevent the use of a split course which would look most unsightly in any work of this nature.

If the tumbling-in is only small, all of the tumbling

courses may be taken down to the same horizontal course (Figure 121). On the other hand, if the work is quite extensive and requires a large number of courses, the tumbling-in may be divided into sections (Figure 122), giving a much more pleasing appearance. These sections should be kept, as far as possible, in similar sizes and shapes so that a reasonable balance is maintained between the horizontal and tumbling courses.

Gable shoulders or springers
These are used at the springing of gables and may be constructed in brick, tiles or concrete (Figures 123–127). If bricks are used, the bond must be adjusted to suit the overhanging courses. These courses may be corbelled 56 or 28 mm at a time, the latter being preferred as it gives a better appearance.

The Building Regulations state: 'that the extent to which any part of a wall overhangs a part below

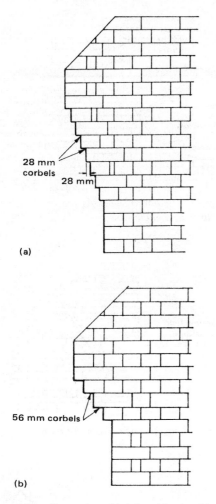

28 mm corbels

28 mm

(a)

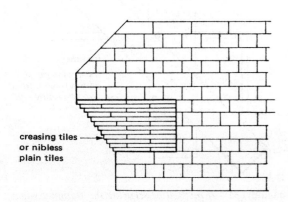

creasing tiles or nibless plain tiles

56 mm corbels

(b)

Figure 123 *Examples of brick gable shoulders*

Figure 124 *A tiled gable springer or 'tiled knee'*

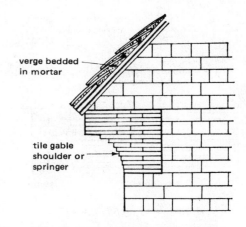

verge bedded in mortar

tile gable shoulder or springer

Figure 125 *Ornamental tiled gable springer*

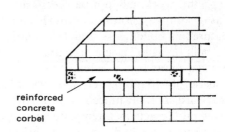

reinforced concrete corbel

Figure 126 *Reinforced concrete gable springer*

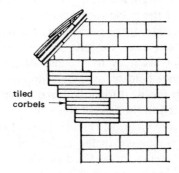

tiled corbels

Figure 127 *Gable tile springer*

shall not be such as to impair the stability of the wall or any part of the wall'.

It is normally considered a safe practice for the overhang not to exceed the thickness of the wall immediately below the overhang.

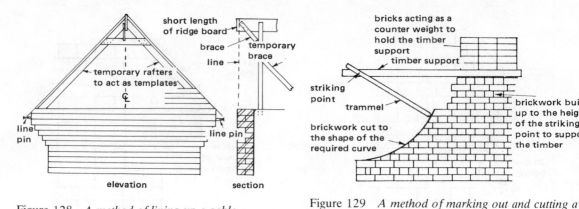

Figure 128   *A method of lining-up a gable*

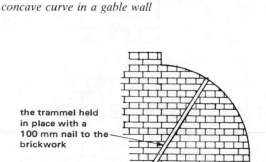

Figure 129   *A method of marking out and cutting a concave curve in a gable wall*

Cutting to gables

Although this work may not be specifically classified as decorative, gables can provide an attractive feature to a building. A straightforward gable may be built up as follows: a temporary profile is first erected immediately behind the gable wall. This consists of two roof rafters and a short length of ridge board carefully braced as shown in Figure 128. This profile acts as a template so that lines may be secured for building up the brickwork. Care must be taken to ensure that the height of the template is correctly predetermined. A line can then be stretched from the lowest course on each side of the gable to the profile and the wall built to this line. If the gable wall involves the use of any curved work, this may be constructed and checked for accuracy by the use of a trammel. This is either held by a timber support which is bedded on the wall for a concave curve (Figure 129) or fixed to the face of the wall by a 100 mm nail for a convex curve (Figure 130). If the striking point is situated in the middle of a brick, a piece of batten may be fixed on the face of the wall by nailing into two bed joints (not necessarily consecutive joints) and the trammel nailed to this batten (Figure 131).

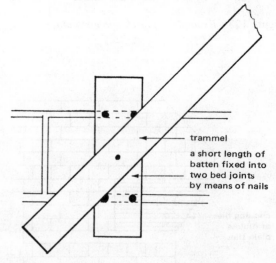

Figure 130   *A method of marking out and cutting a convex curve in a gable wall*

Projecting patterns

Projecting bricks

These are used in many modern structures to form patterns in large plain surfaces of brickwork. A simple method is to use headers which project

Figure 131   *A method of securing the trammel when the striking point is situated in the middle of a brick*

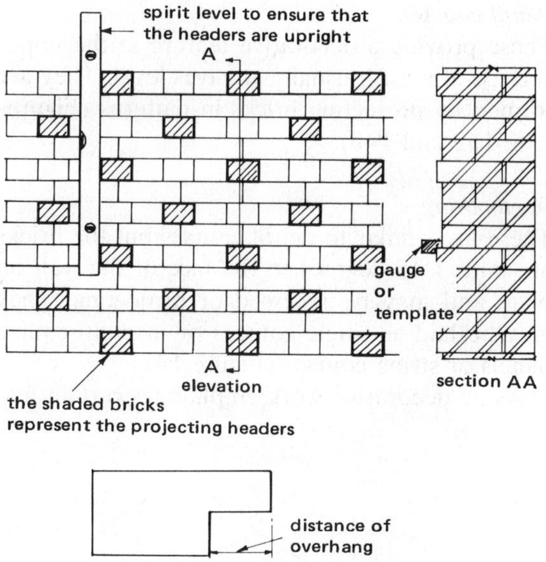
spirit level to ensure that
the headers are upright
A
A
elevation
section AA
gauge
or
template
the shaded bricks
represent the projecting headers
distance of
overhang

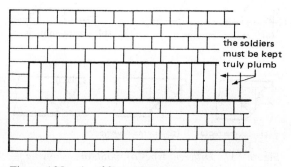

Figure 132 *Plywood gauge or template*

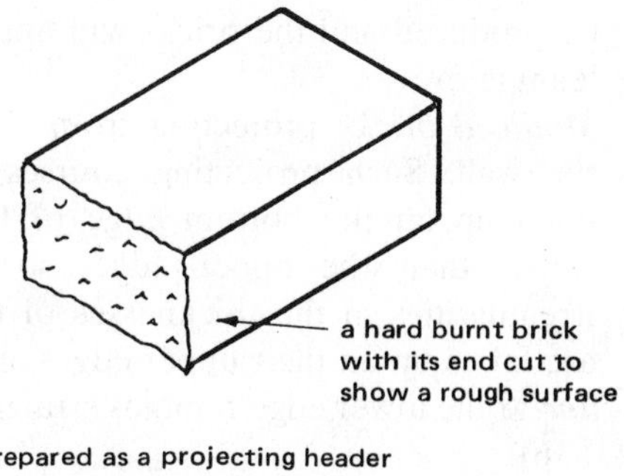
a hard burnt brick
with its end cut to
show a rough surface
a brick prepared as a projecting header

Figure 133 *Projecting bricks for decorative brickwork*

from the face of the wall about 18 mm. These are laid at equal distances apart and kept truly plumb so that straight lines are formed horizontally, vertically and diagonally across the wall. A small template or gauge may be made to assist in checking in an easy manner the accuracy of the projections (Figure 132).

Another method is to cut the ends of the bricks so that a rough surface is left protruding from the face of the wall. Although the surface is rough, care must be taken with the cutting because it is important that the edges are cut square, while the surface is left uneven. For this type of work, it is essential that a hard, well-burnt brick is used so that it will stand up to the weather (Figure 133).

Yet another method is to use small isolated patterns in the wall (Figure 134). This method can be very effective if contrasting coloured bricks are used for the patterns.

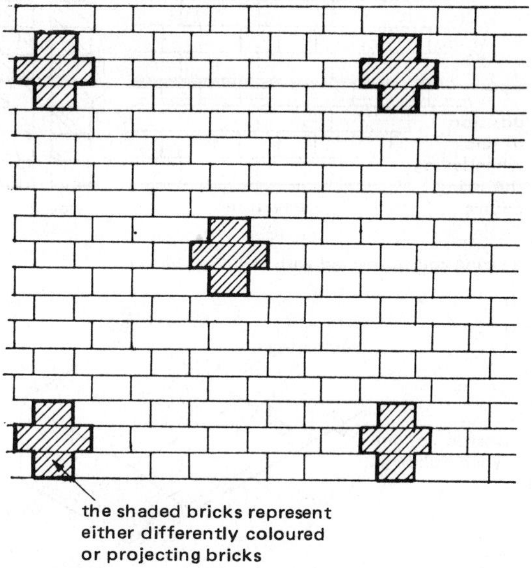
the shaded bricks represent
either differently coloured
or projecting bricks

Figure 134 *Decorative brickwork with contrasting coloured and projecting bricks*

String courses

These are horizontal courses built into the face of walls to form an architectural feature. These may consist of:

1 *Soldier courses* which are bricks laid on end side-by-side (Figure 135). These must be laid truly plumb, otherwise a very poor effect will

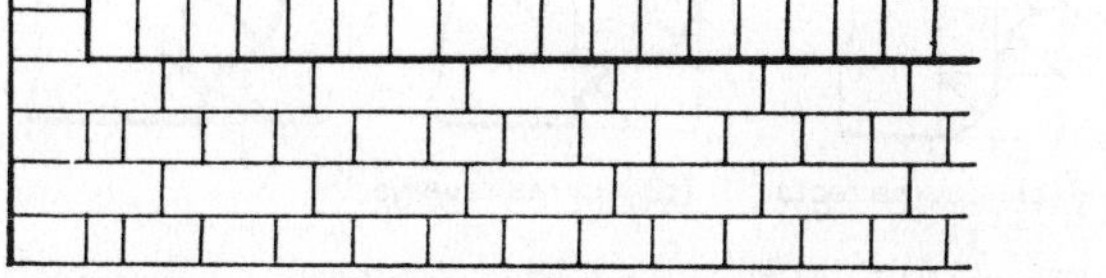
the soldiers
must be kept
truly plumb

Figure 135 *A soldier string course*

be produced and the bricks will appear to be leaning over.

2 *Moulded bricks* projecting from the face of the wall. Such projecting courses must be lined up on the bottom edge of the bricks rather than the upper edge, so that any irregularities in the thicknesses of the bricks are taken up on their upper edges and the *eye line* at the lower edge remains straight (Figure 136).

Various shapes of mouldings are shown in Figure 137.

Dentil courses

These provide a decorative feature at the upper surface of a wall, usually at eaves level. They are formed by projecting bricks in patterns (Figures 138, 139 and 140).

Dogtoothing

These are similar to dentil courses but the bricks are laid at 45 degrees to the face of the wall on plan, and may be recessed or projecting. They may be laid as single courses or in multi-course panels or string courses (Figure 141).

As all decorative work emphasizes certain fea-

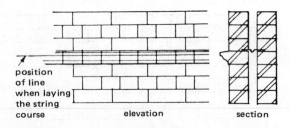

a string course formed with moulded bricks

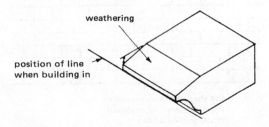

Figure 136 *Details of a typical moulded brick*

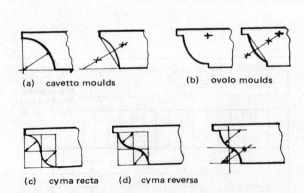

(a)   cavetto moulds   (b)   ovolo moulds

(c)   cyma recta   (d)   cyma reversa

Figure 137 *Different types of mouldings showing methods of their setting out*

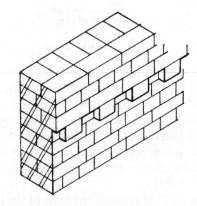

Figure 138 *A single dentil course*

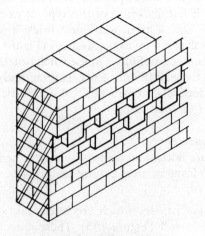

Figure 139 *A double dentil course*

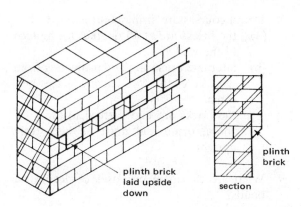

Figure 140 *A single dentil course incorporating the use of plinth bricks*

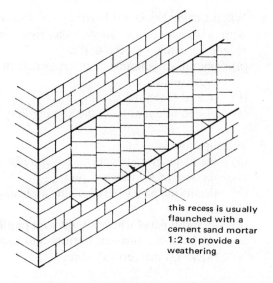

this recess is usually flaunched with a cement sand mortar 1:2 to provide a weathering

tures in general brickwork, it is most important to observe the following points:

1 Take special care to ensure that all work is truly plumb and level.
2 All overhanging work should be lined-in on the bottom edge of each course.
3 Work involving cutting should be carefully set out before building starts.
4 Make full use of templates, trammels, guns or gauges to check the accuracy of the work.
5 Carefully select the bricks to be used on special features and reject any which have their faces damaged.
6 Carefully check the angles at which bricks are cut and laid.

Self-assessment questions

1 Block-bonded corners are those which are built with
   (a) 450 × 225 ×100 mm blocks
   (b) contrasting bricks in block patterns
   (c) contrasting bonds

2 Diaper bond is
   (a) diamond formed in plain walling
   (b) panels of three bricks horizontal and three vertical laid alternately
   (c) similar to (b) but laid at 45 degrees

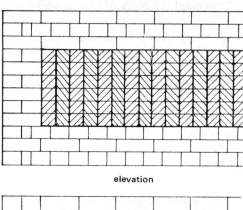

elevation

plan

the bricks in the dogtoothings are laid in opposite directions in alternate courses to form a bond

Figure 141 *Dog toothing*

3 Herring-bone bond is the name given to bricks which are
   (a) laid at 45 degrees to the horizontal plane
   (b) laid at 90 degrees to each other but at 45 degrees to the horizontal plane
   (c) laid at 90 degrees to the horizontal plane

4 When cutting bricks for herring-bone bonds with a hammer and bolster the first cut should be made with the bolster
  (a) placed at right angles to the face at the acute angle
  (b) placed along the sloping line
  (c) placed at 5 mm from the sloping line

5 A tympanum is
  (a) the name given to courses which reduce the size of an attached pier
  (b) the in-fill panel between an arch and lintel
  (c) an in-fill panel which is built with plinth bricks at the top and bottom and cant bricks on the vertical edges

6 A trammel is a piece of timber which is used to
  (a) mark out a concave curve in a gable wall
  (b) line up a gable wall
  (c) to check the corbels in a gable shoulder

7 With reference to Figure 142, a cyma-recta mould is
  (a)
  (b)
  (c)

8 Dentil courses are string courses in which
  (a) the bricks are at 45 degrees to the face of the wall
  (b) alternate bricks are laid projecting from the face of the wall leaving spaces between
  (c) the bricks are laid vertical to the horizontal plane and must be kept truly upright.

9 What are the main purposes of decorative bonds?

10 Describe how coloured mortars may be used to enhance the appearance of brickwork.

11 Make neat sketches of (a) herring-bone bond and (b) basket weave bond.

12 Describe how the 'tumbling-in' to a pier may be checked for accuracy when it is being built.

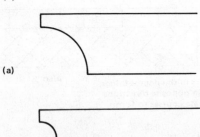

(a)

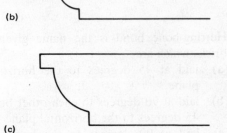

(b)

(c)

Figure 142

Chapter 7

Door and window openings

After reading this chapter you should be able to:

1 Have a sound knowledge of the construction of steps to doorways.

2 Know how to fix door frames in square and recess reveals.

3 Have a good knowledge of the construction and installation of precast and *in situ* lintels.

4 Have a good knowledge of the use of steel lintels.

5 Understand the methods of setting out and cutting brick arches.

6 Know how to place arch centres and install the arches over openings.

7 Know how to build a wheel arch or bull's-eye opening.

8 Have a sound knowledge of gauged and rubbed work.

Door openings: thresholds

Bricks and tiles for thresholds must be well-burnt and able to stand severe weather conditions, as well as wear and tear. Engineering bricks and quarry tiles are eminently suitable as they are water-resistant and have strong wearing properties. The mortar for bedding such bricks and tiles should not be weaker than one part of cement to three parts of clean washed sand.

Thresholds should be laid on a bed of well-compacted concrete with a roughened surface. Before laying the bricks, the concrete must be dampened; if the concrete is very dry it should be saturated first. Then the surplus water should be allowed to evaporate so that the concrete will be only damp when the bricks are eventually bedded on to it. The mortar should be mixed to a dry consistency. (The practice of sprinkling dry cement on to a mortar bed before laying engineering bricks should never be used by any craftsman, as it has a harmful effect on the final strength and wearing properties of the mortar.) The secret of laying engineering bricks and quarry tiles, because of their non-porosity, is to place them firmly into the bed and leave them well alone. The more they are tapped with a trowel the more water will be attracted to the surface of the mortar bed. This will result in the bricks or tiles *swimming on the bed* and cement grout will run down the face of the brickwork and make it dirty.

After the bricks or tiles are bedded, the joints may be pointed with a Portland cement mortar (1:1) to prevent any moisture from penetrating into the bed joints.

When the steps are completed, any stains on them may be cleaned off by applying with a cloth a solution of two parts linseed oil to one part turpentine substitute. This solution will also enhance the colour of the bricks or tiles.

Brick steps should be truly level across their width, but may have a very small slope outwards of about 3 mm, so as to throw off any water which may fall on them. On no account must this slope be excessive or it will be liable to cause a person to slip and fall.

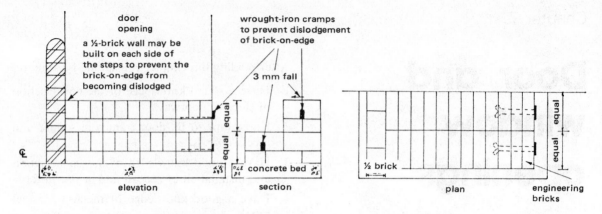

Figure 143   *A simple straight flight of brick steps showing methods of preventing dislodgement of bricks on edge*

Before thresholds are built, the heights and threads of the steps must be carefully determined. If two or more steps are to be built into one flight all the risers must be of equal height and the treads of equal length. This is again extremely important to prevent accidents (Figure 143).

When quarry tiles are used for the surface of steps (Figure 144), a certain amount of cutting will probably be necessary to fit the steps around irregular shapes. Because of their brittleness, these tiles are not easily cut by hand. They create little or no difficulty, however, if they are cut with either a mechanical saw with a carborundum wheel or a patent portable tile cutter with a hardened wheel. A Harris tile cutter (Figure 145) is a very efficient cutting machine.

If, however, one of these tiles has to be cut by hand, place it first, solidly on a flat surface (a heap of sand will also provide a suitable surface) and

lightly hammer and chisel along the mark on the tile with a light hammer and a small sharp chisel. Keep passing from one side to the other until the tile breaks at the required point. Heavy blows with the hammer should be avoided as these will only break the tile in the wrong place. Quarry tiles are difficult to cut and require much care and patience to prevent excessive wastage. A mechanical saw will cut quarry tiles with ease, but such a machine is expensive to buy and requires a sufficient volume of work to make its use an economical proposition.

A Harris tile cutter is simple to operate and very useful for this type of cutting. It consists of a table which carries the tile, and is moved backwards and forwards by a small handle. The hardened wheel is lowered into contact with the surface of the tile by a vertical handle. The sliding table of the apparatus is then traversed backwards

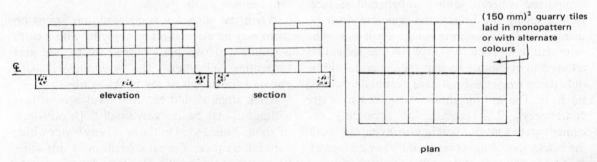

Figure 144   *Brick and quarry tile steps*
This method provides a better proportion of rise to tread than the example in Figure 139

and forwards by a handle on the side of the machine and the cutting wheel lowered to the tile at the required cutting mark. Pressure is applied to the wheel by the upper handle. While the tile is being moved the pressure is gradually increased until the tile breaks to the required shape. This apparatus is inexpensive and easy to carry. It weighs only about 6.8 kg.

Door frames

These may be fixed into position either after the wall is completed, or as the wall is being built.

Fixing door frames after the wall is completed
If the frames are of a high quality timber, it is generally more satisfactory to fix them into the opening after the walling is finished. This will prevent any damage being caused to the frame by wheelbarrows or heavy articles being taken through the opening. If the frame is constructed of oak, under no circumstances should it be built in the wall as the work proceeds because if any lime comes into contact with the oak it will cause bad staining. This staining will be extremely difficult, if not impossible, to remove.

When frames are built in after the walling is completed, the bricklayer must make suitable provision for the fixing of the frame (see *Brickwork 1*, Chapter 9).

Fixing door frames as the walling is being built
This is more convenient, so far as the bricklayer is concerned, as the frame acts as a profile and reduces the amount of plumbing that would otherwise be necessary.

The frame should be held in place with the aid of *two* boards, one at each side of the frame, in order to ensure that the frame remains parallel to the face of the wall from bottom to top and also that it is kept plumb during building operations. Each board may be secured at its base by means of bricks or other heavy objects, and the frame may be held at its head by a block nailed on the board, or by nails projecting from the board and hitched over the head of the frame. It is also very important to ensure that the frame is not squeezed in at the middle, particularly with frames of small cross-section. To prevent this happening, it is a good practice to fix a *stretcher* (a length of batten) across the centre of the frame (Figure 146). Although this may be a nuisance to people who wish to pass through the opening while the work is in progress, it should still be done to prevent an excessive amount of corrective work at a later stage. In any case, the batten can

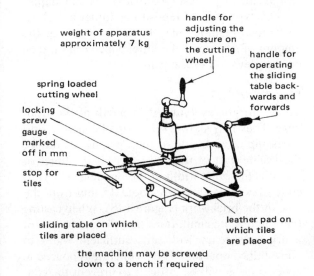

Figure 145   *Harris tile cutter*

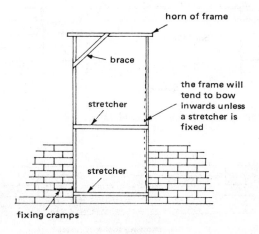

Figure 146   *An elevation showing a method of preventing distortion in a frame during building-in operations*

be removed as soon as the wall is finished so it need only be in place for a comparatively short time.

Once the frame is in position, it should be protected by nailing thin pieces of timber or hardboard in the front so that it is not damaged by wheelbarrows or equipment carried through the opening. When the frame is made from a hardwood and is to be oiled rather than painted after the work is finished, nails must not be driven into the frame when fixing the protective timber, as it will be difficult to hide the nail holes. Protection may be given by constructing a simple cage of hardboard, placing it over the frame and wiring it back to nails driven into the brickwork on each side.

Great care must be taken to ensure that the frame is kept truly plumb while it is being built into the wall. It is very costly and time-wasting to correct a frame which has been built into position without being properly plumbed.

Treatment at reveals
Door frames may be fixed to square reveals or set into recesses (see *Brickwork 1*, Chapter 9). If the recess is to be formed in a cavity wall, it is possible

to bond the reveal into the outer leaf of the wall, but this usually involves so much cutting that it is quite impracticable. Even if the amount of cutting is acceptable it still usually results in an unsatisfactory job, because of the difficulty in obtaining a good tie-in to the wall. It also makes it difficult to provide an adequate damp-proof course. It is, therefore, far more practical to build the reveal with a straight joint between it and the outer leaf (Figure 147). This also allows the damp-proof course to be housed in this joint, but the reveal has to be stabilized to comply with the Building Regulations. This is done by building in extra wall ties as near as is practicable to the opening and at every 300 mm in height.

Door and window heads

The Building Regulations require that adequate means of supporting the superstructure shall be provided over every opening and recess. The number, size or position of openings or recesses in a wall shall not be such as to impair its stability of the wall.

Concrete lintels

The simplest way of bridging an opening is to use a reinforced concrete lintel. This may be either cast *in situ* or precast (see *Brickwork 1*, Chapter 9). This type of lintel tends to be rather unsightly, so various methods may be used to reduce the amount of surface of the lintel which can be seen on the elevation of the wall.

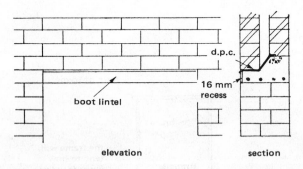

Figure 147 *A 'boot' lintel elevation*

plan showing shape of lintel

Figure 148 *A 'boot' lintel plan*

Boot lintels
These are greatly reduced in depth at the front edge. They may show a thin strip of concrete with a bearing at each side of the opening, or reduce the visible part of the front face of the lintel so that it is the exact width of the opening. The concrete may be recessed by about 15 mm from the face of the brickwork (Figure 148). When casting these lintels, it is important that the concrete is of a dry consistency with only sufficient water to allow full compaction. If the concrete is poured in a wet state, it will be difficult to prevent the concrete from rising above the formwork on the front

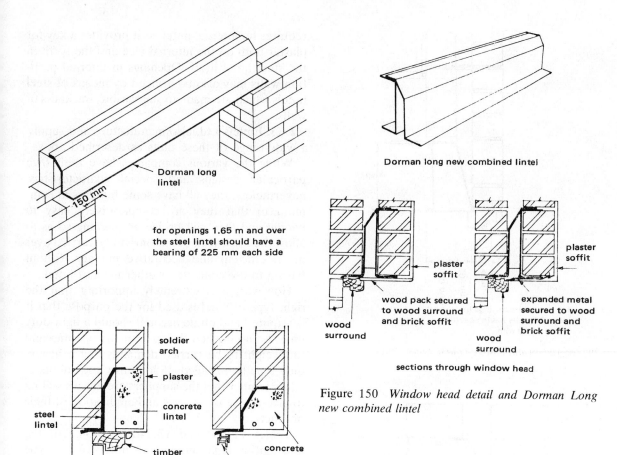

Dorman long lintel

150 mm

for openings 1.65 m and over the steel lintel should have a bearing of 225 mm each side

Dorman long new combined lintel

plaster soffit

plaster soffit

wood pack secured to wood surround and brick soffit

expanded metal secured to wood surround and brick soffit

wood surround

wood surround

sections through window head

Figure 150 *Window head detail and Dorman Long new combined lintel*

soldier arch

plaster

steel lintel

concrete lintel

timber frame

metal frame

concrete lintel

section

section

Figure 149 *Alternative methods of bridging an opening showing different shapes of steel lintels*

edge of the lintel, apart from the fact that it will lose a great deal of strength.

Steel lintels

This is a modern technique of bridging an opening and supporting the walling above. It may be used in conjunction with a concrete lintel, as shown in Figure 149. The steel member is shaped as shown, and may also act as a damp-proof course in the case of cavity walls.

Another type of steel lintel made by the Dorman Long steel company is a combined unit intended to carry both skins of a cavity wall (Figure 150).

Other companies who manufacture lintels

Figure 151 *Superlintel*

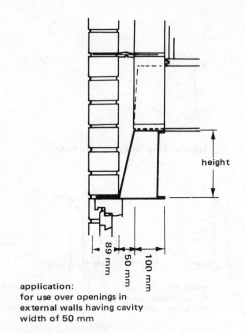

application:
for use over openings in
external walls having cavity
width of 50 mm

Figure 152   *Catnic three course lintel*

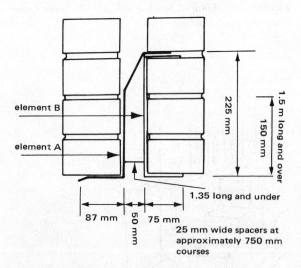

Figure 153   *Steel lintel*

include the Catnic Components Co. Ltd, and Frederick Jones & Son, who supply steel units that may be used in conjunction with any mode of construction, such as brickwork and masonry, and involving the use of concrete or timber lintels on the internal face or even another type, which

requires no internal lintel, as it provides a key for plaster both on the internal face and the soffit in the steel lintel itself. Openings in internal partition walls may also be bridged by means of steel lintels which are made to suit various thickness of walls.

I. G. Lintels Ltd, also manufacture and supply a wide-range of these units as described above.

While the various companies have their own particular designs and special characteristics, nevertheless, they all have some features in common, in that they are comparatively easy to handle and they will bridge an opening so as to allow the brickwork or masonry to be carried over in an efficient and decorative manner without having to use concrete or other form of lintel.

However, it is extremely important that the right type of lintel is used for the purpose that it is required and on no account should a light-duty lintel be used when the span of the opening and the weight to be carried demands that a heavy-duty type be installed. If you have any doubts at all remember that the suppliers are always willing to give advice on the use and application of their products.

Tables 11, 12 and 13 indicate some of the information regarding various lintels of this type but full information concerning their application and loading may be obtained by contacting the companies direct, or at your nearest Building Information Centre.

A brick-faced lintel

Figure 156 illustrates a method of casting *in situ*. Note that a support should be provided at the front of the brick-facing to prevent it from being forced outwards by the pressure of the concrete. The bricks are given added support by tie irons or wires, each of which will have one end built in the joints of the bricks and the remainder bedded into the concrete. The diagram also shows a method that may be used to provide a recess if one should be required.

A stone-faced lintel

This provides a more attractive finish than plain Portland cement concrete. The stone facing may be a mixture of stone dust and white cement (1:2)

Table 11 *Dorman Long steel lintels*

Clear span	Material thickness		Safe UD floor load	Total maximum safe UD load	WT/LIN, 300 mm
	element 'A'	element 'B'			
300 mm–1.05 m	3 mm	3 mm	1016 kgf	2032 kgf	4.5 kg
1.21 m–1.82 m	3 mm	3 mm	1219 kgf	2540 kgf	5.6 kg
2 m–2.4 m	4 mm	3 mm	1219 kgf	2743 kgf	6.1 kg
2.55 m–3.34 m	5 mm	3 mm	1625 kgf	3760 kgf	7.0 kg

Table 12 *Catnic steel lintels*

Lintel type/code	CN8a	CN8b	CN8c	CN8d
Manufactured lengths in increments of 150 mm	2250–2700	2850–3750	3900–4575	4800
Minimum end bearings (mm)	150	150	150	150
Height 'h' (mm)	219	219	219	219
Safe working load (tonnes)	3.0	3.0	3.0	2.6
Weight per metre (kgs)	12.4	15.4	19.2	19.2

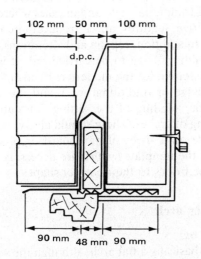

Figure 154 *L1/S for 50 mm cavity wall construction*

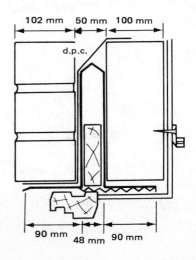

Figure 155 *L1/HD for 50 mm cavity wall construction heavy-duty loading*

Table 13   *I. G. steel lintels*

Lintel type/code	L1/S			L1/HD	
Manufactured lengths	600–1500	1650–1800	1950–2250	600–1500	1650–2100
Height (mm)	120	130	170	210	210
Minimum end bearings (mm)	150	150	150	150	150
Total allowable UDLkN	17	17	22	28	32
Finished weight (kg/m)	8.95	9.47	11.04	14.09	15.56

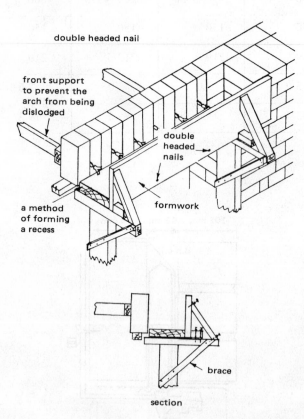

Figure 156   *Brick-faced lintel*

with just sufficient water added to hydrate the cement. This dry mix should be rendered on the soffit and face of the formwork to a depth of about 25 mm. The reinforcement is then placed and the Portland cement concrete poured on the top and behind the stone facing. Care should be taken to ensure that the Portland cement concrete is not tamped right through the stone facing otherwise it will show as a flaw on the face of the lintel when the formwork is removed.

Arches

Arches are not commonly used in modern structures. They are, however, still designed for buildings of traditional style and in cases where special decorative features are introduced in the face work. In addition, repairs and alterations to existing buildings have to be carried out. It is, therefore, essential for the modern craftsman to have a knowledge of traditional work and this includes an understanding of the setting out, cutting and building of arches. These should always be set out full-size on a sheet of hardboard or plywood to obtain the templates which are necessary for cutting the bricks to their correct shapes.

Camber arch

Setting out
This is basically a flat arch, although the voussoirs are set out on an arc. A common method for set-

ting out this type of arch is illustrated in Figure 157 and carried out as follows:

1   The span AB is marked off.
2   The skewbacks are drawn at an angle of 60 degrees to the springing line and extended downwards until they meet at point C.
3   The outline of the arch is completed by drawing the extrados at the required depth of the arch.
4   The intrados of the arch is usually given a rise of 3 mm to every 300 mm of span to counteract any illusion of sagging in the arch.
5   With the aid of a measuring tape, trammel or pair of trammel heads, an arc is drawn with a radius equal to the distance from point C to the crown of the arch at D.
6   The voussoirs of the arch are marked off on this arc. If the arch is to be bonded, an even number of courses must be plotted on each side of the key brick. This ensures that the springing bricks correspond to the key brick.
7   The bed joints of the arch are drawn by radiating them down to point C.
8   The face joints are then drawn parallel to the extrados of the arch.

Obtaining the template

Having set out the arch full-size, a template must be obtained so that the bricks can be cut to the correct shape. Either of the following methods may be used for this:

Method 1

Half of the arch is set out full-size on a sheet of tempered hardboard. When the setting out has been thoroughly checked for accuracy, the vourssoirs are carefully sawn apart with a carpenter's saw. These are used as individual templates for the arch bricks. Each template is used twice, first for the voussoir on the left-hand side of the arch and then for the corresponding voussoir on the right-hand side (Figure 158). The exception to this rule is the key brick.

Method 2

A template is marked out from the key brick on the full-size drawing and checked for accuracy by

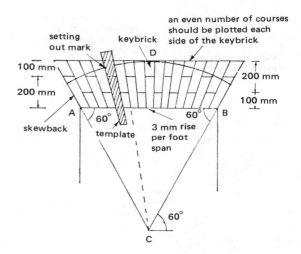

Figure 157   *A method of setting out a camber arch*

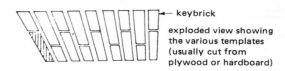

Figure 158   *A method of setting out the templates for a camber arch*

trying it on other voussoir shapes. This template should be of sufficient length to allow for marking off the springing courses. The template is laid over the key brick on the drawing and a mark is made on the template where it touches the setting out curve. This mark is called the *setting out mark*. A mark is also made at the point where the template touches the intrados of the arch. This is called the *cutting mark*. The angle that they key brick makes with the intrados is transferred from the drawing to the template with a bevel. This operation is repeated so that a cutting mark is made on the template for each course of the arch. Care must be taken, when marking off each course, to ensure that the template is placed so that the setting out mark coincides with the setting out curve. The courses are usually marked on the template as follows: 1 L & R; 2 L & R; 3 L & R; and so on (Figure 159).

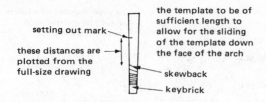

Figure 159   *An alternative method of setting out the template for a camber arch*

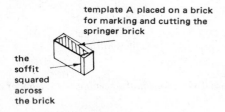

Figure 160   *Marking a voussoir with the aid of a template*

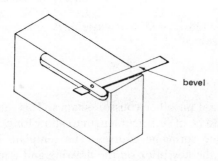

Figure 161   *Transferring the angle that the skewback makes with the soffit from the full-size drawing*

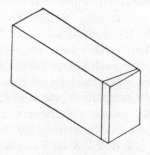

Figure 162   *The brick marked ready for cutting*

Cutting the voussoirs

If Method 1 has been used for obtaining the template, each template, starting from the springer brick, should be laid on the face of the brick and the voussoir carefully marked round it. This should be repeated but with the template placed on its reverse side. The voussoirs for the left-hand and right-hand sides of the arch may be cut at the same time from each template. The soffit of each voussoir should be carefully squared across the brick from the marks on the face (Figure 160).

For Method 2, in which only one template is used, the following procedure for cutting may be adopted:

1   Starting with the springer bricks, with a bevel transfer the angle that the skewback makes with the extrados of the arch to the brick. This should be clearly marked (Figure 161).

2   This mark is carefully squared across the brick, indicating the soffit of the voussoir (Figure 162).

3   The brick is then cut at this mark, trimmed with a scutch and polished with a carborundum stone until an even surface is obtained. Alternatively, it may be sawn with a mechanical brick-cutting saw.

4   The template is then placed on the face of the voussoir with the cutting mark at the soffit, so that the width of the voussoir can now be marked on the brick (Figure 163).

5   The voussoir is cut or sawn along this mark.

6   These operations are repeated for each voussoir. Each cutting mark is used twice: both for the left-hand and again for the right-hand side of the arch.

7   When all the voussoirs are cut they may be placed side-by-side in their correct positions and their lengths marked off by a straightedge along the top. If there are a number of such arches to be cut, it is a good plan to construct a jig into which the bricks are placed as they are cut and which makes the marking of the lengths of the voussoir relatively simple.

8   The voussoirs are now cut off to their correct lengths.

9   Each voussoir is clearly marked as 1 L, 1 R, 2 L, 2 R, and so on to the key brick.

10   The final operation is to cut joggles in the

beds of the voussoirs, with a rasp if the bricks are soft, or comb hammer if they are hard.

Setting the arch

When the cutting of the voussoirs is finished, the procedure for setting the arch in place is as follows:

1 A soffit board is fixed in position and firmly strutted in the opening.
2 The course marks are transferred from the full-size drawing to the top of the soffit board.
3 A length of line should be fixed, if possible, at the point where the angles of the skewbacks meet. This line is used to check the accuracy of the angle at which each arch course is laid.
4 The bricks forming the skewbacks are marked from the soffit board with a bevel, cut and bedded with the brickwork at each side of the arch.
5 Lines should be set up along the face of the arch at the top and lower face of the arch.
6 The voussoirs are bedded from each side of the arch until the key brick is placed in position.
7 When the arch has been checked for accuracy with a straightedge, the joggles are filled with a neat cement grout or mixture of cement and clean, washed sand 1:1.

Three centre arch

This is a false elliptical arch composed of three arcs drawn as continuous curves. It has a similar appearance to a true elliptical arch, but it is easier to set out and mark off the voussoirs because they radiate from a single striking point in each curved section of the arch instead of from two foci as described in Chapter 2.

Setting out

1 The span of the arch AB is plotted on the spring line.
2 A centre line CD is drawn perpendicular to the springing line (Figure 164).
3 The given rise of the arch is marked off at point E.
4 A line is drawn from A to E.

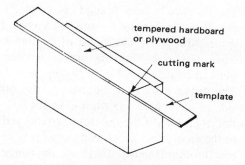

Figure 163 *The template placed on the cut brick ready for marking off the face of the voussoir*

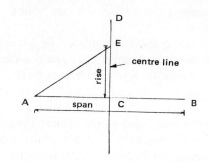

Figure 164 *Marking out the rise and span of a three centre arch*

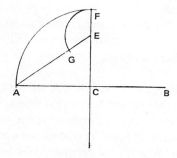

Figure 165 *Marking off the distance to be bisected*

5 With a radius equal to AC (half the span) and centre C, an arc is drawn cutting the centre line at F.
6 With a radius equal to EF and centre E, an arc is drawn by cutting line AE at G (Figure 165).

7   The distance betwen A and G is bisected and the bisector extended until it crosses the centre line at H. The point of contact between this line and the springing line is marked as I.

8   The distance CI is transferred to the other side of the centre line from C to J.

9   Points H, I and J are the three striking points of the arch. Lines are drawn through H and I and through H and J. These are the common normals of the arch (Figure 166).

10 With the compass point on I and a radius equal to the distance from I to A, an arc is drawn from A to the common normal. Using the same radius an arc is drawn from B with the centre at J.

11 The arch shape is completed by extending the compasses from H to E and drawing an arc between the two common normals.

12 To complete the arch outline, repeat operations 10 and 11, but with the radii increased to a distance equal to the required depth of the arch. These arcs are struck from the same centres as the intrados of the arch, that is at points H, I and J. The extrados will thus be parallel to the intrados.

13 The voussoirs are set out on the extrados of the arch and the sections between the common normals are treated separately. It is advisable to plot the courses so that a bed joint, between two voussoirs which are in separate sections, occurs on the common normal.

14 If the arch is to be bonded, an even number of courses should be plotted on each side of the key brick. An arch which is not to be bonded needs only an odd number of courses which allow for the provision of a key brick.

15 The voussoirs radiate from the striking points of the sections in which they are situated (Figure 167).

Obtaining the templates

The method of determining the shape of the templates is exactly the same as that for any semi-circular or segmental arch. While only one template is required, however, for a semi-circular arch, two are needed for a three centre arch – one

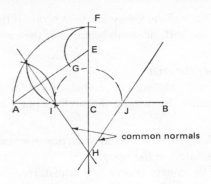

Figure 166 *Bisecting the line AG to determine the three centres*

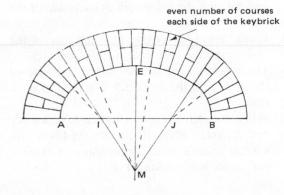

Figure 167 *Setting out a three centre arch*

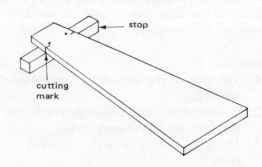

Figure 168 *A template for cutting arch voussoirs*

for the two sections at the haunches of the arch and another for the section at its crown.

1 These are obtained from the full-size drawing and carefully checked for accuracy (see *Brickwork 1*, Chapter 10).
2 The cutting mark is determined by placing the template over the top of a voussoir on the full-size drawing, so that it is completely covered. Place a straightedge against one edge of the template and then slide the template back until the required thickness of joint is showing on the drawing between the template and the bed joint line. The *cutting mark* is marked on each side of the template where it touches the intrados.
3 For convenience a piece of wood may be fixed at the cutting mark to act as a stop (Figure 168).

Cutting the bricks

1 The template is placed on the face of the brick to be cut, and the shape of the voussoir is marked on each side of the template (Figure 169).
2 The soffit of the voussoir is carefully squared from the face marks (Figure 169).
3 The voussoirs are cut, or sawn, to the shape marked from the template.
4 A joggle is formed in both beds of each voussoir (Figure 170).
5 The voussoirs should be marked according to the position in which each is to be placed.

Setting the arch

When the cutting of the voussoirs is finished the setting may be carried out as follows:

1 An arch centre is placed in position and firmly strutted in the opening.
2 The walling is built up on each side of the opening or dead men are erected, so that a line may be pulled across the arch to ensure correct alignment. Lengths of line for radiating the voussoirs are secured at each of the striking points (Figure 171).
3 The spacing of the voussoirs is transferred from the full-size drawing to the timber

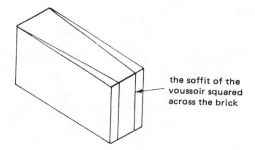

Figure 169   *A voussoir marked ready for sawing or cutting*

the soffit of the voussoir squared across the brick

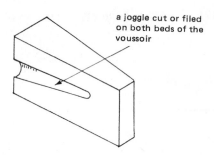

a joggle cut or filed on both beds of the voussoir

Figure 170   *A voussoir joggled ready for setting*

centre. This may be carried out with a pair of dividers or compasses.
4 The voussoirs are laid from each side of the arch until the key brick is placed in position, and care should be taken to ensure that each voussoir radiates from its striking point by using the line fixed at that point.
5 After checking the arch for accuracy in alignment with a straightedge, the joggles are filled with neat cement grout or cement and sand 1:1.

Gothic arches

All of the arches in this group are pointed in shape and include the following types:

Equilateral
Lancet
Drop
Florentine or semi-Gothic
Tudor Gothic

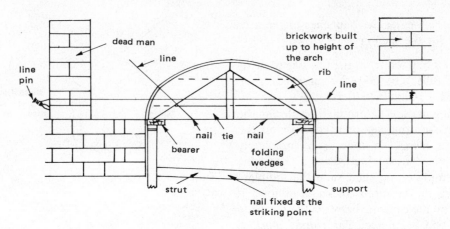

Figure 171   *A method of setting up an arch centre and alternative methods of securing a line for aligning the face of the arch*

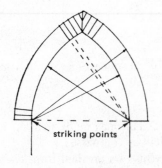

Figure 172   *Equilateral arch*

The equilateral Gothic arch

This is set out by using the two springing points of the arch as striking points and the span of the arch as the radius (Figure 172). The voussoirs are radiated from the striking points, and there is no provision made for a key brick.

The lancet Gothic arch

This has a rise which is greater than that for an equilateral Gothic of equivalent span. Each striking point is determined by bisecting a line drawn from the springing point to the top of the rise, and extending the bisector until it cuts the springing line (Figure 173). The voussoirs are set out on the extrados of the arch and radiate from the striking points.

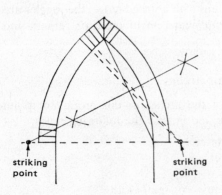

Figure 173   *Lancet Gothic*

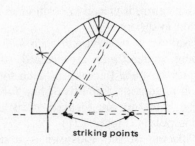

Figure 174   *Drop Gothic*

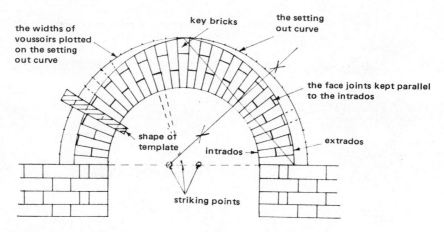

Figure 175   *Semi-Gothic or Florentine arch*

The drop Gothic arch

This has a rise which is lower than the rise for an equilateral arch of equal span, and the method of setting out is the same as for the lancet Gothic arch (Figure 174).

The Florentine or semi-Gothic arch

This is a very decorative arch and combines a semi-circular intrados with a Gothic extrados. Thus, it has a depth on face which is greater at the crown of the arch than at the spring points. The voussoirs in this type of arch all radiate from the centre point of the semi-circular intrados. A semi-circular setting out curve must be drawn on the outside of the arch to plot the voussoirs around the arch, and to ensure that they are normal to the inner curve. The radius of this curve must be equal to the distance from the striking point of the intrados, to the crown of the arch (Figure 175). Provision should be made for a key brick when plotting the voussoirs on the setting out curve. Therefore, an equal number of arch courses should be plotted on each side of the key brick. The face joints of the voussoirs should be drawn parallel to the semi-circular curve on the intrados of the arch.

The cutting of the voussoirs for this type of arch may be carried out as for an ordinary semi-circular one, except in one respect. When the arch bricks have all been reduced to their voussoir shape, their correct lengths are marked by setting the arch out *dry* on a flat surface and marking the outer curves of the arch with a trammel or trammel heads. The voussoirs are then cut to their respective lengths.

A Tudor Gothic or four centre arch

The intrados and extrados are parallel to each other and both Gothic in shape. This means that the arch has four striking points, and the setting out may be done as follows:

1 Set out the given span and rise of the arch AB and CD (Figure 176).
2 In one half of the span, draw a rectangle ACDE.
3 Divide side AE of the rectangle into three equal parts, and mark the two intermediate points as F and G.
4 Draw a line from F to D.
5 From D draw a line perpendicular (90 degrees to line FD) and extend downwards. On this line mark off from D, a distance equal to two-thirds of the rise, at H.
6 With a compass point, or trammel head, at point A and a radius equal to AF draw an arc from F to I on the springing line.
7 Draw a line from I to H, and bisect. Extend this bisector until it cuts line DH at J.
8 I and J are two of the striking points for the arch, and a line drawn through these two points is a common normal.

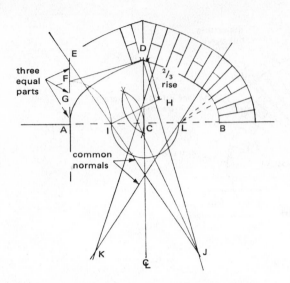

Figure 176   *Tudor Gothic or four-centre arch*

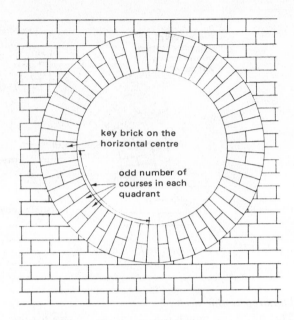

Figure 177   *Bull's-eye or wheel arch*

9   Transfer the points I and J to the opposite side of the centre line of the arch at K and L to obtain the remaining two centres of the arch. A line drawn through K and L provides the other common normal.

10   The outline of the arch is drawn by placing the compass point at I and with a radius equal to IA, an arc is drawn to the common normal. Repeat this operation from centre K, with the same radius. Extend the compasses by a distance equal to the depth of the arch and from points I and K draw arcs parallel to the previous arcs from the same centres.

11   Place the compass point at J and with a radius equal to the distance from J to D strike an arc from the common normal to point D. Transfer the compass point to L, and strike an arc on the opposite side of the arch. Extend the compasses by the depth of the arch, as before, and complete the outline by drawing arcs from point J and L. The voussoirs are plotted on the extrados of the arch, each section being treated independently with the joints of the bricks radiating from the striking point of the section in which they are situated. As this arch is composed of a series of arcs, the method of

obtaining the templates and cutting the voussoirs is carried out in the same manner as for semi-circular and three centre arches.

Bull's-eye or wheel arch

This type of arch is used around any opening which is in the form of a complete circle.

The setting out and cutting is the same as for a semi-circular arch, except that it is common practice to arrange the voussoirs so that a *key brick* is placed at both horizontal and vertical lines (Figure 177). Therefore, if the arch must be bonded on the face, it is necessary to divide each quadrant into an odd number of courses to ensure that the face joints in the arch do not coincide in consecutive courses.

The setting of the arch should be carried out in two main operations: one for the lower half and the other for the upper part of the arch.

To construct the lower part of the arch:

1   The brickwork on each side of the opening is built up to the horizontal centre line, and is either toothed or racked back from the opening.

2   A length of 75 by 50 or 75 by 38 mm timber is placed across the opening so that the horizon-

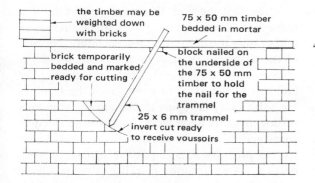

Figure 178 *A method of preparing an invert for a bull's-eye or wheel arch*

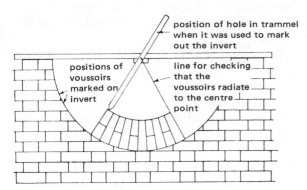

Figure 179 *Method of building up the lower half of the wheel arch*

tal centre line of the arch occurs in the middle of the timber. This timber is carefully bedded down and weighted with bricks to make certain that it will remain firmly in place during building operations (Figure 178).

3 A trammel is cut from a length of 25 by 6 mm batten so that it is about 100 mm longer than the distance from the centre point of the arch to the extrados. The radius of the extrados of the arch is marked from one end of the batten and a small hole is drilled at this point. A nail is inserted in this hole and nailed in the horizontal timber across the opening. The trammel should revolve quite freely around this nail. It is also quite usual to form the other end of the trammel with a blunt point so that

when the bricks are marked, the pencil will be kept on the centre line of the trammel.

4 The brickwork is prepared to receive the arch by marking the bricks with the trammel and cutting them to shape. This may be done by bedding each brick temporarily in mortar or sand and then marking it with the trammel. The brick is removed and cut to the mark and the mortar or sand also removed. When the brick is cut to shape, it is rebedded in position and checked for accuracy with the trammel. This operation is repeated for each brick until the horizontal centre line is reached.

5 The trammel is removed and a fresh hole drilled in it at a distance, equal to the depth of the arch, from the previous hole (Figure 179).

6 The positions of the voussoirs are now marked on the brickwork around the opening (an indelible pencil must not be used) (Figure 179).

7 The arch voussoirs are bedded, starting from the lower *key brick*, building up each side to the horizontal centre line, and checking for accuracy of position with the aid of the trammel.

To construct the upper part of the arch:

1 A timber centre is fixed in position so that the upper part of the arch can be built.

2 A line is secured at the striking point of the arch.

3 The positions of the voussoirs are then marked around the centre.

4 The voussoirs are bedded in position in the same way as for a normal semi-circular arch.

5 The joggles are grouted in with neat cement grout or cement and sand 1:1.

6 The brickwork surrounding the arch is then cut to shape, particular care being taken to form a neat joint around the extrados of the arch (Figure 180).

Centring

While an arch is being constructed a temporary support is necessary. On completion it will be capable of carrying its own weight and that of any superimposed loads. A temporary support must

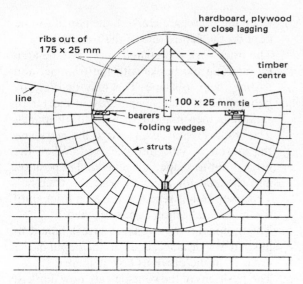

Figure 180   *Method of building the upper half of the wheel arch*

be strong enough to bear the mass of the loading and the arch. It must also be economically constructed so as not to add an excessive item of cost to temporary work.

Timber is generally the most suitable material for this type of work as it is adaptable and easily worked to shape. Although centring is classified as temporary work it is essential that it is constructed with a high degree of accuracy. Any mistakes that are made will be transmitted to the permanent work which may rest upon it.

Centring consists of ribs, ties, laggings, bearers and struts.

The *ribs* form the shape of the arch and may be built up with timbers which have quite a thin section. For large centres they may be stabilized with iron straps and bolts, or with timber dogs (Figure 181).

Ties are used to prevent the ribs from pulling apart.

Laggings form the surface around the ribs and the arch is in direct contact with them. They may be of small section battens laid as:

1 open lagging with open spaces between them; or
2 close lagging where they are laid close together.

In the first method, the spaces can be quite a nuisance. Also, the saving of a small amount of timber may prove to be a false economy, because of the difficulty in marking the positions of the voussoirs around the centre before beginning the building of the arch. In many cases the laggings are sufficiently far apart to prevent the voussoirs resting properly upon them. This causes a delay in construction with consequent extra costs. Close lagging provides a more positive surface to work on as it allows accurate marking of the positions of the voussoirs, and an even surface on which they can be laid. A suitable method of lagging, however, is to fix plywood or tempered hardboard around the ribs. The latter is generally the more economical. These provide a very even surface for laying the bricks and marking out the courses.

Bearers are secured at the underside of the ties and their main use is to provide an even base for the centre to rest upon its supports.

Struts are placed underneath the centre to provide the means of supporting the whole of the framework and the arch. The struts may be of timber. In this case the folding wedges must be used between the strut and the bearer to give a fine adjustment for setting the centre to its correct height. If the opening is high enough, steel floor props may be used as struts. These are very convenient, as they have a screw thread which may be used for adjusting the height of the centre.

Figure 182 illustrates some typical timber centring for various shapes of arches.

Introduction to gauged and rubbed work

Gauged and rubbed work is a very decorative method of arch construction, but, because of high production costs, it is generally used nowadays only on buildings which have special architectural features, or on a structure which is being built alongside ancient buildings where the design must be in keeping with its surroundings. The bricks used for this type of work are of a sandy texture. This allows for easy rubbing and sawing. They are made in various random sizes from 240 by 140 by 90 mm. To obtain the required shapes these bricks are rubbed down to even surfaces, and then

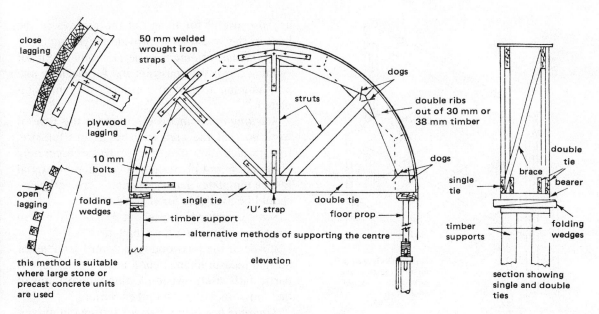

Figure 181 *A suitable centre for an arch having a span of about 4 metres, showing alternative methods of securing ribs*

sawn to shape. They are not cut with the normal cutting tools of a bricklayer. While a mechanical saw is an excellent piece of equipment for general brickwork, it is not so suitable for use in gauged work as it is too fierce in its action. Better results are usually produced by hand.

Equipment or tools that may be required should include:

A cutting bench of convenient height. This should be provided with an overhead beam so that the bricks can be held firmly in position by means of struts while they are being sawn. The bench may be of stout timber construction, but Figure 183 illustrates a suitable method of constructing one with patent slotted and drilled angle iron.

A rubbing stone. A flat piece of York stone of about 375–450 mm square and 50–75 mm thick is excellent for this purpose.

Cutting boxes consist of two sides fixed to a base. These may be of fixed shape or adjustable. Figure 184 shows examples of both types.

A bow saw is used for sawing the bricks. It has a twisted wire for its cutter or *blade*, tensioned by means of a tourniquet at the top of the bow saw

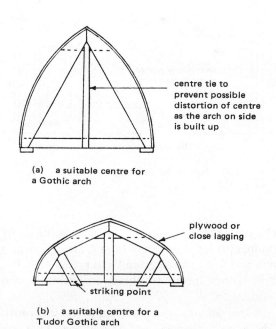

Figure 182 *Typical centres for arches*

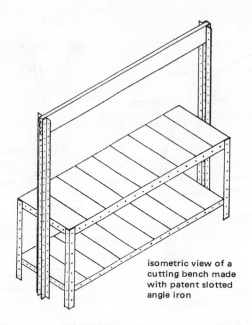

isometric view of a
cutting bench made
with patent slotted
angle iron

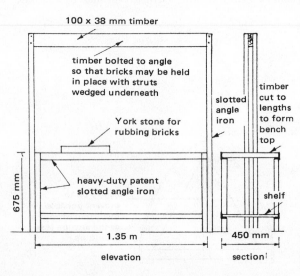

100 x 38 mm timber

timber bolted to angle
so that bricks may be held
in place with struts
wedged underneath

York stone for
rubbing bricks

slotted
angle
iron

timber
cut to
lengths
to form
bench
top

heavy-duty patent
slotted angle iron

shelf

675 mm

1.35 m

450 mm

elevation

section

Figure 183   *Design for a cutting bench*

(Figure 185). The wire blades may be made by doubling a length of steel (about 20 swg) over a nail and fixing the other end to a breast drill. The drill is then turned to obtain an evenly twisted blade.

A selection of flat and half round files and rasps. These are particularly useful for giving a final polish to the bricks after they have been sawn. They

are also useful for filing out the grooves in the beds of the voussoirs to provide joggle joints.

A fine carborundum stone is another tool for rubbing down the voussoirs and for cleaning and polishing the arch when it is in position and completed.

A setting-out board is essential for this type of work so that the arch may be set out full-size, from which the templates may be accurately obtained. 6 mm plywood is a very good material for the templates and a carpenter's saw and plane should be available for shaping them.

Short straightedges of about 375 or 450 mm in length for traversing the templates.

A rule of the boxwood type is very suitable for normal measurements, but a flexible steel tape is particularly useful when plotting the positions of the voussoirs around a timber centre.

Trammel heads are used for setting out curves, in the same way as a pair of compasses. They are used in pairs and are connected by a length of batten (Figure 186).

Dividers are necessary when plotting the voussoirs on the full-size drawing. The most useful type for this work has a screw-locking device to prevent stretching apart when in use (Figure 187).

A bevel with a screw-locking arrangement is used for plotting and transferring angles.

A square is necessary for squaring the voussoirs across their widths for example at the soffit.

A pencil. An ordinary drawing type or an oval carpenter's type is suitable. (An indelible pencil must never be used for this work.)

Procedure for cutting a semi-circular arch in gauged and rubbed work

The arch is set out full-size on the setting out board.

The template is sawn off and planed to the shape of the voussoirs. It is then traversed to check its accuracy of shape. This is an extremely important operation and should be carried out with great care as the joints should only be 1.5 mm thick. This allows for any discrepancy in the shape of the voussoirs. The template should be traversed with two short straightedges (Figure

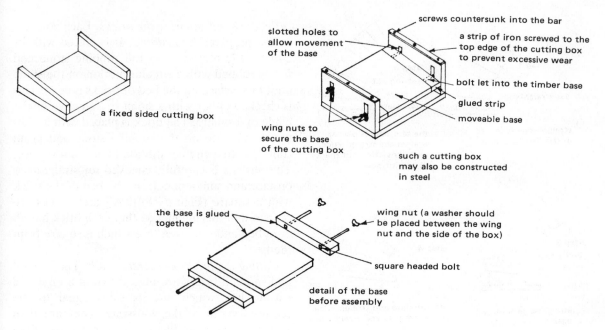

Figure 184   *An adjustable cutting box*

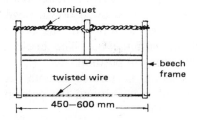

Figure 185   *A typical bow saw*

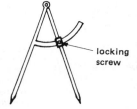

Figure 187   *A pair of dividers with locking attachment*

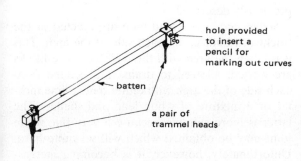

Figure 186   *A pair of trammel heads*

188). Any error in the template should be corrected by planing off to shape, and again rechecked by traversing.

Preparing the cutting box. When the template has been checked for accuracy, it should be cut off to the true length of the voussoir so that it is now the exact shape of the arch bricks to be cut. Two pieces of timber 25 mm thick are cut to the exact shape of the template and screwed to the base on the narrow edges (Figure 184) so that the distance between the sides of the cutting box is about 250 mm.

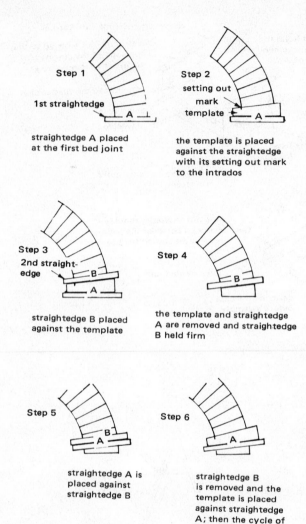

Figure 188   *Traversing a template for an arch*

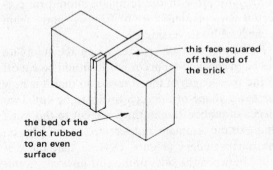

Figure 189   *'Squaring' the brick*

Bedding and squaring the bricks. Each voussoir is first prepared by *bedding*. It is placed with its 240 by 125 mm face on the rubbing stone and firmly rubbed with a circular motion on the stone until the surface on the bed of bricks is even. This is checked either with a small straightedge or the blade of a square. The brick is placed with its 240 by 75 mm face on the rubbing stone and again rubbed with a circular motion to an even surface. This surface is carefully checked for straightness on face and squareness from the bed of the brick with a square (Figure 189). All arch bricks are prepared in this manner so that each brick has an even bed and one even face which is square from the bed.

Cutting the bricks to correct width. The bedded and squared bricks are placed two at a time in a cutting box which has its sides equal to the required width of the voussoirs. They are then strutted down from the overhead beam and sawn off to size and filed to an even surface. All of the bricks are treated in this manner (Figure 190).

Cutting the voussoir shapes or reducing the voussoirs. The bricks are placed in pairs in the cutting box which is prepared from the template (Figure 191). Each pair is strutted down, sawn at each end and along the top with the bow saw and finished off with the file. The bricks are then ready for setting in position.

Joggles should be formed in both beds of the voussoirs with a half round file or rasp (Figure 170).

The arch centre should have either close lagging or a plywood or hardboard surface. This must be carefully marked out with the positions of the voussoirs. A line is fixed at the striking point of the arch curve, and the centre fixed in position as previously described.

Setting the arch. Dead men are erected or the brickwork built up on each side of the arch. This is to align the arch with the wall face. The bricks are wetted, allowed to drain, and bedded from each side of the arch with either a neat lime mortar or a mixture of white lead and shellac. The latter is more suitable because a very fine white joint may be obtained which will set quite hard. Unfortunately, however, it is becoming increasingly difficult to obtain the white lead. The mortar

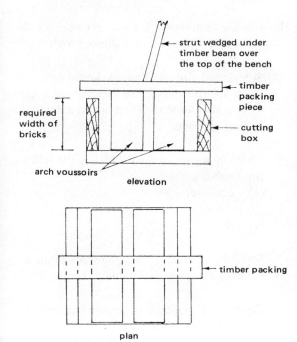

Figure 190   *Method of cutting voussoirs to their correct widths*

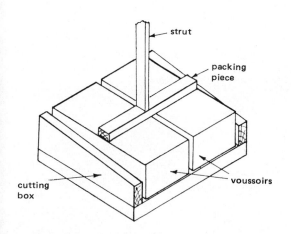

Figure 191   *Reducing the bricks to voussoir shape*

is spread very thinly on the bed of each brick as it is laid and pressed firmly into position. When all the voussoirs are in position, the joggle joints are carefully filled with a neat cement grout. If any grout escapes from the joint on to the face or soffit of the voussoir, it should be removed immediately to prevent staining on the bricks.

Cleaning the face of the arch. When the arch has set, the face should be cleaned and polished with a piece of fine carborundum stone. This should bring the white joints into prominence and give the arch a clean appearance.

Self-assessment questions

1   The minimum mortar mix recommended for laying quarry tiles for steps is
    (a)   one part cement to three parts sand
    (b)   one part cement to four parts sand
    (c)   one part cement to five parts sand

2   Engineering bricks are best laid by
    (a)   sprinkling dry cement on the mortar bed which is laid on the wall to receive the bricks
    (b)   using ordinary mortar and tapping them well-down with the aid of a trowel
    (c)   using ordinary mortar mix and pressing down firmly with the hand and then leaving them well alone

3   When building in a door frame, a stretcher may be used to
    (a)   keep the frame upright
    (b)   prevent it from bowing in the middle
    (c)   keep the frame at the right distance from the face of the wall

4   Boot lintels are
    (a)   those which are reduced in depth at the front edge
    (b)   those which have a brick face
    (c)   concrete lintels which are rectangular in cross-section and are cast *in situ* over the opening

5   The reinforcement for a concrete lintel should be placed at
    (a)   the top of the lintel
    (b)   the middle of the lintel
    (c)   the bottom of the lintel

6   The voussoirs for a camber arch are set out
    on
    (a)   the top edge
    (b)   the bottom edge
    (c)   an arc

7   A three centre arch is
    (a)   a Gothic arch
    (b)   an arch which springs from two skew-
          backs
    (c)   a false elliptical arch

8   An equilateral arch has a rise which is
    (a)   greater than the span of the opening
    (b)   the same as the span
    (c)   less than the span

9   A florentine arch is a
    (a)   Gothic arch
    (b)   a semi-circular arch
    (c)   a combination of Gothic and semi-
          circular arches

10   List the operations that are necessary for the
     cutting of voussoirs for a camber arch.

11   Set out full-size on a suitable board or a con-
     crete floor a three centre arch having a span
     of 900 mm, a rise of 300 mm and a depth on
     face of 200 mm.

12   Show by means of neat sketches the follow-
     ing Gothic arches
     (a)   equilateral
     (b)   lancet
     (c)   drop

13   State the advantages of using steel lintels for
     bridging openings in walling.

14   Describe the method of cutting and building
     a bull's-eye or wheel arch.

15   Describe the meaning of 'bedding and squar-
     ing' a brick.

Chapter 8

Stairways

After reading this chapter you should be able to:

1 Have a good understanding of the design and construction of stairways.

2 Understand the definitions of purpose groups stairways.

3 Understand the construction of tapered steps.

4 Know how to construct precast straight flight cantilever stairways.

5 Know how to install a cantilevered spiral stairway with precast concrete units.

6 Understand the fixing of slate treads and risers.

7 Know how to fix balustrades.

Stairways which are badly designed and constructed can cause many accidents in the home. The most common faults are:

Unequal heights of risers.
Unequal goings to treads.
Too steep a pitch to the stairway.
Insufficient handhold or balustrading.

Building Regulations requirements

The Building Regulations (Approved Document K) lay down stringent requirements for the design and construction of stairways. Although it is not usual for craftsmen to be primarily responsible for the design of stairways, they should be familiar with the regulations concerning their construction, because mistakes may result in work being condemned and having to be replaced, which wastes both time and money.

Definitions
Balustrade includes a wall, screen or railing.

Flight means that part of a stairway or stepped ramp which consists of a step or steps (Figure 192).

Going means the distance between its nosing

and the nosing of the tread above it (Figure 193).

Landing means a platform situated between consecutive flights of a stairway.

Length in relation to a tread means the least distance (measured on plan) between the sides of the tread (Figure 192).

Nosing means the front edge of a tread (Figure 193).

Parallel tread means a tread having uniform width throughout that part of its length which is within the width of the stairway (Figure 192).

Pitch means the angle between the pitch line and the horizontal (Figure 194).

Ramp means any part of a building which pro-

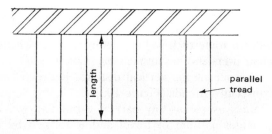

Figure 192 *Plan of a flight of steps*

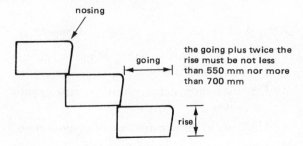

the going should be not less than 240 mm
the rise would not be more than 220 mm

nosing

going

the going plus twice the rise must be not less than 550 mm nor more than 700 mm

rise

Figure 193   *A section showing the going and rise of a step for a single dwelling*

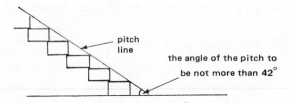

pitch line

the angle of the pitch to be not more than 42°

Figure 194   *Section through a flight of steps showing the pitch line of a private stairway*

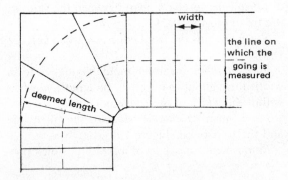

width

the line on which the going is measured

deemed length

Figure 195   *Plan showing the 'deemed length' of a stairway*

vides a route of travel for pedestrians or wheel-chair users and has an inclined surface.

Rise means the vertical distance between two consecutive treads (Figure 193).

Stairway means any part of a building which provides a route of travel and is formed by a single flight or by a combination of two or more

flights and one or more intervening landings.

Tapered step means a tread which has a greater width at one side than at the other.

Tread means the upper surface of a step.

Width. In relation to a tread, width means the least distance from the nosing of the tread to face of the riser, or if there is no riser to the back edge of the tread. In relation to a stairway, width means its unobstructed width between the handrail and the wall or string.

Deemed length. If a stairway contains tapered steps of differing widths all such steps shall be deemed to have a length equal to the length of the shorter or shortest of those steps (Figure 195).

General requirements for stairways and ramps

Buildings are now classified into 'purpose groups' each having its own specific requirements for stairways and ramps, but the following are general requirements which are applicable to all the groups.

1   Any stairway or ramp shall be provided with a landing at the top and bottom. Such landing shall be level and free from obstruction.
2   There shall be a clear headroom of not less than 2 metres measured vertically above the pitch line, or, where there is no pitch line, above the top surface of a ramp (Figure 196).
3   If any flight or ramp is divided into sections the width of each section shall be not less than 1 metre and a handrail shall be provided between the adjacent sections.
4   The landing at the top of an external stairway or ramp may slope at a gradient not exceeding 1 in 12.
5   The rise of any step must be uniform throughout its length and the same as the rise of every other step in the flight.
6   Each tread must be level.
7   The width of each tread measured at any part is not less than the going of the tread at that part.
8   The nosing of any tread which has no riser below it, overlaps on plan, the back edge of the tread below it by not less than 15 mm (Figure 197).
9   All parallel treads have the same going.

10 All consecutive tapered steps have the same going measured at the centre of the tread or the deemed length of each tapered tread, also the same rate of taper.

Specific requirements for stairways

Any stairway within a dwelling serving exclusively one dwelling
1 The width shall not be less than 800 mm (600 mm if it leads to only one room or bathroom, etc.).
2 Must not have more than 16 steps.
3 The height of the rise to be not less than 75 mm nor more than 220 mm.
4 The going of a step must be not less than 220 mm.
5 The aggregate of the going and twice the rise of a step to be not less than 550 mm nor more than 700 mm.
6 The goings of landings to be not less than the width of the stairway.

Any stairway for common use in connection with two or more dwellings
1 The width to be not less than 900 mm.
2 Must have no more than 16 steps.
3 The height of the rise to be not less than 75 mm nor more than 190 mm.
4 The going of a step to be not less than 240 mm.
5 The aggregate of the going and twice the rise of a step shall be not less than 550 mm and not more than 700 mm.
6 The goings of landings to be not less than the width of the stairway.

Tapered treads

For a stairway serving a single dwelling
1 The going of any part of a tread within the width of the stairway to be not less than 75 mm.
2 The going of a step to be not less than 220 mm.
3 The aggregate of the going and twice the rise of a step to be not less than 550 mm nor more than 700 mm.
4 The pitch to be not more than 42 degrees.

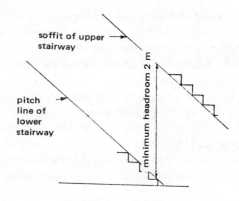

Figure 196 *The minimum headroom for a stairway*

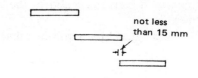

Figure 197 *Open riser stairs*

5 The going, rise and pitch shall be measured at the central points of the length (or deemed length) of a tread if the stairway is less than 1 metre in width, or at points 270 mm from each end of the length if the stairway is more than 1 metre in width.

For a stairway for common use in connection with two or more dwellings
1 The angle (measured on plan) formed by the nosing of the tread and the nosing of the tread immediately above it to be not more than 15 degrees.
2 The going of a step to be not less than 240 mm.
3 The aggregate of the going and twice the rise of a step to be not less than 550 mm nor more than 700 mm.
4 The pitch to be not more than 38 degrees.
5 The going, rise and pitch shall be measured at points 270 mm from each end of the length of a tread.

Guarding of stairways and landings

1 Any flight with a total rise of more than 600 mm shall be provided with a handrail:

    (a) On each side of the flight if the width is 1 metre or more.

    (b) On the side where the tapered treads have the greater going.

    (c) On at least one side in any other case.

2 Any such handrail shall:

    (a) Be so designed so as to afford adequate means of support to persons using the flight.

    (b) Be continuous for the length of the flight.

    (c) Be securely fixed at a height of not less than 840 mm nor more than 1 metre (measured vertically above the pitch line).

    (d) Be terminated by a scroll or other suitable means.

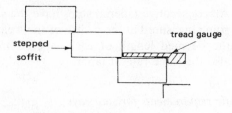

Figure 198 *Rectangular section concrete steps*

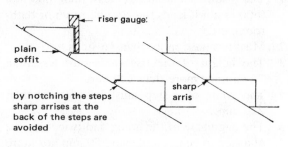

Figure 199 *Spandril steps*

Precast concrete stairs

These may be one of several types:

Straight flight
Doglegged
Spiral or circular

The straight flight

These stairs may be precast in flights and hoisted into position by a crane. They are usually cast with the steps downwards and the soffit of the flight uppermost. They are fixed in between an upper and lower landing. Where heavy lifting equipment is not available, steps may be precast in single units in one of the following sections:

1 Rectangular (Figure 198);
2 Spandril (triangular in section) (Figure 199);
3 Open riser steps (Figure 200).

All of these types of steps may be built in so that they are either supported at both ends of each step or supported at one end only; that is, cantilevered from the wall (Figure 201). Spandril steps provide greater headroom and a plane soffit, as against the stepped soffit of rectangular section steps. The steps may be fixed after the walling has been built or built in the wall as work is in progress.

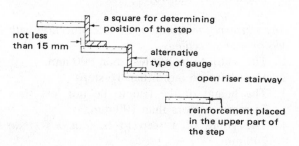

Figure 200 *Methods of checking the accuracy of the position of the steps*

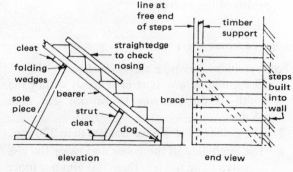

Figure 201 *Timber framework for supporting cantilevered stairways*

Fixing steps after the walling is finished
The following points should be noted:

1 The position of the stairway should be carefully set out as the wall is being built to ensure that the sand courses which have been left for each step are correctly placed. A generous allowance should be made for each step as it is more economical to build in brickwork for the steps than to cut it out.

2 Before building the steps into the wall, the sand courses should be removed and all of the loose sand brushed out of the indentations and the wall dampened.

3 A height rod should be set out for the distance between two floors, and the number of steps required marked on it so that they all have an equal rise.

4 The total going of the stairway should be carefully measured and accurately divided into the number of steps to be bedded in the flight.

5 Riser and tread gauges may be made to allow for ease of checking when laying the steps (Figure 200).

6 The first step is bedded in a cement/sand mortar (1:2), across the width of the stairway and levelled in both directions – across the width and parallel to the going – and checked for correct height with the riser gauge. The end of the step is then built solidly into the wall.

7 If the stairway is of the cantilever type, a temporary strutting (Figure 201) is erected at the free end of the steps. The construction, of course, should be strong enough to carry the weight of the stairway.

8 The steps are generally heavy and cumbersome to handle. Therefore, when the mortar has been spread, three small wedges should be placed on the step, one at either end and one at the back, where it joins the wall, so that the workmen's fingers are protected as the steps are placed on the mortar beds. By gradually easing the wedges from under the step, it may be easily levelled and checked for accuracy in the height of the riser. The wedges also save the mortar from being squeezed out due to the sudden weight of the step being dropped on to it. If several steps are being laid in a continuous operation, the wedges may be left until the mortar has hardened sufficiently to carry the weight of the the steps. They can then be removed and the small holes in the bed joints pointed in solidly with mortar.

9 A straightedge laid against the nosings of the steps will keep an accurate check on the laying operation.

10 Similarly, a line should be used to check the alignment of the steps at their free end.

11 As each step is fixed into position, it should be carefully built into the wall after it has been checked for accuracy and well-pinned at the upper side of the step at its bearing.

Fixing the steps as the work proceeds
This method is more straightforward because sand courses do not have to be provided, and pinning down the steps while building the wall is very much easier than within a recess. However, as the flight develops it becomes cumbersome for the bricklayer to work both on the top and underneath the flight of steps.

The rules that apply for the fixing of steps to a wall which is in the process of being built are also followed when bedding steps to a wall which is finished in so far as they must be well bedded, level, and of even tread and rise. If the steps are cantilevered, a temporary support must be provided as previously described.

Open riser stairways

These should be laid in a similar manner as described for precast steps, but the nosing of each step must overlap the step below by at least 15 mm. A method of checking this measurement is shown in Figure 200. The distance of the overlap is marked on the step previously laid and a square is used from this mark to position the next step above. Another type of gauge that can be made is similar to a square but with a 15 mm projecting piece at the back. It can be placed directly on the lower step with the projecting piece flush with the back edge of the step. The

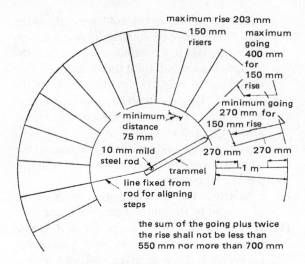

Figure 202   *Plan of a circular stairway showing the application of the Building Regulations*

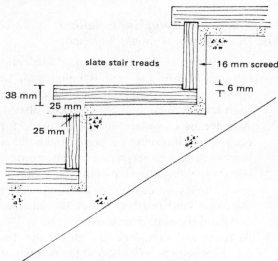

Figure 203   *Fixing slate stair treads and risers to concrete bases*

upper step may be laid to the vertical blade of the gauge.

The spiral or circular stairway

The total maximum and minimum goings on the setting out lines, which are measured 270 mm from each side of the stairway, are carefully calculated (using the usual formula, that the circumference is equal to 3.14 times the diameter) (Figure 202). The number of steps is then divided into these distances to calculate the maximum and minimum goings.

A 12 or 16 mm diameter mild steel rod secured in the centre of the stairwell will allow a trammel to be used to check the alignment of the steps, and a line stretched from the rod will enable a check to be made on the radial lines of the nosings. The bedding of the steps is carried out in a similar way to that previously described.

Slate stair surfacing

Concrete stairs may be provided with an attractive surface finish by covering them with a thin stone. One excellent material extremely suitable for this purpose is slate as it provides a non-slip

and easily cleaned surface. The treads are usually 38 mm thick and the risers 25 mm. These are fixed and housed as shown in Figure 203. The slabs should be bedded on a cement and sand screed of about 16 mm.

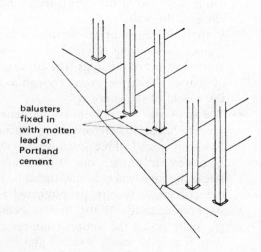

Figure 204   *A method of fixing balustrates into the stair treads*

Balustrades

Holes may be provided in the steps for the fixing of balustrades. These may either be in the tread or in the end of the step. The balustrades should be firmly strutted in position and carefully plumbed. The holes should be cleaned out thoroughly and the balustrades secured with either molten lead or neat Portland cement mortar (Figure 204).

Self-assessment questions

1 The 'going' is the
   (a) total length of the flight
   (b) distance from the nosing to the back edge of the step
   (c) distance between the nosing of one tread and the nosing of the tread of the step above it

2 The 'rise' is the
   (a) total height of the flight of steps measured vertically
   (b) height between two consecutive treads
   (c) total height of the flight measured along the pitch line

3 The 'width' of a tread is the distance
   (a) from the nosing to the back edge of the tread
   (b) from the nosing to the nosing of the tread above it
   (c) from the riser of one step to the riser of the step above it

4 The 'width' of a stairway is the distance
   (a) between the balustrade and the wall string
   (b) across the stairwell
   (c) between the sides of the tread

5 The 'deemed length' of a tapered step is equal to
   (a) the longest of the tapered steps in the flight
   (b) the overall 'going' of the tapered steps
   (c) the shortest of the tapered steps in the flight

6 A stairway shall have a minimum headroom of
   (a) 1.90 metres measured at right angles to the pitch line
   (b) 2.0 metres measured at right angles to the pitch line
   (c) 2.0 metres measured vertically from the pitch line

7 The nosing of a tread which has no riser below it must overlap the tread below by not less than
   (a) 10 mm
   (b) 15 mm
   (c) 20 mm

8 The 'going' for a stairway for a single dwelling shall not be less than
   (a) 220 mm
   (b) 240 mm
   (c) 260 mm

9 The 'going' plus twice the rise of a stairway must not be greater than
   (a) 700 mm
   (b) 750 mm
   (c) 800 mm

10 The maximum rise for a common stairway is
   (a) 190 mm
   (b) 200 mm
   (c) 210 mm

11 Sketch a method of avoiding a sharp acute angle when casting precast units for stairways.

12 By means of a sketch, show how a flight of precast cantilever steps may be supported during their installation.

13 Describe the method of building a spiral stairway using precast units.

14 Describe a method of securing a balustrade into precast steps.

Chapter 9

Chimneys and flues

After reading this chapter you should be able to:

1 Know the definitions applicable to chimneys and flues.

2 Have a good knowledge of the structural requirements for chimneys and hearths.

3 Know how to construct chimneys and stacks.

4 Know how to prevent dampness from entering chimney stacks.

Building Regulations

Approved Document J sets out to ensure that appliances producing heat are designed and installed to work efficiently and safely without giving rise to nuisances and without harmful effect on the structure. Adequate provision is to be made for the discharge of the products of combustion from the heating appliances to the outside air. Heat producing appliances, flue pipes and chimneys are to be installed and/or constructed so the risk of the building catching fire from these sources is reduced to a reasonable level.

Definitions

The following definitions relate to the construction of chimneys, flue pipes, hearths and fireplace recesses;

Chimney. Any part of a structure of a building forming any part of a flue other than a flue pipe.

Constructional hearth. A hearth forming part of the structure of the building.

Flue. A passage for conveying the discharge of an appliance to the external air and includes any part of the passage in an appliance ventilation duct which serves the purpose of the flue.

Flue pipe means a pipe forming a flue but does not include a pipe built as a lining into either a chimney or an appliance ventilation duct.

Superimposed hearth. A hearth not forming a part of the structure of the building.

Class I appliance. An open fire or a solid fuel or oil-burning appliance having an output rating not exceeding 45 kW.

Class II appliance. A gas appliance having an input rating not exceeding 45 kW.

High-rating appliance. A solid fuel or oil-burning appliance, having in either case an output rating exceeding 45 kW. A gas appliance having an input rating exceeding 45 kW.

Insulated metal chimney means a chimney comprising a flue lining, non-combustible thermal insulation and a metal outer casing.

Main flue means a flue serving more than one appliance.

Room-sealed appliance means a gas appliance which draws its combustion air from a point immediately adjacent to the point where it discharges its products of combustion and is so designed that the inlet, outlet and combustion chamber of the appliance, when installed, are isolated from the room or internal space in which the appliance is situated.

Subsidiary flue. A flue which conveys the discharge of one appliance into the main flue.

Structural requirements for chimneys

Chimneys, flues and hearths must be so constructed that:

1 The materials used are of a non-combustible nature and of such a quality and thickness that they will not be adversely affected by heat, condensation or the products of combustion.

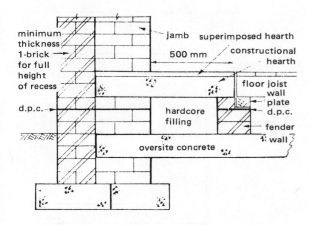

Figure 205 *Section through a ground floor fireplace recess*

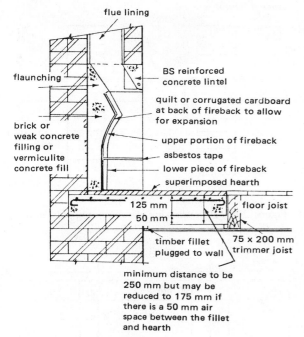

Figure 206 *Section through an upper floor fireplace recess*

2   They will be so constructed and of such thickness as to prevent ignition of any part of the structure.
3   They will prevent any smoke or products of combustion escaping into the building.
4   Any flue pipe shall:
   (a) Be placed or shielded so as to ensure that, whether the pipe is inside or outside the building, there is neither undue risk of accidental damage to the pipe nor undue danger to persons in or about the building;
   (b) Be properly supported;
   (c) Discharge into a chimney or open air.
5   If provision is made for a solid fuel fire to burn directly on a hearth, secure means of anchorage for an effective fireguard shall be provided in the adjoining structure.
6   If a flue serves an appliance which burns solid fuel or oil, the opening into the flue shall be constructed so as to enable the flue to be cleaned and shall be fitted with a closely-fitting cover of non-combustible material.

Construction of hearths

Ground floors
Hearths in ground floors may be supported by fender walls (Figure 205). If the hollow space under the hearth and behind the fender walls is filled in solidly with clean hardcore, there is no need to use any reinforcement in the concrete hearth.

Upper floors
The simplest method of forming a hearth in an upper floor is to use reinforced concrete. If such a hearth is being supported by the wall, it is most important to remember that it is a cantilevered slab and therefore the reinforcement must be placed within the top part of the slab, about 25 mm from the upper surface. If timber formwork is used between the trimmer joist and the fireplace recess so that the concrete hearth may be cast *in situ*, such timbering must be removed if it is within 250 mm of the upper surface of the hearth (Figure 206).

Fireplace recesses for Class I appliances

With appliances, it is also necessary to provide a hearth in order to reduce the fire risk. Each appliance shall have a constructional hearth which shall be:

1   Not less than 125 mm thick.

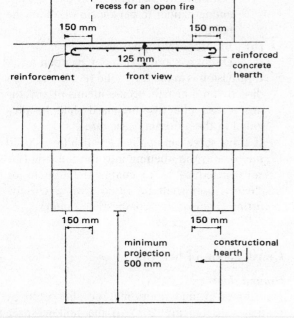

Figure 207 *Minimum dimensions for a constructional hearth*

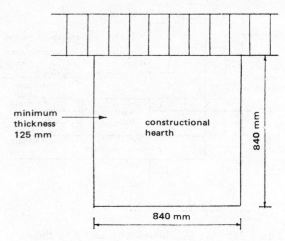

Figure 208 *Minimum dimensions for a hearth not constructed within a recess*

2 Not lower than the surface of any floor built of combustible material (Figures 207 and 212).
3 Extended within the recess to the back and jambs of the recess and projected not less than 500 mm in front of the jambs and not less than 150 mm each side of the jambs (Figure 207).
4 Not less than 840 mm square if the hearth is not constructed within a recess (Figure 208).

Fireplace recesses should be constructed so that:

1 The jamb on each side of the opening is not less than 200 mm thick.
2 The back of the recess is a solid wall not less than 200 mm thick or a cavity wall, each leaf of which is not less than 100 mm thick, such thickness must extend for the full height of the recess. If the recess is situated in an external wall and there is no combustible cladding across the back of the recess then this back may be a solid wall less than 200 mm thick but not less than 100 mm thick. If the recess serves as the back of each of two recesses other than in a separating wall, then it may be a solid wall less than 200 mm thick but not

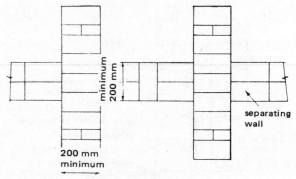

Figure 209 *Plan showing the minimum thickness of the back of a fireplace in a 1-brick wall*

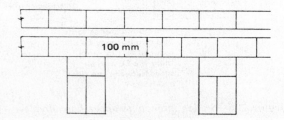

Figure 210 *Plan showing a recess which is backed by a cavity wall*

less than 100 mm thick (Figures 209–211). (The thickness of any fireback may not be included in the foregoing dimensions.)
3 No opening shall be made in the back of a fireplace recess which does not communicate with a flue.
4 No combustible material, other than timber

fillets supporting the sides of the hearth where it joins the floor, shall be placed under a constructional hearth serving as Class I appliance within a distance of 250 mm measured vertically, unless such material is separated from the underside of the hearth by an air space of not less than 50 mm (Figure 206).

5 An ash pit may be constructed under a constructional hearth if the sides and bottom are constructed of non-combustible material and not less than 50 mm thick; no combustible material is built into a wall within 225 mm of the inner surface of the pit. Any combustible material placed elsewhere must be separated from the outer surface of the pit by an air space of at least 50 mm.

6 If a duct is to be constructed under a hearth for the admission of combustion air to an appliance then the duct must be smoke-tight and constructed of non-combustible material.

Flues and chimneys

A flue should be at least 175 mm in diameter (Figure 219) and must be lined to provide a chimney which is resistant to acids and the products of combustion, particularly in the case of solid fuel burning appliances. The three main substances obtained from the burning of coal are water, sulphur dioxide and carbon dioxide. When either of the two dioxides are mixed with the water they will produce acids. Sulphur dioxide, when mixed with water, will produce sulphurous acid; carbon dioxide, when mixed with water, will produce carbonic acid. Although these acids are not in a concentrated form, their continual application inside a flue will eventually harm the mortar and, in some cases, the bricks. When the gases leave the fire they are hot and contain a lot of moisture vapour (where the temperature of the gases is above 100°C this would be steam), but as it cools down it is capable of holding less moisture in suspension. If this happens inside the chimney, the flue gases will condense on the sides of the flue, and it is this condensate that is acid and harmful to the construction of the chimney.

With slow burning appliances, the flue gases do not flow so rapidly, and there is a greater risk of these gases condensing much earlier than with open fires. It is, therefore, a very good practice to insulate the lining of the flue with a loose non-combustible material, for example, exfoliated mica or mineral wool. This will allow the lining to warm up quickly because it will not lose its heat to the surrounding brickwork too rapidly. Thus, the flue gases will not cool off so quickly and the amount of condensate will be kept to a minimum. The more efficient an appliance is, the more products of combustion are obtained from the fuel, which means, in turn, that chimneys and flues must also be much more resistant to acids.

Chimneys for Class I appliances

The chimney is the part of a building most vulnerable to fire risks, therefore great care must be exercised to reduce these risks to an absolute minimum. The Building Regulations state they

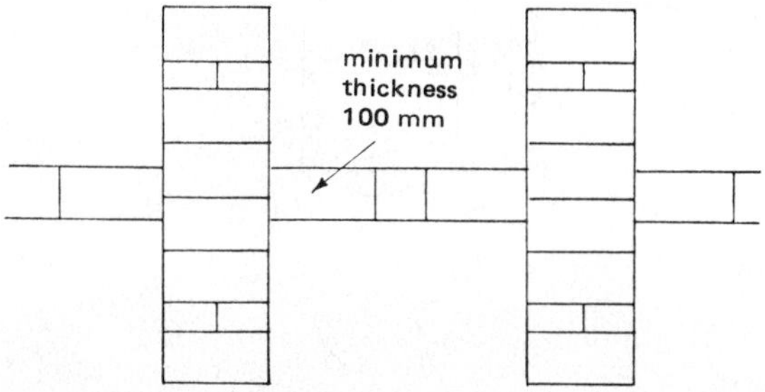

Figure 211 *Plan showing the minimum thickness of the back of a fireplace recess in a wall other than a separating wall*

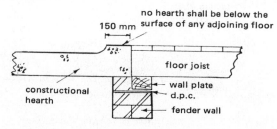

Figure 212 *Section through a sunken hearth*

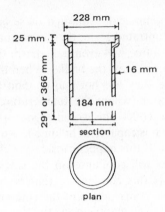

Figure 213   *Section through a straight unit*

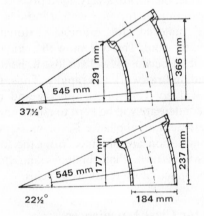

Figure 214   *Sections through curved units*

shall be either:

1   Lined with any one of the following:
  (a)   rebated or socketed clay flue linings complying with BS 1181 (Figures 213, 214, 215, 216, 217 and 218);
  (b)   rebated or socketed flue linings made from kiln-burnt aggregate and high alumina cement;
  (c)   glazed vitrified clay pipes and fittings complying with BS 65: 1965.
2   Constructed of concrete flue blocks made of, or having inside walls made of, kiln-burnt aggregate and high alumina cement and so made that no joints between blocks other than bedding joints adjoin any flue.

Flue linings

Any linings or blocks shall be jointed and pointed with cement mortar and any linings shall be so built into the chimney that the socket of each component is uppermost (Figure 219).

They shall be made from fireclay or terra-cotta, be free from defects and give a clear ring when struck with a light hammer. They may or may not be vitrified; or be either glazed or unglazed.

Clay flue linings are available in straight or curved units. Straight units are nominally 300 or 375 mm long including a joint. Rebated and socketed flue linings shall have ends which fit properly leaving an annular space. Such flue linings

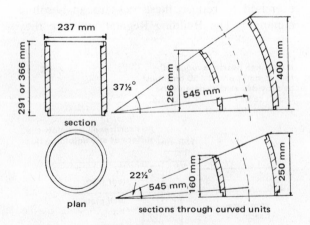

Figure 215   *237 mm diameter rebated flue linings Also available in 191 mm diameter units*

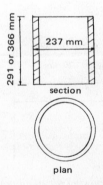

Figure 216   *237 mm diameter butt-ended flue linings Also available in 37½ degree and 22½ degree units*

should be accurate in shape and Figure 220 shows methods of checking these for accuracy.

Chimney construction

1 If a chimney is constructed of bricks or blocks of concrete and lined with one of the materials previously described then any flue in the chimney shall be surrounded and separated from any other flue in the chimney by solid material not less than 100 mm thick, excluding the thickness of the lining.

2 If a chimney is situated in a separating wall then the part of the chimney forming part of this separating wall shall be not less than

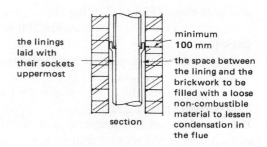

the linings laid with their sockets uppermost

minimum 100 mm

the space between the lining and the brickwork to be filled with a loose non-combustible material to lessen condensation in the flue

section

Figure 219 *Section showing the method of building in linings and insulating them against excessive condensation*

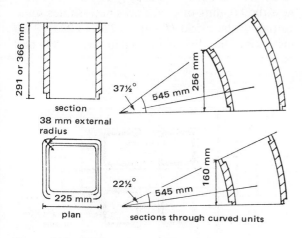

291 or 366 mm

section

38 mm external radius

225 mm

plan

37½°

545 mm

256 mm

22½°

545 mm

160 mm

sections through curved units

Figure 217 *225 mm square rebated flue linings*

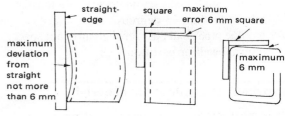

straight-edge

square

maximum error 6 mm square

maximum deviation from straight not more than 6 mm

maximum 6 mm

Figure 220 *Methods of checking accuracy of shapes of flue linings*

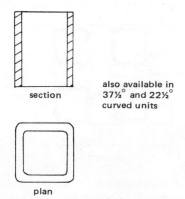

section

also available in 37½° and 22½° curved units

plan

Figure 218 *225 mm square butt-ended flue linings*

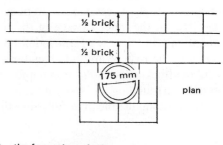

½ brick

½ brick

175 mm

plan

(a) the formation of a flue in a cavity separating wall

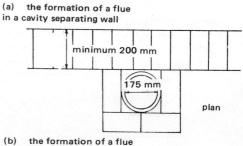

minimum 200 mm

175 mm

plan

(b) the formation of a flue in a 1-brick separating wall

Figure 221 *Flue formations*

200 mm thick (Figure 221(b)). In a cavity wall, each leaf should not be less than 100 mm thick (Figure 221(a)).

3 A flue in a chimney serving a Class I appliance shall be such as will contain a circle having a diameter of not less than 175 mm measured in cross-section (Figure 221(b)).

4 If a flue does not communicate with a fireplace recess, it will terminate at its lower end in a chamber which:

   (a) has a means of access for inspection and cleaning fitted with a close-fitting cover; and

   (b) is capable of containing a condensate collecting vessel.

5 No flue shall make an angle with the horizontal of less than 45 degrees.

6 No flue pipe shall pass through any roof space, internal wall or partition.

Proximity of combustible material

It is most important to ensure that no materials are built around any fireplace recesses in such a position that they are liable to create a fire hazard. The Building Regulations lay down the following minimum requirements:

1 No combustible material shall be placed in a chimney or fireplace recess, so as to be nearer to the flue, or the inner surface of the recess than 150 mm in the case of a wooden plug or 200 mm in the case of any other material.

2 Where the thickness of solid non-combustible material surrounding a flue is less than 200 mm, no combustible material other than a floorboard, skirting board, dado rail, picture rail, mantel shelf, or architrave shall be so placed as to be nearer than 38 mm.

3 No metal fastening which is in contact with combustible material shall be so placed in any chimney or fireplace so as to be nearer than 50 mm to a flue or the inner surface of a fireplace recess.

Bonding for chimney stacks

The dividing walls between the flues are called *withes*, and should be of a minimum thickness of 100 mm. To obtain the greatest amount of stability in the chimney stack, the withes should be properly bonded into the outer walling of the stack. Because they are usually 100 mm in thickness the bonding of such stacks necessitates some cutting of the bricks (Figures 222 and 223). Two methods of bonding are shown in Figures 224 and

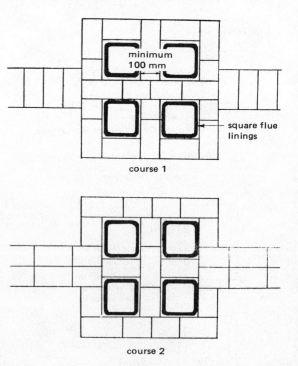

Figure 223 *Plans showing the minimum requirements for the construction of a chimney stack and a method of bonding the brickwork*

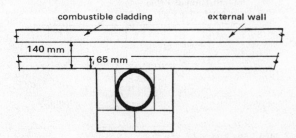

Figure 222 *The minimum permissible dimensions for a flue in an external wall*

225. It is also good practice to use a fairly strong mortar such as Portland cement and sand 1:3 or 1:4, a cement lime and sand 1:3:6 or 1:2:9, or a masonry cement and sand 1:3.

Outlets of flues

1 The outlet of any flue in a chimney shall be so situated that the top of this chimney (excluding any chimney pot) is not less than 1 m above the highest point of contact between the chimney and the roof (Figure 226).

2 If the roof has a pitch on each side of the ridge of not less than 10 degrees and the chimney passes through the roof within 600 mm of the ridge, the top of the chimney may be not less than 600 mm above the ridge (Figure 226).

3 It should not be less than 1 m above the top of a window or skylight which can be opened, which is not more than 2.3 m measured horizontally from the chimney.

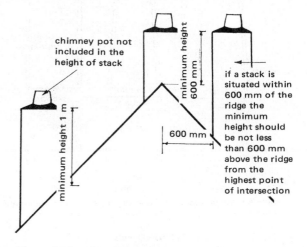

Figure 226 *The minimum heights of chimney stacks at different positions on the roof*

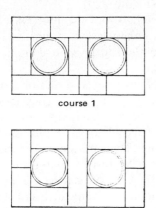

course 1

course 2

Figure 224 *A two-flue stack*

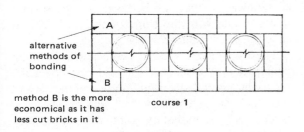

alternative methods of bonding

method B is the more economical as it has less cut bricks in it

course 1

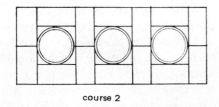

course 2

Figure 225 *A three-flue stack*

Chimney pots

These may be made of either plain clayware or salt-glazed ware, and may be either circular in cross-section or circular with a square base. The former should be used with circular flue liners and the latter with liners that are square in cross-section. Chimney pots are usually tapered off at the top to reduce the cross-section of the outlet. This lessens the possibility of downdraught by increasing the upward flow of the flue draught thus preventing the wind blowing down the flue (Figure 227).

The chimney pots must be securely fixed at the top of the stack to prevent dislodgement by the wind, and built well into the brickwork, preferably for at least three courses. They should also project 100 to 175 mm above the flaunching or weathering placed on top of the chimney stack to shed the rainwater. The flaunching may be a mixture of Portland cement and coarse or clean washed sand 1:3 or 1:4. It can be applied in a stiff consistency and trowelled off to an even surface, or finished off with a wooden float (Figure 228).

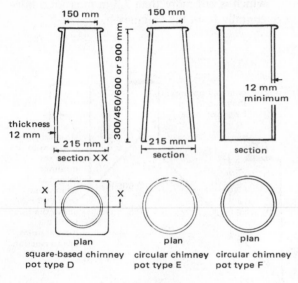

Figure 227   *Types of chimney pots*

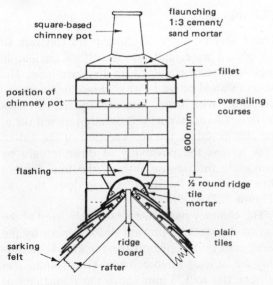

Figure 228   *A method of building in a chimney pot*

Damp prevention in chimney stacks

Chimney stacks are very vulnerable to damp because of their exposed position and the junction between the brickwork and the roof. In the case of a flat roof, the method of damp prevention is relatively simple. A damp-proof course is laid across the chimney stack and allowed to protrude from the brickwork. When the roof surface is laid, a skirting is dressed up the chimney stack to a minimum height of 150 mm and tucked into a chase in the brickwork. The chimney damp-proof courses may then be dressed over the top of the roof finish (Figure 229).

With a pitched roof the junction between the roof and the chimney stack requires a rather more elaborate method to prevent dampness entering the building.

If the roof covering is of tiles or slates, soakers must be cut from a non-ferrous metal such as copper, lead or zinc. These are equal in length to the gauge of the tile or slate plus the lap and 25 mm for fixing. They are about 175 mm in width, 75 mm of which is turned up to form a right angle (Figure 230). A soaker is placed in between each tile course at an abutment, such as a chimney, and turned up so that it is covered by the flashing. The flashing is fixed into the bed joints of the brickwork and may be bedded in one bed joint all round the chimney stack or by using the more economical method of bedding it into several joints in line with the slope of the roof. This is called *stepped flashing*.

The front of the stack is protected from damp penetration by a sheet of metal dressed over the tiles, which is called a front apron, and the back of the stack has a chimney back gutter. A cover flashing is fitted to seal the joint between the back gutter and the stack (Figure 231).

As a final protection against the penetration of dampness into the chimney stack, a damp-proof course should be placed across the stack (Figure 233). When the flashings are built into the joints there are several points which should be observed so that a perfect barrier is provided against the penetration of rainwater, and also that the damp-proofing material remains securely in place after the completion of the work:

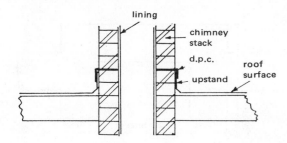

Figure 229 *Section showing a method of waterproofing a chimney stack where it passes through a flat roof*

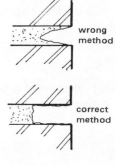

Figure 232 *Method of raking out bed joints for flashing*

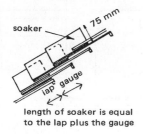

Figure 230 *Detail of a soaker*

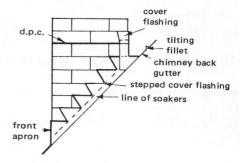

Figure 233 *Stepped cover flashing*

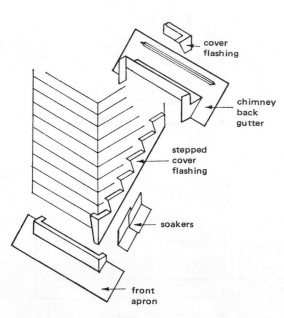

Figure 231 *An exploded view of a chimney showing a method of waterproofing a chimney stack*

1 The joints should be raked out to a depth of about 25 mm.
2 They should be raked out cleanly, and not with a sloping section (Figure 232).
3 When the flashing is in position and plugged in the joints, the bed joints should be carefully brushed out so as to remove any loose particles, then dampened. The mortar is trowelled firmly into the joints and pointed on completion.

Self-assessment questions

1 A flue is the
 (a) brickwork projecting above the roof to carry off the smoke and gases
 (b) brickwork surrounding the passage from the appliance to convey the gases
 (c) passage for conveying the discharge of an appliance

2 The minimum thickness of a hearth used in conjunction with a Class I appliance is
   (a) 100 mm
   (b) 125 mm
   (c) 150 mm

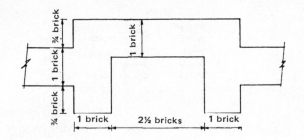

3 The minimum projection of a hearth used in conjunction with a Class I appliance is
   (a) 450 mm
   (b) 475 mm
   (c) 500 mm

Figure 234

4 If a hearth is not constructed within a recess it must be not less than
   (a) 830 mm²
   (b) 840 mm²
   (c) 850 mm²

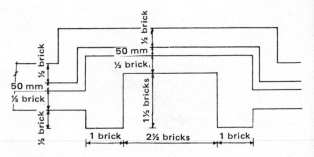

5 The space behind a fireback should be filled with
   (a) a lightweight concrete
   (b) a dense concrete
   (c) loose bricks or non-combustible rubbish

Figure 235

6 If an upper hearth is cantilevered from the chimney breast then the reinforcement must be placed
   (a) at the bottom
   (b) in the middle
   (c) at the top

7 The jambs on each side of a fireplace recess should be not less than
   (a) 200 mm
   (b) 225 mm
   (c) 250 mm

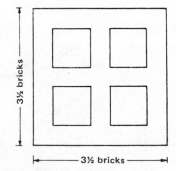

8 A flue should have a diameter of not less than
   (a) 150 mm
   (b) 175 mm
   (c) 200 mm

Figure 236

9 The outlet of any flue in a chimney shall project above the highest point of contact between the roof and the chimney not less than
   (a) 914 mm
   (b) 974 mm
   (c) 1 m

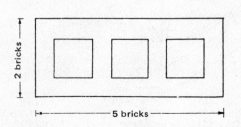

Figure 237

10 The outlet of any flue projecting from the ridge of a roof shall be not less than x mm above the ridge. What is the value of x?
    (a)   550 mm
    (b)   600 mm
    (c)   650 mm

11 A soaker is the piece of sheet metal which is
    (a)   the unit formed at right angles and placed between the tiles or slates
    (b)   placed at the back of the stack to form a gutter
    (c)   placed at the front of the stack to form an apron

12 Draw the bonding arrangement for the recesses shown in Figures 234 and 235.

13 Draw the bonding arrangements for the chimney stacks shown in Figures 236 and 237.

Chapter 10

Fire appliances

After reading this chapter you should be able to:

1 Have a sound appreciation of the importance of the correct fixing of appliances.

2 Have a sound understanding of the method of fixing an open fireplace.

3 Know how to fix an inset open fire.

4 Know how to install an inset fire with an underfloor primary air supply.

5 Understand how to install back boilers and free standing appliances.

6 Have a good understanding of the installation of convector units and fully appreciate the importance of correct sealing of the unit and the air ducts.

7 Know how to fit a soot door or cleaning access unit.

8 Know how to connect a flue pipe into a main flue.

In recent years rapid development has taken place in the design of heating appliances and many efficient types are now available. Maximum efficiency can only, however, be achieved if these appliances are installed correctly and in accordance with the manufacturers' instructions. The construction of open fires used not to demand close attention and consequently they were generally wasteful because of high fuel consumption and loss of heat from the building. Nowadays much more consideration is being devoted to these points, and as heating appliances become more efficient, so more care must be taken with their installation.

There is a wide variety of appliances suitable for heating domestic premises and it would be beyond the scope of this book to detail the fixing of each individual type. General fixing methods are given below so that the manufacturers' fixing instructions may be easily understood and the reasons for the importance of correct fixing appreciated.

Heating appliances may be classified into the following groups:

Open fires
Inset fires
Inset with underfloor primary air supply
Open fires with back boilers
Convector open fires
Free-standing convector open fires
Independent boilers

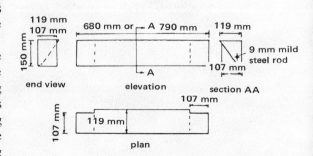

Figure 238 *BS concrete lintel for fireplace openings*

Open fires

The recess for an open fire should be 2.5 bricks wide and 1.5 bricks deep. The height of the opening should be 570 to 600 mm above the upper level of the superimposed hearth. The cross-section of the concrete lintel, which in this case is roughly triangular in shape, is shown in detail in Figures 238 and 239. In other cases a precast concrete or fireclay preformed throat unit may be needed and, to ensure that sufficient room is allowed, the lintel may be fixed at about 1.22 m above the constructional hearth. This lintel can be the conventional type which is rectangular in cross-section (Figure 240).

The flue liners should be built within the chimney as soon as the flue commences from the recess. The fireback (or firelump) may be constructed of either fireclay or refractory concrete, which is usually a mixture of high alumina cement and crushed firebricks. The fireback should be composed of at least two pieces. It may even be four or six. This makes it lighter to handle and easier to replace, particularly when the surround does not have to be removed. It also reduces the amount of cracking that would occur if the fireback were composed of a single unit. This is because the lower half of the fireback gets hotter and consequently expands more than the top half. Cracking is, therefore, bound to occur in a single unit owing to the differing rates of expansion. If joints are introduced, movement can take place without causing unsightly cracks to appear in the fireback.

The joints in the fireback are best made with flat asbestos tape which allows movement due to expansion better than would be the case with fire cement.

The back of the fireback should also be provided with an expansion joint by placing a sheet of corrugated paper, mineral wool blanket or thin strawboard behind the fireback before filling in with a mixture of lime/sand/broken brick 1:2:4, brickwork built with lime/mortar. The layer of soft material placed between the filling and the fireback will allow for movement by expansion (Figure 241).

The filling behind the fireback must never be of

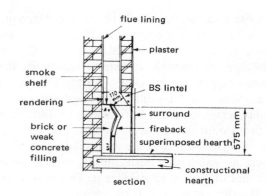

Figure 239 *The positioning of a BS lintel in relation to an open fireplace*

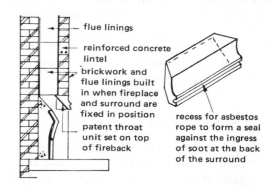

Figure 240 *Section showing the formation of a fireplace in a large recess*

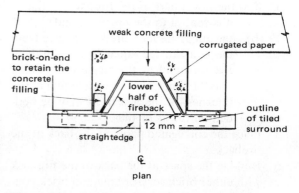

Figure 241 *Fixing the lower half of a fireback*

a loose material, but should be stabilized by using a lime mortar or a concrete. This is because the loose fill will gradually settle and may in time dislodge the fireback. In extreme cases the surround may be forced away from the face of the wall. When the loose fill settles it will leave large voids, which are likely to fill with soot and create a fire hazard in the back of the recess. Another method of filling is to use an insulating material such as exfoliated mica mixed with a small amount of cement to stabilize it. This is an especially efficient method if the chimney is built on an external wall as it reduces the amount of heat escaping through the wall.

The fireback may be finished off smoothly at the top at an angle of about 45 degrees (Figure 243), or with a preformed throat unit (Figure 240). A smoke shelf may be formed above the fireback (Figure 239). This has the advantage of keeping the effect of downdraughts to a minimum, but on the whole it is probably better to have a properly formed throat unit rather than consider this type of construction.

Installing the fireback

1   Its position should be carefully set out by measuring the depth of the surround at the return at the ends and where the fireback meets the surround.
2   Lay a straightedge along the face of the chimney breast at a distance from the face of the wall equal to the depth of the surround at the return (Figure 241).
3   Mark the centre line of the fireplace recess.
4   Bed the lower part of the fireback so that:
    (a)   it is central to the opening; and
    (b)   the edges are measured a distance from the straightedge equal to the depth of the surround at the fireplace opening plus 12 mm, and at a height equal to the thickness of the hearth. It may be bedded on bricks or tiles.
5   Place the corrugated paper at the back of the fireback.
6   Build in the space at the back of the fireback with either brickwork or lime and brick concrete.

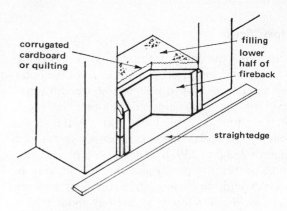

Figure 242   *Method of setting out an open fireplace*

7   Lay asbestos tape on the top edge of the fireback.
8   Place the upper half of the fireback on the tape so that it is slightly set back from the edge of the lower half by about 2–3 mm (Figure 242). This prevents the edge from burning away.
9   Place the corrugated paper or mineral wool blanket and build in the space behind the fireback.
10   Finish off the top with a smooth surface at an angle of about 45 degrees. When fixing the fireback, it is sometimes wise to place a prop against it if there is a possibility of the filling pushing it out of place. If brick in-filling is used, strutting the fireback in place should not be necessary.

Fixing the surround

Tiles, brick, polished concrete, stone or slate may be used for providing a decorative feature around a fireplace opening. The method of fixing is common to all types and varies only in small details. An expansion joint should be provided at the front edge of the fireback with asbestos rope of 25 mm diameter. An asbestos rope seal should also be provided at the top of the opening or a metal strip plugged to the wall (Figures 243 and 244). If the asbestos rope is dipped in a solution of silicate of soda, this will act as an adhesive to hold it in place while fixing the surround.

The hearth is bedded in place, carefully levelled in all directions, and the surround placed on the top. (In some types, the surround is fixed first and the hearth bedded last.) The positions of the fixing lugs are marked on the wall, holes drilled (preferably with a brick drill) and metal plugs inserted. It is advisable not to use wood or fibre plugs because they are liable to shrink with the heat and become loose. If this happens, there is a possibility of the fixing being spoilt. The surround is securely screwed into the plugs, with at least 50 mm screws. The plaster can now be made good around the surround. If there is space between the surround and the face of the chimney breast, this should be filled solidly with lime mortar or concrete up to the height of the fireback where the flaunching is made good with the same angle as the previous flaunching. This is to prevent the possibility of soot collecting in open voids at the back of the surround and creating a fire risk. An asbestos tape joint is made between the tiled hearth and the back hearth and the back hearth is then cast.

Throat units

If the opening is made high enough to accommodate a preformed unit, the fireback is built in as previously described, and when the throat unit has been placed on the top of the fireback, the sides and top are built in solidly. Asbestos rope is placed in the groove provided in the front of the throat unit and the surround fixed in position (Figures 240 and 244).

Fixing an inset open fire or all-night burner

The dimensions of a fireback are shown in Table 14, and it is most important that the appliance fits neatly into the fireback. The firebars on many of these appliances are notched so that the bars may be adjusted in length to suit the fireback. When adjustment is necessary it should be done with care, otherwise there is a possibility that the bars will break off at the wrong point. One method is to clamp the bottom firebars in a vice so that the notches are just above the jaws. A sharp blow with a hammer will break off each of the bars at the required point. If the shape of the bars makes it impossible to use this method, these may be placed firmly on a hard surface with the notches immediately above the edge. Sharp blows will break the ends to the required length. A 6 mm clearance should be allowed between the bars and the fireback to allow for expansion.

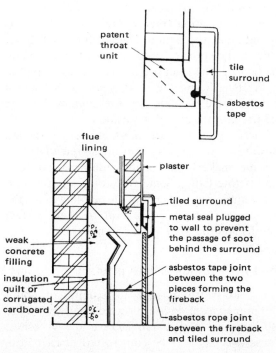

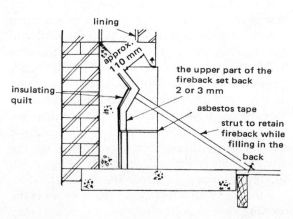

Figure 243 *Fixing the upper portion of the fireback*

Figure 244 *Sealing the space behind a tiled surround to prevent the entry of soot*

Table 14

	Dimensions in mm		
Size of fire	A	B	C
350 mm	330–342	203–215	170–182
400 mm	380–393	254–266	170–182
450 mm	430–445	304–316	170–182

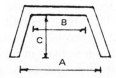

Figure 245   *Dimensions of a firebrick*

The inset fire should be offered in place to mark the positions of the holes for the plugs. It should then be removed and the hearth drilled and plugged with metal plugs. Asbestos rope or tape should be placed at the edges of the fireback with a solution of silicate of soda (waterglass) to hold it in position (Figure 246). Fire cement is spread along the bottom edge of the inset stove, which is then pressed firmly down into position on the hearth. The inset fire is screwed down tightly to the hearth and the joint between the hearth and the grate pointed with fire cement. Finally, the firebars are placed in position.

These appliances are most efficient provided they are fixed correctly. They are simple to install, but the maker's instructions must be carefully read before fixing. Some types of inset grates do not require any plugging or bedding and the firebars are simply broken off to their correct lengths and the grate placed in position.

Inset fire with underfloor primary air supply

The back hearth is sunk to a depth of about 250 mm to form an ash pit which houses a large ash pan capable of containing several days' ashes. These ash pits may be constructed of cast iron, concrete or firebrick and the minimum thickness of the walls must be not less than 50 mm.

Air for the fire may be supplied from underneath the floor. The ash pit usually incorporates a short length of pipe in which is contained a butterfly valve acting as the air control (Figure 247). This pipe is then connected to a duct which, in the case of solid floors, may be constructed of concrete or salt-glazed pipes jointed in the usual manner with cement and sand mortar 1:2. If the duct is underneath a suspended timber floor, either a piped duct may be used or the air from underneath the floor utilized with a duct provided that the air vents are completely clear and that there is a good draught of air in the underfloor space. When ducts are used, it is a good practice to have two inlets on the external walls, preferably at right angles to each other, to offset the possibility of the wind creating a suction effect instead of supplying air to the fire (Figure 248). This might happen if only one inlet pipe were used. All underfloor ducts must be constructed of non-combustible material so that there is no possibility of a fire hazard in the event of the fire being drawn downwards because of wind suction.

Open fire with boiler

The recess can be constructed in the same way as for an open fire, but the dimensions will differ according to the type of appliance. The throating should not exceed 100 mm in width to prevent excessive heat loss up the flue. The back hearth should be laid and allowed to harden before setting the boiler which should be set up on the floor first to check its correct assembly. The space behind the boiler may be filled with an insulating non-combustible material, for example exfoliated mica and cement, to prevent loss of heat from the boiler through the external walls. The boiler should be set at the correct height above the hearth and in accordance with the manufacturer's instructions. It should never be lower than the firebars and preferably about 38 or 50 mm above them. This will prevent cold air from below the firebars entering the boiler flue and cooling down and thus reducing its output (Figure 249).

If there are any firebrick cheeks to be set in the opening, care should be taken to ensure that they fit together accurately and, if necessary, are trimmed before being set into position. If the fireback projects from the face of the chimney breast, it is good practice to make the brick in-filling project so as to give added protection to the fireback and safeguard it from burning away at the edges. It will also act as permanent formwork if a lightweight aggregate and cement filling or lime/sand/broken brick mixture is being used for the in-fill. Holes should be cut or provided in one of the jambs of the chimney breast. (In new work, sand-courses should be left to save cutting with hammer and chisel.) The boiler is fitted and the primary flow and return pipes connected. Sleeves should be placed over these pipes where they pass through the wall to allow for expansion of the pipes. These sleeves need only be a size larger than the diameter of the primary flow and return pipes and the space between can be filled with asbestos string, although this is not necessary. The boiler should be checked for leaks before building the sleeves in solidly.

Some types of back boilers are fitted with a cast iron damper and throat unit which should be carefully placed in position and bedded solidly. The brickwork can then be made good and flaunched up between the damper and the flue liners. When this is finished, the damper should be cleaned off and checked for its sliding or opening action. The tiled hearth and surround can now be fitted as previously described.

Fixing the convector open fire

Convector fires are more efficient than ordinary open fires because they provide radiated heat. They also heat a supply of air which is convected within the room. It is, however, essential that these appliances are installed with the utmost care to ensure that there is no possibility of a leak between the fireplace opening and the convection chamber. Otherwise, the warmed air may be drawn up the chimney, or smoke escape into the

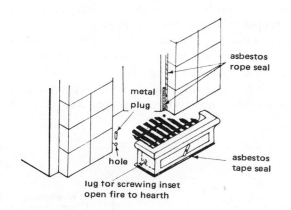

Figure 246   *Fixing an inset open fire*

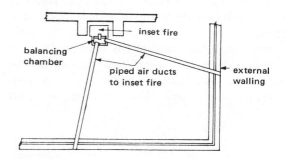

Figure 248   *Pipe ducts from external walling to an inset fire*

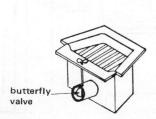

Figure 247   *Inset fire with primary air supply and ash pit*

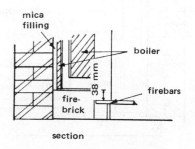

Figure 249   *Method of setting a back boiler*

room. Some appliances are free-standing and made with the convection chamber as an integral part. With these, there is no chance of a leakage in the convection chamber, but the bricklayer should ensure that there is a good seal where the chimney enters the flue (Figure 250). Asbestos rope may be used for this purpose, or in some popular types the chimney is flaunched up from the appliance flue connector. Often expanded metal is provided to ensure a key for the mortar or the fire cement (Figure 251).

If the convector is to be provided with a convection chamber constructed in the brickwork, the bricklayer must make certain that every joint between different types of materials is carefully sealed with asbestos rope or tape (Figure 252). The air for convection may be drawn from the room or from outside the building through ducts or pipes. If the fireplace is built on an external wall, air bricks may be fitted and the convected air taken direct through the wall from the outside into the convection chamber. This method is the simplest way in which warmed fresh air may be supplied to a room (Figure 253). The chamber should also be rendered with cement mortar and trowelled to a smooth finish. This not only ensures that the chamber has been sealed, but also provides a smooth surface so that the flow of air is not unduly restricted by friction on the convection chamber walls. The flue connector must

be fitted with a flanged flue adaptor which fits tightly to the concrete slab built over the top of the opening and is sealed with asbestos rope (Figure 254).

Free-standing convector open fires

These require a superimposed hearth of at least 40 mm thick, which projects from the front of the appliance by at least 300 mm in addition to the constructional hearth (Figure 250). The appliance may be installed in front of the surround or in a recess.

If it is set in front of the surround, a hole must be provided to receive the flue connector, which should be sealed with asbestos rope and fire cement (Figure 255). A soot door, of the double plate type (Figure 256), may be provided at the back of the flue if the fireplace recess is built on an external wall. This has the great advantage of allowing access for sweeping the flue from the outside of the building, thus avoiding the messy job of cleaning it from the inside. If the fireplace recess is not built in an external wall, access for sweeping the flue must be made by providing a removable box plate behind the appliance. When the flue is to be cleaned the appliance is removed, also the box plate, thus allowing access for the brush to enter the flue. This method is not very convenient, however, if the appliance is fitted

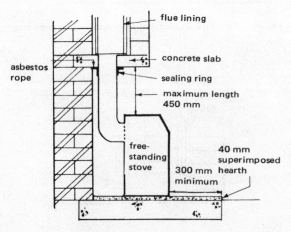

Figure 250   *Sealing the flue of a free-standing stove*

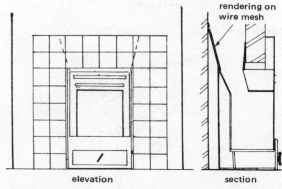

Figure 251   *Sealing an inset convector fire*

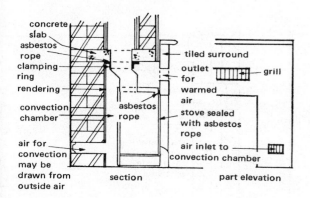

Figure 252 *Sealing a convection chamber*

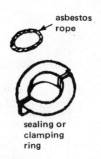

Figure 254 *A sealing or clamping ring*

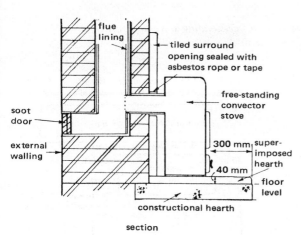

Figure 253 *Method of providing a soot door for a free-standing stove*

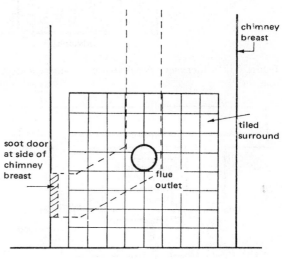

Figure 255 *Elevation showing a method of providing a soot door in a chimney breast*

with a back boiler since the draining of the water system is also required. In this case, a soot door may be provided in the side of the jamb with access to the flue and this will allow the flue to be swept without moving the appliance.

If the heating appliance has to be set in a fireplace recess, a concrete slab provided with a hole for the connecting flue should be built in over the top of the recess. The connecting flue is then inserted into the hole in the concrete slab and sealed with a clamping ring and asbestos rope (Figure 252). The maximum length of such a connecting flue pipe should be 450 mm from the top of the appliance. If there is sufficient room in the

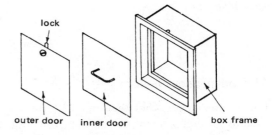

Figure 256 *Detail of a soot door*

recess, a soot door may be provided above the concrete slab (Figure 257) by building a junction pipe in the flue; alternatively, a soot door may be built in the outside of the building provided that the recess is on an external wall.

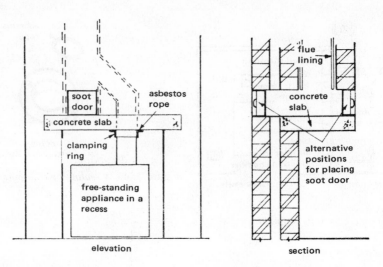

Figure 257 *Alternative positions for providing a soot door for a free-standing stove in a recess*

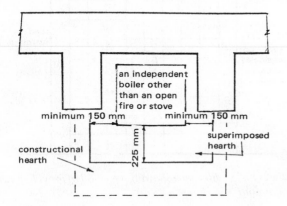

Figure 258 *Fixing an independent boiler other than an open fire or stove in a recess*

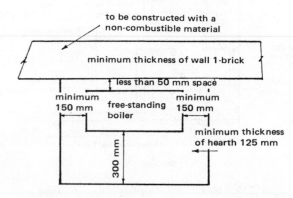

Figure 259 *Plan showing minimum thickness of walling at the back of an independent boiler which is less than 50 mm from the wall*

The independent boiler

For an appliance, other than open fire or stove, such as an independent boiler, the projection of the superimposed hearth should not be less than 225 mm in front of the stove and 150 mm on each side (Figure 258). If the space between the back of the boiler and the wall is less than 50 mm, the wall must be a minimum of 200 mm thick and constructed of non-combustible material (Figure 259). If the distance is 50 mm or more, the wall must still be constructed of non-combustible mat-

erial but need only be 75 mm in thickness (Figure 260). The wall must be built of non-combustible materials for at least 1 m above the boiler, and there must be no combustible material nearer than 225 mm to the flue pipe where it enters the wall.

The flue pipe from the boiler should never be of asbestos as this is liable to split when it becomes very hot. Therefore, the pipes must be of metal. This pipe should enter the brick chimney at an angle of 135 degrees to the horizontal and a cleaning eye should be provided at the bend. The flue pipe should be passed through a sleeve at the point where it passes through the brickwork to allow for expansion (Figure 261). The gap between the pipe and the sleeve is sealed with asbestos rope. This sleeve may be of asbestos and have a diameter of about 12 mm larger than the outer diameter of the flue pipe. The base of the flue should have a catchpot for collecting the condensate which is liable to occur in the flue. The flue should be extended to a depth of about 750 mm below the entrance of the metal flue pipe. Insulating material, such as exfoliated mica, sand or mineral wool, placed around the flue liners, will keep the amount of condensate to a minimum, and thus safeguard the chimney against damage due to acid attack (Figure 262).

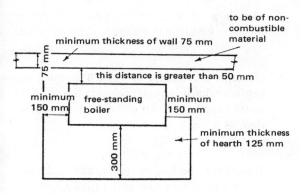

Figure 260 *Plan showing minimum thickness of walling at the back of an independent boiler which is more than 50 mm from the wall*

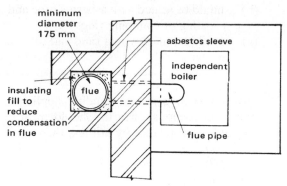

Figure 262 *Plan showing the insulation of the flue lining*

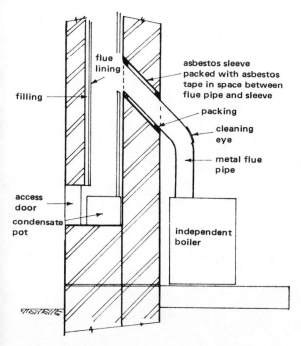

Figure 261 *Section showing a method of entering a flue pipe into a flue*

Self-assessment questions

1 The flue liners should be built within the chimney
   (a) as soon as the flue commences from the recess
   (b) 500 mm above the recess
   (c) from where the flue pipe enters the main flue

2 A fireback should be built in
   (a) solidly with dense concrete
   (b) with loose bricks at the back
   (c) using a lightweight concrete

3   When installing an inset fire with underfloor primary air supply it is recommended that the air supply should be obtained
    (a)   from the room in which the appliance is situated
    (b)   through a single duct system from the external air
    (c)   through a two duct system from the external air

4   Where a flue pipe from a convector appliance enters the main flue through a concrete slab, the space between the flue pipe and the concrete slab
    (a)   may be left open
    (b)   should be sealed with asbestos rope and a sealing or clamping ring
    (c)   should be filled with a sand and cement mortar

5   When installing a free-standing appliance, the constructional hearth should project beyond the appliance by not less than
    (a)   200 mm
    (b)   250 mm
    (c)   300 mm

6   If an independent boiler is installed in a recess, the hearth should project in front of the appliance by not less than
    (a)   200 mm
    (b)   225 mm
    (c)   250mm

7   Sketch a method of bridging a fireplace recess in which an open fire is to be installed.

8   Describe the method of fixing a fireback and explain why it is preferable for the fireback to be supplied in two or more pieces rather than as a single unit.

9   Describe a method of sealing the space between a tiled surround and a fireback.

10 By means of a sketch show how a soot door may be installed
    (a)   for an independent boiler inside a dwelling; and
    (b)   in conjunction with a free-standing stove in an external wall.

Chapter 11

Wall surface finishes

After reading this chapter you should be able to:

1 Have a sound knowledge of the building of internal fair-faced brickwork.
2 Know how to lay glazed bricks and tiles.
3 Know how to lay glass blocks.
4 Have a good knowledge of slate and tile hanging.
5 Have a good knowledge of the method of rendering external wall surfaces.

Fair-faced brickwork

This is becoming increasingly popular as an internal surface finish to walls of living-rooms or sun lounges in domestic premises. The bricklayer has to exercise a great deal of skill in erecting these walls so that they are pleasing to the eye. Small defects which would not be noticed on external walls may be very conspicuous in a living-room and can easily create an objectionable finish. Extra special care in building is, therefore, essential and the following points should be observed:

1 The walling must be kept perfectly clean and free from mortar stains.
2 If multicoloured bricks are used, the various colours should be evenly distributed throughout the wall face.
3 No chipped bricks should be visible on the face of the wall.
4 The joints must be kept to an even thickness.
5 The pointing must be of a high standard. Recessed joints are probably the most popular form of finishing off the work and these recesses should all be maintained at the same depth. The colour of the mortar must be kept even throughout the wall.
6 Perpends must all be kept truly plumb.
7 The correct bond must be maintained throughout the wall.
8 The wall must be kept truly plumb, level and straight along its face.
9 On completion, the wall is sometimes sealed against the penetration of dust by applying a coat of transparent silicone sealing compound or a solution of linseed oil and turpentine 1:2 or 1:3 which will have both a sealing effect and enhance the colouring of the bricks. The solution may be applied to the brickwork with a small paint brush.
10 The walls must be protected from staining when other tradesmen, such as painters and plasterers, are working nearby. Any accidental staining must be removed at once.

Glazed bricks and tiles

In some types of building, such as food stores, abattoirs and hospitals, cleanliness and hygiene are essential and, therefore, require wall surfaces which are bright and easily cleaned. In these cases, glazed bricks or tiles provide an excellent wall finish as they are smooth and hard, and any dirt which collects on the surface is easily wiped off with a damp cloth.

Both of these products are moulded from refractory clay and burnt. Then, when cooled, they are either *dipped* into liquid *slip*, or, more usually, conveyed on a belt underneath a spray. This liquid slip varies in composition depending on the manufacturer and the colour required, but its base is usually a metallic oxide such as tin or zinc. After the spraying process, the brick is subjected to further heat treatment in a continuous kiln (often gas-fired), and the slip forms a glass-like surface similar to that on cups and saucers.

A variety of colours is available, and though the one which is the most common is white, this can be obtained in a great number of shades. It is, therefore, good practice to use the bricks from a single manufacturer so as to be reasonably certain of keeping a constant colour. If different manufacturers' products are used, varying shades will be seen in the wall instead of one even colour.

Laying glazed bricks

This is not a very easy type of brick to lay and the following points should be observed if a first-class finish is to be achieved:

1 The bricks should be well soaked and then allowed to drain thoroughly so that there is no surplus water on their surfaces before laying.
2 The sand used in the mortar should be of a fine texture, free from stones to make for ease of laying, and free from organic impurities to prevent the possibility of staining the bricks.
3 The brickwork should be kept strictly to gauge, which means that in the case of the thicker types, the joints must be kept very thin, sometimes only equal to the thickness of a two pence piece.
4 After each course is laid to a line, the tops of the bricks should be rechecked for straightness with the aid of a straightedge to ensure that there are no *humps* or *bumps*.
5 The face of each course should be checked for straightness with a straightedge.
6 The perpends must be carefully plumbed and marked out on each course before laying the bricks.
7 When the wall is finished, the face joints may be filled in with a neat cement or white or coloured cement. This is often carried out by rubbing the cement mixture into the joints with a piece of rag or cloth, and then cleaning the surface of the wall with a clean cloth.

If a broken bond is incorporated in a wall built with glazed bricks this will involve the cutting of the bricks, which may be done with either a mechanical saw, or a hammer and bolster. If the hammer and bolster are used, the brick is first marked and then cut at a point about 6 mm from the mark. A second cut is then made on the mark and finally finished off with the aid of a piece of carborundum stone. If an attempt is made to cut the brick in one operation by placing the bolster directly on the mark, there is a possibility of the glaze being spalled at the edge (Figure 263) whereas by taking two cuts a cleaner cut may be obtained.

Fixing glazed tiles

There are two common methods which may be used for the fixing of wall tiles:

1 With a cement mortar; or
2 With a rubber-based adhesive.

Fixing with cement mortar

1 The walls, which are to be tiled, should be wetted and then rendered with a cement mortar 1:3 or 1:4 to a thickness of about 12 mm.
2 The surface of the rendering should be roughened after it has been floated to an even finish.
3 When the rendering has hardened and is ready for the tile fixing, it must be wetted.
4 The tiles should be thoroughly soaked and allowed to drain so as to be free from surplus water on the surface of the tile.
5 A batten is fixed to the wall at the width of one tile course above the floor or floor screed. This is to allow the tiles to be started from a truly level surface and one which is straight. When the tiles have set, the batten is removed and the course which is adjacent to the floor is fixed last so that the tiles can be scribed to any irregularities which may be in the floor surface (Figure 264).
6 The mortar for bedding should be composed of Portland cement and sand 1:3; the sand to be fine enough to allow for a 6 or 7 mm bed. It is not a good practice to use a mortar which is richer than that suggested, because of the possibility of excessive shrinkage, which may cause cracking in the bed and dislodge the tiles.

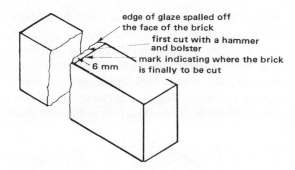

Figure 263 *Method of cutting a glazed brick*

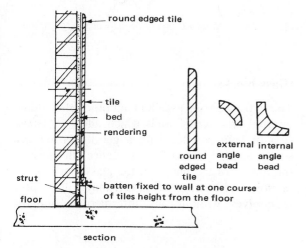

Figure 264 *Fixing tiles to a partition wall*

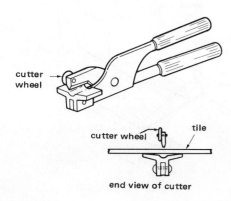

Figure 265 *Tile cutter*

7 The tiles are buttered with the mortar and then tapped securely to the wall. Skill is required to judge the correct amount of mortar. If too much is buttered on the tile, there is a possibility of dislodging the next-door tile. If insufficient mortar is used, the tile will not be soundly bedded, since there will be a void behind the tile.

8 The joints in between the tiles should be about 2 mm thick and filled in or grouted with a white or coloured cement; then cleaned off with a piece of cloth.

9 The tiles may be laid either half-bond with each other or with straight joints. Straight joints generally give a better appearance but half-bond is better when the tiles vary a little in size then slight discrepancies are not so easily noticed. If the tiles are to be laid with straight joints and the tiles vary somewhat in size, it is usual to sort out the various sizes before beginning and to lay the different sizes in separate courses.

10 Round-edged tiles and angle beads (Figure 265) may be used for finishing off the top courses of tiles when the whole wall is not required to be tiled, or for angle returns.

11 Tiled work must be truly plumb, level and each course checked for straightness along both the top edge and face of the tiles. Any irregularity on the face of the wall will be accentuated by the sun or any light shining on it at an angle.

12 Glazed tiles may be cut with:

   (a) A patent tile cutter which is a tool similar to a pair of shears, having a cutter wheel on one side and the jaws having one knife edge and the other with two flattened surfaces a small distance apart. See Figure 265. The tile is marked and the hardened wheel is run along the mark to scratch the surface. The tile is then placed in the jaws with the marked line between the two flattened surfaces. The jaws are then tightened and the tile will break along the line scored with the hardened wheel.

   (b) A glass cutter.

   (c) By running the point of the trowel

along the mark on the tile.

When using either method (b) or (c) the surface is first scratched and then broken with the hands or by using a pair of pincers.

Fixing tiles with an adhesive

1   The surface to which the tiles are to be fixed must be flat and even, as any irregularity which is in the rendering will reproduce itself on the tiled surface.
2   The surface should be free from dust, oil and grease.
3   Adhesive usually has an *open time* of about an hour. Therefore, too large an area should not be spread on the wall ready to receive the tiles. (Approximately 1–2 m^2 is usually sufficient.)
4   The adhesive is best spread with a laying-on trowel and then evenly distributed with a notched trowel (Figure 266).
5   The tiles must not be soaked; they are fixed dry and laid straight from the carton and pressed on to the adhesive.
6   Most modern tiles are fitted with 'nib spacers' which allow the joints to be kept even in size without having to worry about their adjustment to keep the tiles straight along the top of the courses. But this does mean that careful sizing should be done before each course is laid.

   Tiles which do not have these 'nibs' should not be butt jointed, instead they should have joints of about 2 mm between them.

   It is also quite common practice to have thin slivers of wood or matchsticks sharpened down, to insert in the joints to adjust the tiles when straightening them along their top edges.
7   Any adhesive on the face of the tiles should be thoroughly cleaned off before it sets hard.
8   The filling of the joints should be left until the adhesive has hardened and the tiles are well-secured to the wall surface.

When using adhesives it is very important that the tins or drums should be kept sealed by replacing the lids after the containers have been opened.

When tiling on partition walls which are built with breeze blocks or a similar type of material, care should be taken to ensure that the partitions are dried out before tiling. These types of partitions are subject to a high shrinkage rate and if they are wet when tiling, the shrinkage is liable to cause a failure in the tiled surface as the wall dries out.

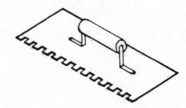

Figure 266   *'Notched' laying on trowel for spreading adhesive*

Glass blocks

These provide an excellent method of building internal or external walls which allow transmission of light coupled with a good thermal and sound insulation and fire resistance. Because of the nature of the material, the glass blocks must be non-load-bearing. However, they will support themselves without any intermediate support

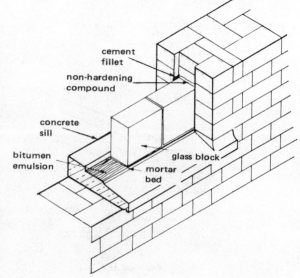

Figure 267   *Isometric view of a glass block panel*

quite safely in panels up to a maximum of 11.148 m² with a maximum height or width of 6.10 m. Provision must also be made at the ends and top of the panels to allow for expansion and also for any movement in the structure.

Laying the glass blocks

1 Glass blocks are non-absorbent and, therefore, a fatty mortar which is not too wet should be used. A suitable mix may be composed of cement, lime and sand 1:1:4. The sand must be clean and free from stones.
2 The sill at the base of the panel should be coated with a bitumen emulsion. This will allow for slight movement either in the panel or in the structure around it without creating cracks in the mortar bed underneath (Figure 267).

3 The blocks are bedded with the mortar and each course is carefully lined-in along the top of the course and along the face of the wall.
4 In all panels, the top and sides must be built independent of the main walling so that no stresses are imposed on to the glass blocks. A recess of at least 12 mm must be allowed and this may be filled with a mineral wool or a non-hardening compound. This recess must also be kept free from any mortar droppings or chips of brick or stones. The faces of the joint between the glass panel and the walling should be pointed with a mastic or non-hardening compound (Figure 268).
5 Reinforcing metal strips should be built into every third, fourth or fifth course depending on the size and position of the panel. These should be built into the main structure. The reinforcement should be of a non-rusting open-mesh type, not wider than 62 mm (Figure 269).

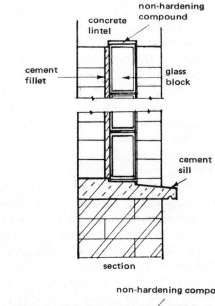

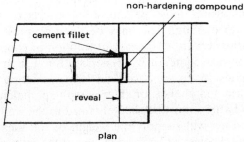

Figure 268 *Fixing a glass block panel*

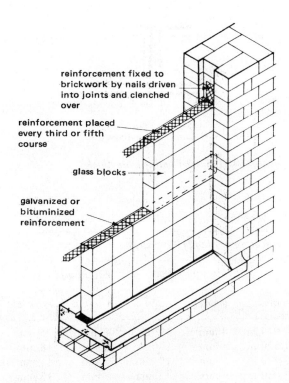

Figure 269 *Method of reinforcing a glass block panel*

6 The joints on the face of the panel may be pointed as the work proceeds, or afterwards, just as in normal brickwork. Coloured mortars may also be used for pointing.
7 Special *prismatic blocks* are available. It is essential that these are placed the right way up and with the correct face on the outside. These blocks are clearly marked 'top out' and should be laid accordingly.
8 When setting out openings for glass block panels, it is essential to measure accurately so as to allow for the recesses at the ends of the panel, and for the panel to be built with complete blocks. Broken bonds cannot be permitted in such panels because of the difficulty in cutting the blocks. Half-blocks, however, are available if required for forming a half-bonded panel.
9 Curved glass blocks are also available for curved walling. The method of laying these is similar to normal panels which are straight in plan, except that *vee* joints are used to build

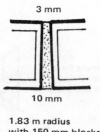

3 mm

10 mm

1.83 m radius
with 150 mm blocks

Figure 270   *Detail of radius glass block*

Table 15

Vertical joints obtained by various radii

	150 mm blocks		200 mm blocks	
radius	internal	external	internal	external
0.914 m	4 mm	19 mm	4 mm	25 mm
1.520 m	5 mm	14 mm	5 mm	18 mm
2.290 m	5 mm	10 mm	5 mm	11 mm
3.050 m	6 mm	12 mm	6 mm	13 mm

walls of various radii. Generally, the recommended minimum radii are 1.83 m for 150 mm blocks. The inside and outside dimensions are given in Table 15.

Slate and tile hanging

Although these two materials are very different the method of fixing them to a wall is basically the same in both cases. Slates are mined from quarries in various parts of the country such as Cornwall, Wales, and the Lake District in the north of England. Each area produces slates with special characteristics peculiar to that district, the main differences being their colour and texture.

A good slate should be:

1 Uniform in colour;
2 Compact and one that will give a sound ring when struck with a stone or light hammer;
3 Hard and rough to the hand;
4 Non-absorbent.

Plain tiles are the type normally used for tile hanging on wall faces. Their size is 266 mm in length by 164 mm in width, and they are made either of concrete or from clay. Each tile has two small projecting nibs or a projecting rib at the top or head of the tile, and two small holes to allow for nailing.

Tile hanging provides both an ornamental and efficient surface finish to a wall since it will also protect it against the penetration of rainwater. The tiles may be fixed to battens which are either plugged direct to the wall or nailed to counter battens, placed at 350 to 450 mm centres and secured to the wall. These battens should, if possible, be treated with a preservative to protect them against possible attack by insects or the growth of fungi. This may be done by pressure treatment with a 10 per cent solution of copper-chrome-arsenate, or by immersion for at least 10 minutes in either a coal-tar oil; a solution of chlorinated phenol; or chlorinated naphthalenes. The battens must be securely fixed to the wall so that they will support the weight of the tiles or slates. They must be fixed by one of the following methods:

1 By driving masonry nails through the battens into the wall with a hammer.
2 By firing special fixings through the battens into the wall with a power tool or *gun*.
3 By drilling holes with a power tool and tungsten-carbide tipped drills, plugging the holes and screwing the battens to the plugs.

The first two methods are most likely to be used for this purpose as the third method would be rather expensive if there was a considerable amount of work to be done, although it is a most efficient method for fixing battens.

The gauge of the battens, the distance from centre to centre, may be calculated with the following formula:

$$\text{gauge} = \frac{\text{length of tile} - \text{lap}}{2}$$

Thus, for a 266 mm tile the gauge with a 38 mm lap

$$= \frac{266 - 38}{2}$$

$$= \frac{228}{2} \text{ mm}$$

$$= 114 \text{ mm (this would be suitable for wall tiling)}$$

Tile and half-tiles may be used at the stopped end of the wall so that half-bond can be maintained in the tiling (Figure 271). For external angles special returns can be obtained to form a return in the tiling (Figure 272). These are ordered as left- and right-handed external returns. Similar tiles would be used for internal angles and ordered as left- or right-handed internal returns.

Window reveals may be rendered in between the tiles and the frame, thus saving uneconomical cutting of tiles (Figure 273). An alternative method would be to project the window frame

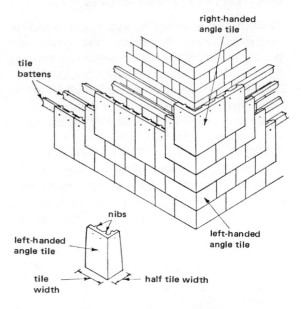

Figure 272 *Alternative shape of angle tile*

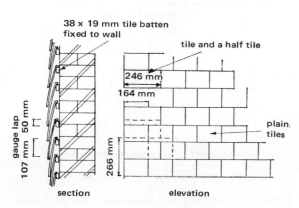

Figure 271 *A stopped end in tile hanging*

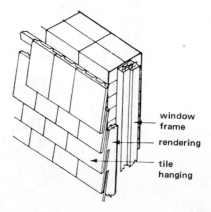

Figure 273 *A method of finishing tile hanging at a reveal*

from the brickwork and finish the tiles flush with the frame (Figure 274).

Slates or tiles should not be reduced to too small a size when being cut. In slating, a minimum size of 150 mm should be maintained. Plain tiles should not be cut so that they are less than their full length on one side. No tile should be cut so that it is reduced in width in any part to less than half the width of a tile (Figure 275).

Rendering external wall surfaces

The wall surface should be well keyed to receive renderings either by raking the joints out thoroughly, or by the better method of building the wall with grooved or keyed bricks (Figure 276). The wall should be cleaned of all loose dirt and wetted so that the surface is damp when the rendering is applied. The rendering should not be of a rich cement and sand mix as this is liable to shrinkage and cracking. There is also a possibility, in large industrial areas, of there being a considerable quantity of sulphates in the atmosphere, which may cause damage to the cement and, therefore, crazing in the rendering. This deterio-

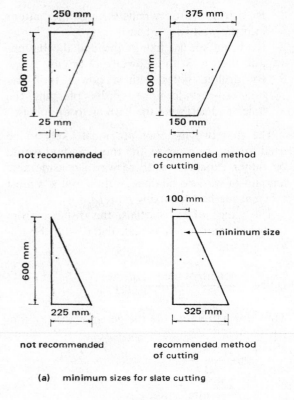

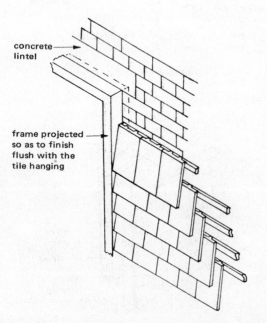

Figure 274 *An alternative method of finishing off tile hanging at an opening*

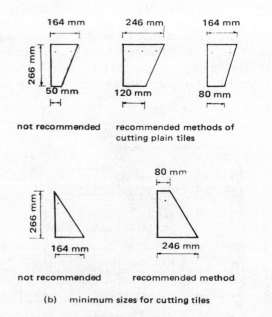

Figure 275 *Recommended minimum sizes for cutting slate and plain tiles*

ration is caused by sulphate-alumina action and may be recognized by the large pattern of cracks which may be seen in renderings which have been attacked in this way. On the other hand, external renderings should not be too soft or pliable otherwise they will not withstand the action of the weather. Therefore, a mix of cement, lime and clean, washed sand 1:1:6 would be suitable for external work.

It is essential that the sand should be of good quality – clean and well graded. Two-coat work is preferable to applying the rendering in one coat only. Each coat must be applied so that it has good contact on the whole of the surface area. The first coat should be allowed to set properly before applying the second and should be well scratched to give a good key. Mixtures may be added to waterproof the rendering and thereby give extra protection against the penetration of rainwater. Pigments may also be added to the mix

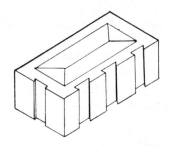

Figure 276   *A grooved or keyed brick*

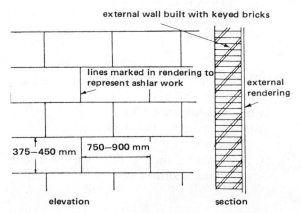

Figure 277   *Finishing off an external rendering to a brick wall*

if a coloured rendering is required. These should be added in the proportions recommended by the suppliers.

These renderings can have a monotonous appearance which can be improved by:

1 Marking neat lines in the surface of the rendering, while it is just setting, to represent ashlar stonework. The horizontal lines would be at about 375 or 450 mm apart measured vertically, and the perpendicular lines half-bonded at 750 to 900 mm intervals (Figure 277).

2 Pebble-dashing. This is done by throwing 9.5 or 12.7 mm gravel, at the rate of 0.62 m^3 per 100 m^2 of wall surface, on to the surface of the rendering while it is still wet. This finish has the advantage that any cracks or crazing are not visible on the wall surface. It will also not discolour in streaks as is the tendency with the smoother finishes, but will tend to discolour more evenly over the whole surface.

The stones which do not stick to the surface and fall to the ground or floor should be collected and washed for re-use.

3 Cullamix Tyrolean finish which is a special cement/lime/sand mixture 1:1:6 containing a pigment. This mix is spattered on the wall surface with the aid of a hand-operated machine into which is poured the wet mix. A series of flexible wires are attached to a handle. When this handle is turned the wires flick the mortar on to the wall. This forms a most decorative and excellent finish to a wall area.

4 A further wall finish may be produced by using Sandtex or similar material which can be obtained in various colours and may be applied by brush, or some types, by trowel. These finishes are resin bonded and waterproof and provide a long lasting decorative wall finish.

In the case of the finish for application by brush, this is suitable for painting direct on to cement and sand renderings, therefore, base treatment to the surface is normally not necessary.

All of the surfaces described in 1, 2 and 3 may be further decorated by painting, but it is important to remember when using ordinary paints that cements are normally alkaline. It is, therefore, wise to treat the surface with a cement primer before painting, but there are paints which are specially prepared for painting cement rendered surfaces. Even so, when using these, the manufacturer's instructions should be carefully observed before applying them to the wall surface to prevent the possibility of failures. If the external renderings are applied to hard dense bricks, the first coat may be of Cemprover Cement Plaskey, or some other similar solution, to ensure that good adhesion may be obtained between the rendering and the wall surface.

The Plaskey mix consists of two parts of Portland cement with two parts clean sand gauged with sufficient Cemprover diluted with an equal measure of water to form a thick slurry.

The surface to which the Plaskey is to be applied must be clean and free from oil and efflorescence, and the Plaskey applied by brushing it vigorously into the wall surface with a soft brush, leaving a 'stippled' finish. This should be left for three to seven days before applying the undercoat of the rendering.

Self-assessment questions

1   When laying glazed bricks, they should be laid in a
   (a)   dry state
   (b)   damp state
   (c)   soaked state

2   When cutting a glazed brick with the aid of a club hammer and bolster, the first cut should be made
   (a)   along the mark
   (b)   6 mm away from the mark
   (c)   10 mm away from the mark

3   When using an adhesive for fixing glazed tiles the surface of the wall
   (a)   may be left rough and the irregularities made up with the adhesive
   (b)   must be wetted
   (c)   must be smooth and dry

4   When tiling with an adhesive, the filling of the joints should be done
   (a)   as soon as the tiles are fixed
   (b)   one hour after the tiles are fixed
   (c)   when the adhesive has hardened

5   When tiling on newly-built partitions it is better to fix the tiles when the walls
   (a)   have dried out thoroughly
   (b)   are partially dried and in a damp condition
   (c)   are still wet

6   The recommended mortar mix for laying glass blocks is
   (a)   one part cement to three parts sand
   (b)   one part lime to three parts sand
   (c)   one part cement, one part lime and four parts sand

7   A bitumen emulsion is laid on a sill at the base of a panel
   (a)   to allow for slight movement
   (b)   as a damp-proof course
   (c)   to provide adhesion between the sill and the glass blocks

8   The gauge for wall tiles 300 mm long with a 50 mm lap would be
   (a)   115 mm
   (b)   125 mm
   (c)   135 mm

9   The quoin of a wall which is being tile hung may be carried out
   (a)   by using angle tiles
   (b)   by butting the tiles on each face together
   (c)   rendering up the edge with a strong cement mortar mix

10   What are the important points to observe when building internal fair-faced brickwork?

Chapter 12

Cladding

After reading this chapter you should be able to:

1 Have a good knowledge of the various types of cladding and their application in building.

2 Understand the important points that must be observed by the designer and the fixer of cladding units.

3 Have a sound knowledge of the various types of cramps and other fixings used in conjunction with cladding.

4 Understand the formation and use of bonder courses.

5 Understand the necessity for the introduction of expansion and compression joints and how they are formed.

6 Realize the importance of protecting cladding after it has been fixed and the methods that may be adopted to ensure adequate protection.

7 Know how to receive cladding units and store them.

The term *cladding* is used when precast brick panels, thin concrete, stone, granite, marble or slate is employed as a facing in addition to the normal structural requirements. It should not be fixed too tightly to the structure, for some measure of give must be allowed so that the cladding does not bear the strain of the finished construction.

Cladding has several advantages over traditional types of construction.

1 The units can be prepared in a factory, where their production is not hampered by bad weather conditions, and where good quality control can be maintained.

2 They can be produced in readiness for fixing while the framework is being built.

3 The units do not carry any structural loads (other than their own weight) and therefore they may be comparatively thin.

4 A wide variety of surface finishes is available.

5 The framework and internal lining can be erected comparatively quickly, so that the internal finishes and services can be put into operation very soon after fixing the external cladding.

Certain points, however, must be observed if failures are to be avoided with this type of construction. Some, of course, are the responsibility of the designer, but the cladding fixer must also play his part by making certain that the fixings are securely made and that all types of joints are constructed in accordance with approved practice.

Important points for the designer

The designer must keep the following points in mind to prevent failures. Designers should:

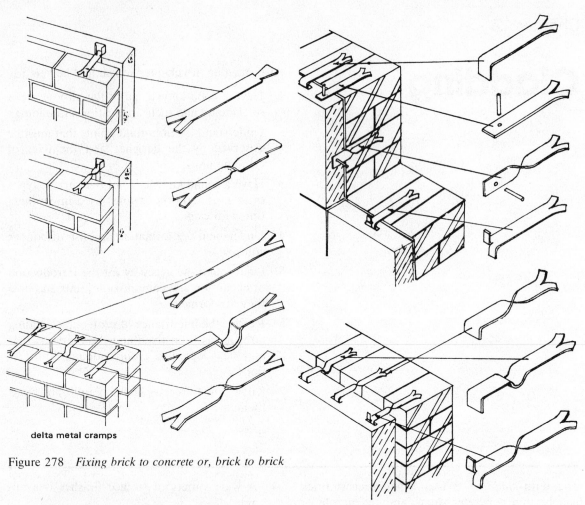

delta metal cramps

Figure 278   *Fixing brick to concrete or, brick to brick*

delta metal cramps

Figure 279   *Fixing stone to brick showing the application of various types of fixing cramps*

1 Allow for the thermal movement of the structure.
2 Allow for movement due to drying shrinkage. (The fixing of the slabs should not be started too soon after the main structure. Some time must be allowed for the shrinkage in the framework to take place.)
3 Allow for elastic deformation particularly with wind loading on tall slender buildings.
4 Allow for *creep*, which is a gradual compression of the structure due to sustained stress. Therefore, great care must be taken with the compression joints.
5 Allow for uneven settlement of the structure.
6 Avoid the use of a cladding material which is too thin, thus preventing adequate and safe fixing methods from being used.
7 Provide well designed cramping details.
8 Ensure that bonder courses or other means of supporting the weight of the cladding are provided at each storey height.
9 Avoid using slabs of too large an area which would reduce the number of joints and probably absorb movement.
10 Specify the correct metal for the fixing cramps.

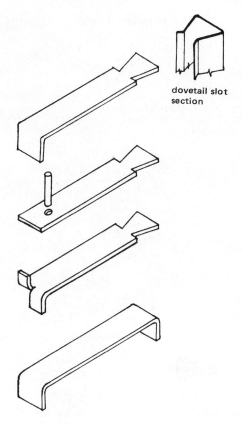

dovetail slot
section

Figure 280   *Typical cramps for fixing stone to concrete*

Important points for the cladding fixer

Cladding fixers should:

1 Point the joints thoroughly to prevent the percolation of water behind the slabs. (This will have a particularly harmful effect in the winter if the water freezes.)
2 Use the correct type of fixing cramps as specified and not substitute different types of metals.
3 Make certain that the bonders or supporting nibs are well constructed.
4 Ensure accurate setting out of the fixing holes and slots.
5 Not use hard mortars for the joints.
6 Have sufficient thickness of the joints.
7 Construct expansion and compression joints in accordance with the designer's requirements.

8 Ensure that the correct *gap* is maintained at a maximum of 18 mm and a minimum of 6 mm. (If these limits are exceeded then the cramps will be either too short or too long and liable to lead to makeshift adaptations.)
9 Take precautions against rusting of the reinforcement, which might cause damage to the cladding, if for any reason the concrete structural wall has to be cut back.

Cramps and other fixings

These should be made from:

Non-ferrous metal, for example copper, gunmetal, phosphor bronze
Stainless steel alloys
Sherardized steel

It is preferable that all the fixings on each job are of the same metal to prevent the possibility of electrolytic action taking place between dissimilar metals. This is likely to cause deterioration in at least one of the metals. Iron or steel are not generally suitable for use as cramps or fixings even though they may be coated, as the coating may become damaged and allow the steel to rust and cause staining on the cladding surface, or expansion which is likely to damage the cladding at the joints, or by spalling of the surface. Figures 278–282 illustrate various types of fixings and cramps which are in common use with cladding.

Cramp holes or mortises

These should be cut or drilled in the cladding without fracturing or spalling the material immediately surrounding the hole.

Bonder courses or supports

It is important that the weight of each storey height of external cladding is transferred to the structural frame of the building. This can be achieved by:

1 Introducing a bonder course of sufficient depth and thickness to carry the weight and to bear on the structural wall (Figure 283). The bearing on the wall should be at least twice the

special fixings

slate, granite, marble, and mosaic

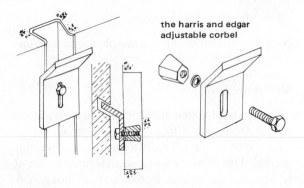

the harris and edgar
adjustable corbel

Figure 281   *Corbels and adjustable corbels for load-bearing*

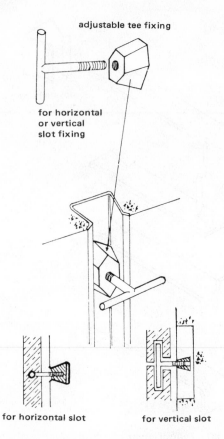

adjustable tee fixing

for horizontal
or vertical
slot fixing

for horizontal slot   for vertical slot

Figure 282   *Adjustable fixing for slate, granite, and marble*

distance of the projection from the wall and in no case less than 112 mm.

2　A concrete boot lintel or nib can be cast integrally with the concrete frame at each floor level. This method is recommended for use where the cladding is 100 mm or more in thickness. The slabs may be notched or grooved to fit around the nib and held back by cramps (Figure 284). The minimum projection of such nibs should not be less than 62 mm and they should also be reinforced.

3　To provide a horizontal channel in the main wall and to use a wrap-over supporting course at floor level (Figure 285).

4　For thin cladding slabs (up to 75 mm thick) non-ferrous metal corbel plates may be provided at each storey height. These corbel plates should be arranged to coincide with the vertical joints of the cladding slabs so that each plate supports two slabs (Figure 286).

The mortar

This should not be too hard or it will be likely to cause spalling on the face of the slab should there be any slight movement. The sand should be clean and free from any organic impurities which are liable to cause staining. The colour of the mortar should be constant and should also blend in with the cladding.

Expansion joints

For continuous lengths of cladding the provision

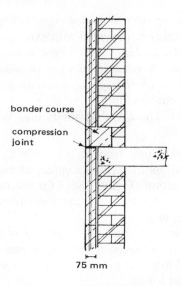

Figure 283 *Supporting thin cladding upon bonder courses*

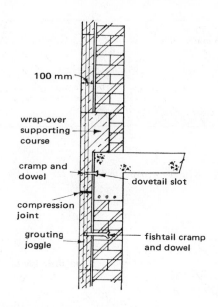

Figure 285 *Supporting cladding with a bonder course at floor level*

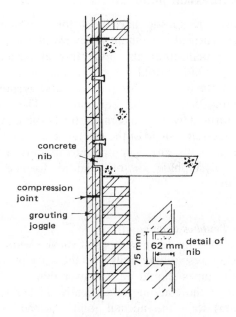

Figure 284 *Supporting cladding upon concrete nibs*

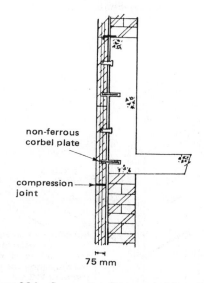

Figure 286 *Supporting 75 mm cladding upon corbel plates*

of open vertical joints at 6–9 m intervals should be adequate to allow for thermal lateral movement. These joints should be kept completely free from mortar to allow freedom of movement in the cladding. They should be filled with a non-

hardening compound or sealer such as:

Bituminized foamed-polyurethane; or Polysulphide compound (Figure 287).

They may also be protected from water penetra-

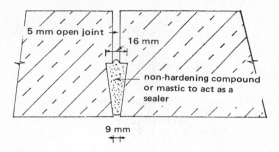

Figure 287   *An expansion joint*

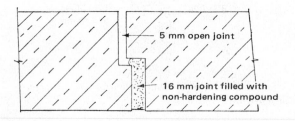

Figure 288   *A sliding expansion joint*

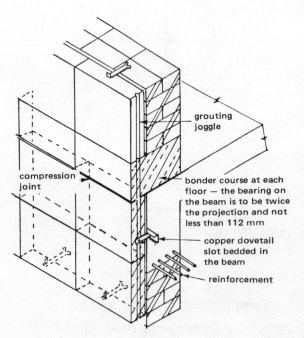

Figure 289   *Detail showing positioning of compression joint*

tion by using bent or folded copper strips. If the main structure is provided with expansion joints, those in the cladding should be made to coincide with them. A suitable method of allowing for expansion is by the use of a sliding joint introduced in the cladding to take up any expected movement. These sliding joints may be formed by:

1   Allowing one face of the cladding to slide behind another (for example, at an internal intersection (Figure 288)) for the full height of the structure with the joint filled with a sealer; or
2   Bonding the courses of cladding in the usual manner but using a soft mortar for the horizontal joints at this point and a sealer for the vertical joints.

Compression joints

These are elastic horizontal joints which will allow vertical movement. They should be placed at frequent intervals, preferably at each floor height, and should be positioned immediately below the bonder or supported course as shown in Figures 283, 284, 285, 286 and 289. These joints are formed by using a comparatively soft and elastic material instead of the mortar. These materials are normally either compounds of butyl rubber or polysulphide or bituminized foamed-polyurethane.

Butyl rubber compounds

These are made up in tapes of various widths and thicknesses and are built in as the work proceeds. These tapes should be narrower than the thickness of the cladding and slightly thicker (about 2 mm) than the normal joint. As the load is applied the tape will be squashed and will spread over the area of the cladding, and the joint will eventually be the same as the others. The tape should also be kept back from the surface of the cladding to avoid its projecting from the face of the work. The joint surface should be thoroughly clean and free from dust and grit. This type of compound is very durable (Figure 290).

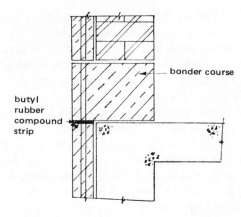

Figure 290 *Detail of a compression joint*

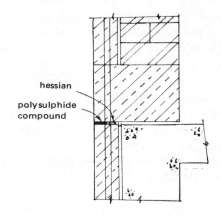

Figure 291 *Detail of a compression joint*

Polysulphide compounds

With these, the compression joints are left open and unfilled. On completion of the fixing, the joints should be loosely plugged with hessian or other similar material which must be kept well back from the face of the cladding. The joint is then filled by gunning in the compound under pressure. This type of filling is usually carried out by specialist firms (Figure 291).

Bituminized foamed-polyurethane

This does not spread when a load is applied to it so it may be used in correct widths and no allowance for spread need be made. As it is black it is normally kept back from the face of the wall to allow for the joint to be pointed to match the normal mortar joints in the walling. When applying the compound, the joint surfaces must be perfectly clean and dry. The adhesive is applied and allowed to become tacky (for about an hour under normal weather conditions) and then the strip is applied. This material is durable and has great elasticity.

Grouting at the back of cladding

Generally thin slabs for cladding are not grouted solidly at the back. These are normally fixed against dabs of mortar and the cavity in between the slabs and the wall left void. Weep holes should be left at each floor level and flashing or a damp-proof course provided to throw any water away from the face of the wall which might penetrate the cladding (Figure 292). With thicker cladding the cavity is normally filled solid with a cement/sand grout from 1:4 to 1:6. The mortises or pockets for the metal fixings should be filled with a neat cement or 1:0.5 cement/sand mix.

Weathering

Overhanging courses should be provided with steep weathering upper surfaces to throw off rainwater, and they should have deep throating or drips.

Concrete cladding

Concrete cladding has become very popular in modern construction because of its flexibility in size and shape and the infinite range of patterns which can be cast or formed on the surface, as well as for the wide variety of colours and surface treatments which can be introduced.

The Claddings Slabs Sub-Committee of the British Cast Concrete Federation makes the following recommendations: 'Plain slabs of constant thickness should not be less than 50 mm thick nor exceed 1 m in any one direction or 0.85 m² in area. When framed panels are used the thickness of the concrete should generally be not less than 50 mm. If, however, the maximum size of the aggregate does not exceed 9 mm and the rein-

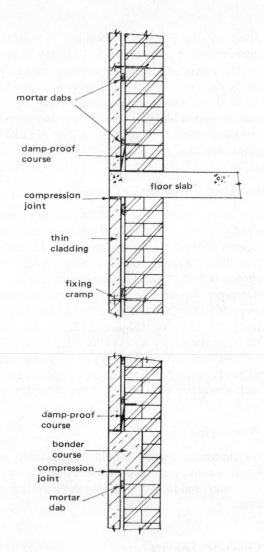

Figure 292 *Sections showing the provision of damp-proof courses*

the weight of the slab to about 54 kg, as this is the most that two people can normally handle. Above this weight mechanical lifting aids become necessary. (1 m² of concrete 25 mm thick weighs 60 kg.) Once mechanical lifting becomes necessary, it is more economical to lift larger slabs than smaller ones. In such cases it is difficult to cast large panels without slight deformations due to shrinking or twisting. Therefore, the slabs are normally cast with chamfered joints so that these slight defects may not be noticed so easily. It is better to avoid sharp arrises because of their liability to become damaged.

When mechanical appliances are used for lifting, some provision must be made in the slab so that it can be attached to the hoisting gear. These attachments must be strong enough to carry the weight of the slab quite safely and securely. A simple method is to provide loops of reinforcement from the top edge of the concrete slab and hook into these. A more elaborate method is to cast threaded plates into the slab and screw lifting hooks with screw threads into them. Any type of lifting apparatus cast into the slab should be carefully placed so as to ensure that when the slab is hoisted it is reasonably level and upright and that handling is, therefore, simple when it is placed into position.

The most usual method of using concrete cladding for light forms of construction is for the slabs to span from stanchion to stanchion or column to column, and for them to be clamped back against a strip of bitumen damp-proof course material. This permits a certain amount of movement in the structure or the slabs without impairing the efficiency of the joints (Figures 293 and 294). The horizontal joints are usually rebated and sealed with a weak mortar or preformed mastic cord.

When brick or *in situ* concrete walls are being faced with precast slabs, a cavity of not less than 18 mm should be provided between the slabs and the main wall. It is generally better not to grout this cavity solid owing to the difficulty in ensuring that it is completely filled. In this case voids would probably be left and fill with water, thus causing more trouble with moisture penetration into the inner wall than if the cavity were left hollow and weep holes provided at each floor level. Bonders

forcement is confined to the ribs, the thickness can be reduced to 38 mm providing that the spacing of the ribs in any one direction does not exceed 1 m centres. Any unribbed portion of a framed panel should have a thickness of not less than 50 mm. If aggregate larger than 18 mm is required to be used, the slabs must be increased in thickness.'

The weight of the concrete slabs is also an important factor. If the slabs are being lifted and positioned by hand, it is a good practice to limit

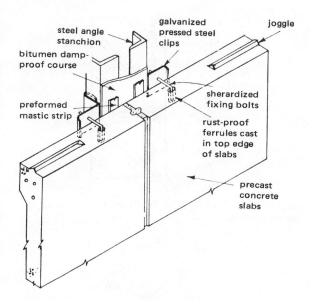

Figure 293 *A method of fixing a precast concrete slab to a stanchion*

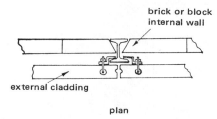

Figure 294 *A method of fixing cladding to a stanchion*

should be arranged at every 3–3.66 m of height (Figures 289–292).

The handling and stacking of the concrete units on site should be done with much care and thought. For example:

1   They should be stacked in such a manner that they are easily accessible when required for use.
2   The edges should be protected against damage by setting them down carefully when handling. Hoisting cable should not be allowed to come into contact with the face of the slab.
3   Pinch bars should not normally be used on the face for moving the slab. If one must be used, then a pad should be placed between it and the slab.

4   Slabs should not be walked upon.
5   The slabs should be stacked on timber battens and not directly upon the ground.
6   Only clean sacks should be used for packing underneath or against the slabs; greasy or dirty sacks are liable to cause bad staining.
7   Slabs should never be stored under roofs where rainwater can wash dirt from the roof surface on to the slabs and thus discolour them.
8   When slabs are stacked against each other on edge, a packing should be placed between the slabs. A suitable method would be to use either short lengths of clean rope or short timber spacers.

Slate cladding

Slates may be obtained in four types of finishes:

1   *Frame sawn:* a rough texture with a vertical emphasis.
2   *Natural riven:* the natural split texture.
3   *Sanded:* a fairly smooth finish.
4   *Fine rubbed:* an eggshell finish.

Slates are usually supplied in sizes up to about 1.8 by 0.762 m in all finishes except riven. To facilitate handling on the site, it is recommended that sizes should not exceed 1.22 by 0.7 m (a 25 mm thick slab at this size weighs 50.8 kg). Thicknesses are usually 38, 25 and 12 mm.

The size of the natural riven finish slab is limited to 610 by 450 mm because of the natural foldings in the rock which produce cambers which can be accentuated if split into large sizes. The thickness of riven slate is usually 25 mm for the larger slabs and 12 mm for slabs 450 by 300 mm.

All fixings must be of non-ferrous metal and serve two functions:

1   Support of the dead weight of the slab.
2   Retention of the slabs in their correct position.

At least one support should be provided to each slab of a particular course. The lowest course of the slate cladding may be bedded on a plinth or a corbel at an upper floor (Figure 295). Metal corbels may be used and these can be supplied in either short or continuous lengths (Figures 296 and 297).

The cramps used for retention of the slabs may be:

1 Double toed (Figure 298)
2 Pin type (Figure 299)
3 Single cramps
4 'S' hooks (Figure 300)

Three types of joints may be used at external angles:

1 Plain joint
2 Plain joint with throating or recess
3 Birdsmouth mitre (Figure 301)

Granite cladding

Riven slabs are of 50 mm nominal thickness and sawn slabs are generally 18, 25 or 30 mm but may be thicker if specially requested. The method of fixing granite slabs is basically the same as for slate cladding.

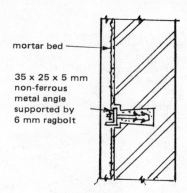

Figure 296   *Section showing the method of fixing an angle support*

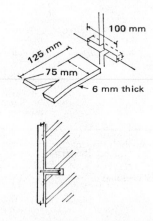

Figure 297   *6 mm copper corbel for fixing slate slabs*

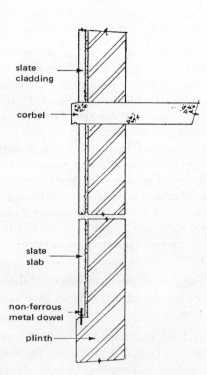

Figure 295   *Method of supporting slate cladding on a plinth or corbel*

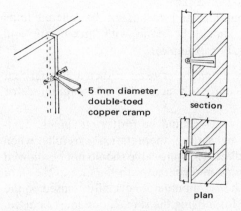

Figure 298   *Methods of retaining slate cladding in position*

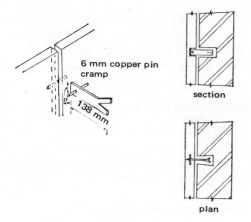

Figure 299 *Copper pin cramp*

Stone cladding

The minimum thickness of stone cladding is usually 62 mm and the maximum size between 0.900 and 1.22 m according to the thickness of the stone. The slabs may be supported on projecting nibs or on bonders as previously described (Figures 283, 284, 285, 286, 289 and 292).

The recommended mortar mix for stone blocks is two parts white cement/five parts hydrated lime/seven parts stone dust. Joints and beds should be 5 mm thick and there should be 12 mm grouting between the stone and the structural

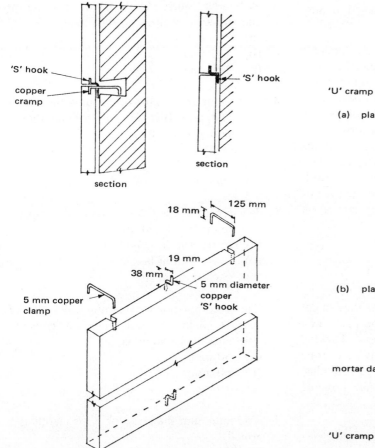

Figure 300 *The positions for placing copper cramps and 'S' hooks for slate cladding*

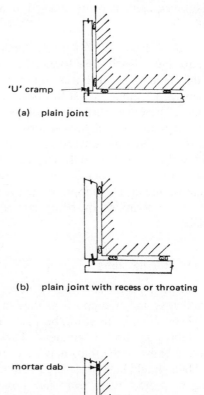

Figure 301 *Types of joints for external angles*

wall. When fixing to reinforced concrete walls the fixing cramps should be non-ferrous metal dovetail anchors and dowels, and channels should be let into the concrete to receive them (Figure 289). When fixing to brick structural walls the stone cladding is secured by the same types of clamps previously described (Figure 283).

Protection of the cladding after fixing

After the cladding has been fixed into position it must be protected against possible damage from:

1 Staining from other trades.
2 Wheelbarrows.
3 People carrying heavy equipment or materials.
4 Tools or material being dropped from above.
5 Material or equipment being stacked against the wall.

Careful supervision will obviously prevent many mishaps, but it is still wise to give full protection to the cladding because it is so expensive to repair damaged walling once it has been fixed into position. Therefore, thin slats of timber should be fixed at all external angles, vertical and horizontal. If there are any concreting operations nearby, the walling must be fully covered with clean hessian or sacking or plastic sheeting. Similar treatment should also be adopted when painting or plastering operations are being carried on near the slabs.

Stacking and storing slabs

Slabs are thin and brittle and should never be stacked flat across timber supports as they might be broken. They should, therefore, be stacked on edge preferably on timber runners. Packing pieces inserted between the slabs may be of rope or timber. Slabs should be well-covered with plastic sheeting to protect them from any possible staining.

Handling large slabs

Mechanical lifting aids should be used when heavy slabs are being handled. The lifting should

be smooth since if it is applied jerkily the slab may be cracked or broken. It may also swerve and become damaged by hitting other slabs or material nearby.

Self-assessment questions

1 Cladding units are designed to carry
   (a) structural loads
   (b) some structural loading
   (c) no structural loading

2 Cramps for cladding are made from
   (a) non-ferrous metals
   (b) steel
   (c) galvanized iron

3 A bonder course should have a bearing on the structural wall of not less than
   (a) 100 mm
   (b) 112 mm
   (c) 120 mm

4 For continual lengths of cladding the provision of open vertical expansion joints should be made at intervals not exceeding
   (a) 6 m
   (b) 7.5 m
   (c) 9 m

5 It is recommended that horizontal compression joints be placed at
   (a) every 4 m in height
   (b) every 5 m in height
   (c) each floor height

6 The recommended minimum thickness of precast plain concrete slabs of constant thickness for cladding is
   (a) 50 mm
   (b) 60 mm
   (c) 70 mm

7 The minimum thickness of stone cladding is usually
   (a) 50 mm
   (b) 62 mm
   (c) 75 mm

8 The recommended mortar mix for stone blocks is
   (a) one part white cement/five parts lime/ seven parts stone dust
   (b) two parts white cement/three parts lime/seven parts stone dust
   (c) two parts white cement/five parts lime/ seven parts stone dust

9 Describe the points that must be observed when stacking and storing cladding units.

10 Describe the method of fixing slate cladding.

Chapter 13

Drainage: clay products

After reading this chapter you should be able to:

1 Have a good understanding of the Building Regulations concerning drainage.

2 Have a good knowledge of clay pipes and the various types of joints commonly used.

3 Know the various types of fittings used in drainage and their uses.

4 Understand the uses of various types of interceptors.

5 Know how to lay drains and to determine required falls.

6 Know how to carry out soundness tests on drains.

7 Understand the construction of manholes and intercepting chambers.

Although drainage is taken very much for granted by most people, it needs to be constructed with care, and in accordance with the Building Regulations, otherwise it can create a definite hazard to health. Obnoxious odours may escape which are not only unpleasant, but also dangerous.

A *drain* is a length of pipe laid to remove soil water, waste water or rainwater from the building or buildings which are situated within one boundary. It is the property of one owner who is solely responsible for its maintenance and repair.

A *private sewer* is a length of pipe removing soil, waste or rainwater from buildings which are situated within two or more boundaries. It is jointly the property of two or more owners who are responsible for its upkeep.

To protect public health, stringent rules are necessary for the installation of soil and waste appliances, and for the conveyance and disposal of soil and waste water. The local authority has the power to order the removal or repair of any drain which is not up to standard. It is, therefore, most important to know the relevant Building Regulations to ensure that all work in connection with

drainage or private sewers agrees with these requirements.

Building Regulations: Part H Sanitary pipe work and drainage

Requirements for drainage and waste disposal are numbered as follows;

H1 Sanitary pipework and drainage.
H2 Cesspools, septic tanks and settlement tanks.
H3 Rainwater drainage.
H4 Solid waste storage.

It is important that the following points be observed when installing drainage systems to ensure that they operate in an efficient manner with only minimal maintenance being necessary during their working life.

1 Any drain or private sewer shall be of sufficient strength and capable of carrying the maximum loads to which it may be subjected.

2 Where necessary it should be protected against injury.

3 It must be constructed of durable materials which will not only resist the corroding action of the ground and subsoil water, but also the soil water which passes through it.

4 All joints must remain watertight under all working conditions, including any differential movement such as may occur between the pipe and the ground.

5 The joints must not form any obstruction in the interior of the drain.

6 The pipes shall be laid in a straight line between points where changes of direction or gradient occur.

7 They shall be so laid at such a gradient (unless the contents are pumped) as to ensure that they are self-cleansing and efficiently carry away the maximum volume of matter which may be discharged into them.

8 They shall be of adequate size to carry the maximum volume of matter and in no case be less than the diameter of the outlet of any appliances, or less than 100 mm in diameter for the conveyance of soil water, or 75 mm in any other case, such as rainwater.

9 Where a drain passes through a building then:
  (a) it shall be adequately supported throughout its length, such support being securely attached to the building;
  (b) there shall be no restriction on the thermal movement of the drain;
  (c) it shall be so placed so as to be reasonably accessible throughout its length for maintenance and repair.

10 Where any drain or private sewer passes under a wall or any part of a building such precautions shall be taken to prevent damage to or loss of watertightness in the drain by differential movement.

11 Any drain shall, after the completion of the work (including haunching or surrounding the drain with concrete and backfilling the trench) be capable of withstanding a suitable test for watertightness.

Means of access to drains and private sewers

1 Any drain shall have a satisfactory means of access for inspection and cleansing.

2 There shall be an inspection chamber:
  (a) where there is a change of direction or gradient which would prevent the drain from being readily cleaned within it;
  (b) on a drain within 12.5 m from a junction between it and another drain, unless there is an inspection chamber at that junction;
  (c) at the highest point of the drain unless there is a rodding eye at that point.

3 The maximum distance that any part of a drain should be from an inspection chamber must not be more than 45 m (this also includes the maximum distance between chambers).

4 Inspection chambers shall:
  (a) be constructed strong enough to sustain all loads which are liable to be imposed upon them;
  (b) exclude subsoil water;
  (c) be watertight;
  (d) be of such a size as to permit ready access to the drain for inspection, cleansing and rodding;
  (e) have a removable and non-ventilating cover of adequate strength and durability;
  (f) have such step irons or ladder or other fitting which will provide safe access where the depth of the chamber so requires;
  (g) be provided with benching having a smooth, impervious finish and so formed as to guide the flow of matter into the pipe and also to provide a safe foothold.

5 Any inspection chamber within a building shall be:
  (a) so constructed with a frame and cover as to be watertight when subjected to the maximum internal pressure which could be caused by the blockage of the drainage system at any point below the chamber;
  (b) be fitted with a removable and non-

ventilating cover of adequate strength;

(c) fitted in a frame with an airtight seal;

(d) secured to the frame by removable bolts made of corrosion-resistant material.

Junctions

Any connection between drains, or drains and private sewers, or private sewers shall be watertight under all conditions of working and shall be made so that the tributary drain discharges its contents into the other drain obliquely in the direction of the flow of the main drain.

Soil and ventilating pipes

1 Generally no soil pipe shall be placed outside the external wall of a building unless the building was erected under former control (including such a building which has been altered or extended) or a building having not more than three storeys.

2 Any soil water appliance discharging into the soil pipe must be provided with an adequate trap.

3 The soil pipe must be capable of withstanding an air or smoke test for a minimum period of 3 minutes at a pressure equivalent to a head not less than 38 mm of water.

4 Must have sufficient access to permit internal cleansing.

5 Must be adequately supported throughout its length.

Any ventilating pipe shall be carried up to a sufficient height and so positioned so as not to transmit foul air in such a manner as to become prejudicial to health or a nuisance. It must be fitted at its topmost end with a durable wire cage or other cover which does not unduly restrict the flow of air.

Rainwater pipes

Rainwater pipes must be of adequate size and composed of durable materials. They must be securely fixed to the building throughout their length. No rainwater pipe shall be so constructed as to discharge into, or to connect with, a soil water drain unless provision is made in the design of the sewerage system for the discharge of rainwater.

uPVC soil and underground pipes

These are plastic units which may be laid to required falls and then surrounded in concrete. They are light, easy to handle, and readily adaptable for any system of soil drainage. Adjustable bends are available, which allow lengths of drains to be laid at any desired angle, they also have high strength and are quite flexible, which allow them to remain watertight even though there may be considerable movement in the soil.

Glazed vitrified clay pipes

The British Standard Specification for these types of pipes is BS 65. This specification lays down minimum requirements for pipes and fittings which are manufactured in accordance with this Standard, and includes the following headings:

The scope – pipes and fittings
Description and marking
The materials used in manufacture
General quality and glazing
Dimensions and tolerances
Dimensions of pipes and fittings
Crushing strength
Absorption tests
Hydraulic proof tests
Acid and alkali tests
Inspection and testing by the manufacturer

The pipes and fittings must be sound and free from visible defects which would impair their efficiency. They must give a sharp clear note when tapped with a light hammer.

The interior of the pipes and fittings should be glazed. The outside surface of the barrel and the inside and outside of the socket need not be glazed, but if they are, they can still be used in accordance with the Standard Specifications.

The British Standard covers two main methods of glazing pipes:

1 Salt glaze
2 Ceramic glaze

Salt glaze

The pipes are made by first moulding them from a refractory clay which has been carefully selected and mixed with a *grog* (an aggregate consisting of finely crushed pipes from previous firings). The clay and grog are mixed together and formed into a *pug* which is then moulded into shape with a hydraulic press, and cut off to its correct length.

The moulded pipes are then carefully dried in a heated chamber and stacked on their socket ends on a slatted floor. The heat, which is often extracted from the kilns, then passes through the floor and around the pipes, and extracts the moisture from the pipes and fittings. This must be done gradually as rapid drying will cause excessive shrinkage resulting in cracked pipes or distorted shapes.

When thoroughly dry, the pipes are stacked in either a coal or an oil-fired kiln, usually of the down-draught type. When fully loaded, the kiln is then sealed at the entrance and the temperature raised until it reaches about 1100°C. This takes about three to four days. Common salt is then introduced into the kiln. This salt volatilizes and forms glass-like compounds on the surfaces of the articles which are in the kiln. If these are left for several days, the compounds will build up into quite a thick layer which provides the glaze necessary to make the pipes impervious to moisture. The cooling down process must also be gradual and the fires are dampened down after the salt has been put into the kiln. The temperature is slowly lowered until the kiln entrance can be reopened and the products are then removed and stacked ready for dispatch to the sites, once they are cool enough to handle.

Ceramic glaze
These are made by moulding the pipes in the same way as for salt-glazed bricks and tiles. They should be fired until *biscuit hard* and then re-fired once a *slip* has been applied to the surface. This produces a quality of glaze similar to that for glazed tiles or bricks.

All pipes which are manufactured in accordance with the requirements of the British Standard Specification should be clearly marked with BS 65: 1963 and the identifying mark of the Institute stamped on them.

If the purchaser requires pipes which have been tested in accordance with the crushing strength requirements, these should be stamped with the word 'EXTRA'. If the purchaser requires hydraulically tested pipes, the word 'TESTED' should be stencilled or stamped on them.

Some pipes and fittings will not meet the full requirements of the British Standard Specification, and therefore must not be sold as branded goods. However, they are quite suitable for use under many conditions, and are sold as *second quality*. They should be marked with a black band to identify them from the best quality.

Joints

All salt and ceramic glazed pipes may be connected with spigot and socket joints. The spigot should either be grooved or roughened. (Such roughening should not exceed 2 mm in depth.) The socket may be either a special flexible jointed type (Figures 302–304), or the standard conical type (Figures 305 and 306).

Patent flexible joints
These have several advantages over the rigid type of mortar joint:

1   As they are flexible, they will allow differen-

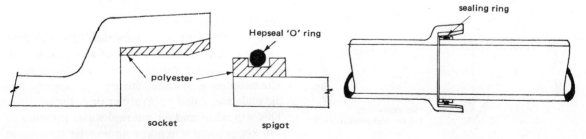

enlarged detail of a flexible joint

Figure 302   *The Hepseal joint*

tial movement between the drain and the ground without any leaks in the joints.

2 They are simple to install in bad weather and allow for rapid testing and backfilling.

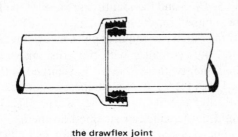

the drawflex joint

Figure 303   *Flexible joints in drainage*

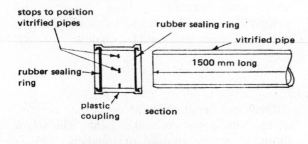

stops to position vitrified pipes

rubber sealing ring

vitrified pipe

1500 mm long

rubber sealing ring

plastic coupling   section

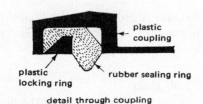

plastic coupling

plastic locking ring   rubber sealing ring

detail through coupling

Figure 304   *Hepsleve joint*

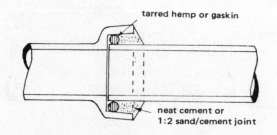

tarred hemp or gaskin

neat cement or 1:2 sand/cement joint

Figure 305   *A method of jointing vitrified clay pipes with an inflexible joint*

3 These joints are usually self-centring. As soon as the pipes are joined together, a level invert is obtained.

4 Some types do not require a concrete bed and may be laid on a granular base.

The Stanford joint

This has a band of bitumen inside the socket and another on the spigot. One pipe is inserted into another by forcing it into place.

The Hassall's joint

This may be obtained as double-lined or single-lined (Figure 307) and also has bitumen bands on the spigot and in the socket, which are sealed with neat cement grout.

The Drawflex joint

This is formed by moulding a band of resilient plastisol on the spigot and inside the socket (Figure 303). When joining two pipes, both plastisol surfaces are lubricated with the special compound and the pipes pushed firmly into place. This type will allow angular movement up to 5 degrees per joint and a linear draw of 18 mm per joint. Proof crushing strengths are not less than 27.1 kN/m for 100, 150, 175 and 225 mm diameter pipes.

The Hepseal joint

This has two polyester mouldings: one on the spigot and the other inside the socket. A rubber sealing ring is placed in the groove in the polyester moulding. When the pipes are joined together, the rubber ring is compressed and forms a seal which will stand a pressure of 140 kN/m^2, and allow movement up to 5 degrees per joint and a linear draw of 18 mm per joint (Figure 302).

The Hepsleve system

This consists of vitrified pipes each 1500 mm long with plain ends, joined together with plastic couplings and incorporating blocked-in sealing rings. The coupling is moulded from polypropylene and the ends are sealed by a rubber ring (Figure 304). This will withstand an internal water pressure of 140 kN/m^2, and will allow an angular movement of 5 degrees and a linear draw of 18 mm as well as a displacement of 9 mm at each joint. The joint is

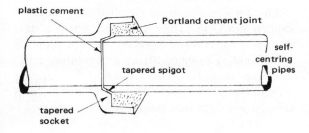

Figure 306   *Knowles free flow joint*

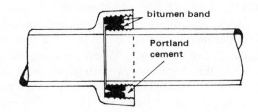

Figure 307   *Hassall single-lined joint*

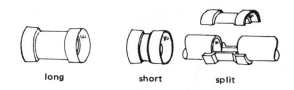

Figure 308   *Types of double collars*

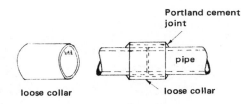

Figure 309   *A loose collar for joining two butt ends of clay pipes*

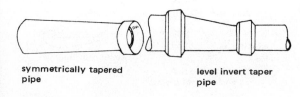

Figure 310   *Taper pipes*

made by spreading a special lubricant on one end of the pipe and pushing the coupling firmly over the pipe. The next pipe is lubricated, and pushed firmly into the sleeve or coupling and so on until the drain is completed (Figure 304).

Types of fittings

There is a wide variety which includes the following:

Double sockets or connecting sockets

Split double sockets are very useful in repairing a drain where one or more pipes have been damaged. A butt pipe is placed on the lower stream side of the double socket and the lower half of the socket is jointed to the pipes on each side. The top half of the socket is then bedded on to these pipes and the whole repair is encased in concrete (Figure 308). This double socket is particularly useful when a w.c. pan is to be replaced and where the socket of the pipe has been broken while removing the old pan. Figure 309 shows a loose collar and its method of application.

Taper pipe

These may be supplied in two types:

1   With a symmetrical taper.
2   With a level invert (Figure 310).

They are used for enlarging the internal diameter of the drain when the flow of sewage has increased owing to the number of inlets or tributaries in the drain.

Junctions

These are used:

1   Where a tributary drain joins a main drain without an inspection chamber being built at that point;
2   To provide a ventilating pipe into the main line of drains; or
3   For a tumbling bay or back-drop manhole.

They may be divided into single square, curved or oblique junctions, or double square, curved and oblique junctions. Some typical shapes are shown in Figures 311–314.

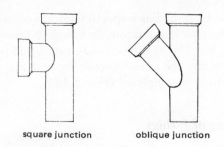

Figure 311   *Single junctions*

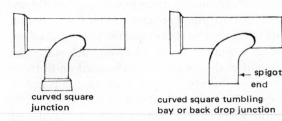

Figure 312   *Square junctions*

Junctions may also be supplied as joinder or capped junctions. These are used where a new drain is being laid and a junction is to be supplied for a building to be constructed at a future date. The cap may be easily removed by tapping around the groove below the capping with a sharp chisel and a light hammer (Figure 315).

Saddle junctions

These are used when a new drain is to be connected to an existing one. A hole is carefully cut with a hammer and sharp chisel into the old drain. The saddle junction is then bedded over the hole with either neat cement or a mix of 1:0.5 cement and clean, washed sand. When ordering such junctions, the diameters of both pipes must be quoted with the tributary diameter first; for example, 100 on 150 mm, or 150 on 225 mm (Figure 316).

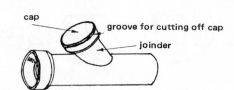

Figure 315   *Capped or joinder junction*

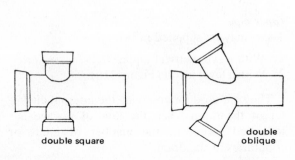

Figure 313   *Double square and oblique junctions*

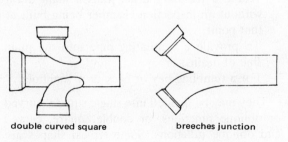

Figure 314   *Double junctions*

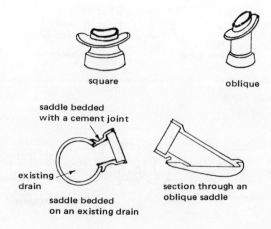

Figure 316   *Saddle junctions*

Stop-tap pipes

This is not specifically a drainage accessory, but can be very useful when a simple stop-tap chamber is required (Figure 317).

Bends

These are usually described by the number required to form a complete circle; for example, a quarter bend means that four joined together will make a circle. A sixth bend requires six for a circle, and an eighth eight, and so on up to one-thirty-second.

Very small quadrant bends are called *knuckle* or *short knuckle bends* according to their size. One particularly useful bend is a w.c. bend which is long enough to allow the barrel to pass right through a cavity wall without having a joint in the middle of the wall. This reduces the danger of sewer gas entering the building because of a defective joint in the middle of the wall (Figures 318 and 319).

Channels

These are divided into two groups:

1 Half-section channels; and
2 Three-quarter section channels.

In both cases, and for all junctions and curved channels, it is important that they are ordered as either right-hand or left-hand sections. An easy way to remember which is left or right is to face against the flow of the drain, or upstream. The channels that are required for the right-hand side are right-handed, and those on the other side are left-handed. Half-sections are similar in all respects to normal pipes, except that they are cut in half. The junctions and bends are the same as those used for pipes except that they are handed.

Junctions are, for example, *half-section single-channel junction left-hand square* or *right-hand oblique*. Bends are *half-section channel-bend one-quarter bend left-hand* or *right-hand* as the case may be, and so on (Figure 320).

Three-quarter section bends are used to connect a tributary drain to a main drain when the junction is being made within an inspection chamber (Figure 321). These must also be ordered as either right- or left-handed three-

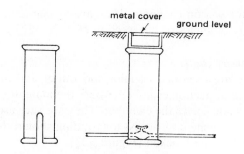

Figure 317 *Stop tap pipe*

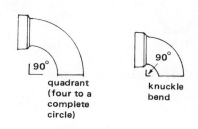

Figure 318 *Bends*

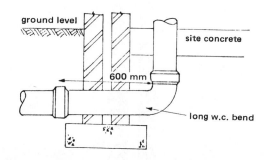

Figure 319 *Section showing the use of a long w.c. bend*

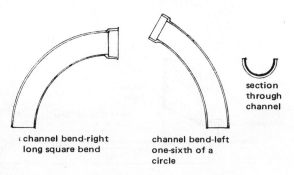

Figure 320 *Channel bends*

quarter section channels. They are available in a variety of angles of intersection (Figure 322).

Stoneware chutes

These are classified as inlet and outlet and are used in inspection chambers where the main drain enters and leaves the chamber. They are very useful in allowing easy access for rodding should the drain become blocked (Figure 323).

left hand   right hand

Figure 321   *Three-quarter section channels*

left-hand   right-hand
section   section

Figure 322   *Three-quarter section channels*

Intercepting traps

These are used in some parts of the country and are installed in the final inspection chamber at a point just before the drain enters the public sewer. They prevent the sewer gases from passing into the domestic drainage system, but also prevent fresh air from entering the sewer, thereby keeping the gases concentrated instead of diluting them. Two types of interceptors are illustrated in Figure 324.

The rodding eye on an interceptor may be sealed with a simple type of stopper (Figure 325). It can be either bedded in with a mastic or other non-hardening compound, or screwed or fixed by a lever-locking system which has a chain on one side of the lever (Figure 326). The other end of the chain is built into the brickwork of the inspection chamber just below the inspection cover, so that if the drain becomes blocked and the chamber filled with water, the chain is pulled and releases the stopper in the rodding eye. The water can then escape down the pipe to the sewer. If such a device were not used, under these circumstances it would be very difficult to release an ordinary stopper, and it might even be necessary to pump the water out of the chamber before the blockage could be cleared. Interceptors must also be installed where a drain enters a cesspool.

Special types of interceptor are made with the socket at the opposite end to normal – at the outlet end (Figure 327). These *reverse action interceptors* are used when a new drain has to be connected to an existing sewer. The junction is made in an inspection chamber and the new drain has to be trapped. The method of using such an interceptor is illustrated in Figure 328.

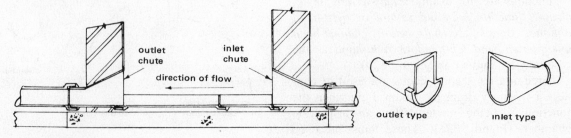

outlet chute   inlet chute

direction of flow

outlet type   inlet type

Figure 323   *Drain chutes*

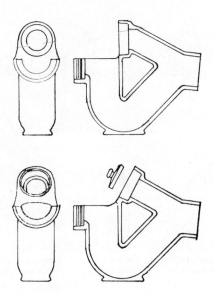

Figure 324 *Interceptors*

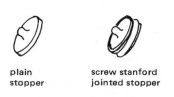

plain
stopper

screw stanford
jointed stopper

Figure 325 *Types of stoppers*

Figure 326 *Lever-locking stopper*

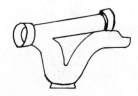

Figure 327 *Reverse action interceptor*

Yard gullies

These are obtainable with either P, Q, or S traps, and the trap required should be clearly stated when ordering (Figure 329). They are also made with no inlet, or back or side inlets (Figure 330). Such inlets are also available as horizontal or ver-

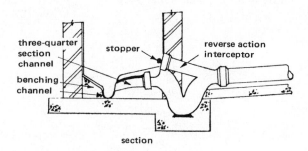

three-quarter
section
channel

benching
channel

stopper

reverse action
interceptor

section

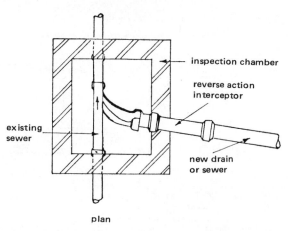

inspection chamber

reverse action
interceptor

existing
sewer

new drain
or sewer

plan

Figure 328 *The application of a reverse action interceptor*

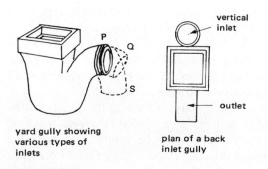

P

Q

S

vertical
inlet

outlet

yard gully showing
various types of
inlets

plan of a back
inlet gully

Figure 329 *Yard gullies*

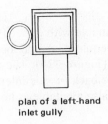

plan of a left-hand
inlet gully

Figure 330   *A left-hand inlet gully*

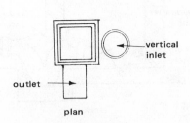

vertical
inlet

outlet

plan

Figure 331   *A right-hand inlet gully*

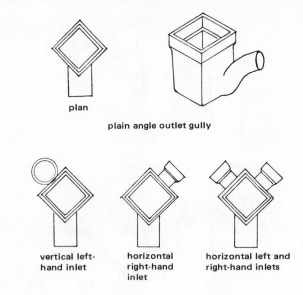

plan

plain angle outlet gully

vertical left-
hand inlet

horizontal
right-hand
inlet

horizontal left and
right-hand inlets

Figure 333   *Angle outlet gullies*

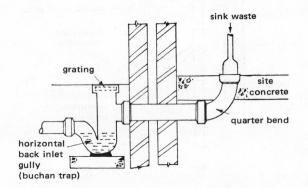

sink waste

grating

site
concrete

quarter bend

horizontal
back inlet
gully
(buchan trap)

Figure 332   *A method of connecting sink waste to a drain*

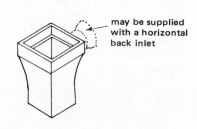

may be supplied
with a horizontal
back inlet

Figure 334   *Raising piece for a gully*

tical inlets (Figures 331 and 332). The type must also be quoted when ordering.

Gullies may also be supplied as square where the grating is parallel to the wall of the building, or as angle gullies. In this case the gully is at 45 degrees to the structure (Figure 333).

If it is necessary to fix a gully deeper in the ground or if the ground must be raised, a raising piece or hopper may be supplied to raise the height of the gully (Figure 334). Gullies may also be obtained with inspection eyes so that the drain

rodding eye

Figure 335   *Inspection gully*

from the gully may be rodded in case it becomes blocked (Figure 335).

Method of laying drains

Setting out the alignment

This may be carried out by either using sight rails, profiles, or pegging out lines, depending on the position of the drain. For example, if a short length of drain is to be laid from a gully to a main drain in an inspection chamber, the alignment can be drawn up and the work set out by stretching lines from the gully to the inspection chamber, showing the width of the trench to be dug.

If, on the other hand, 35 m of drain is to be laid between two inspection chambers, whose invert levels have to be determined when the trench has been dug, it would be better to set out this work by using either profiles or sight rails. The profiles would only be used for stretching the lines to indicate the width of the proposed trench, but if sight rails were used, they would not only show the width of the proposed trench but would be set at a predetermined height so that the levels of the bottom of the trench could be sighted from the rails (Figures 336 and 337).

Determination of the fall

A drain should have just sufficient fall to gain enough velocity in the effluent to make it self-cleansing. It is not necessary to lay drains with steep falls, where the flow of effluent may leave solid matter behind because of the fast flow of water. In a constant flowing drain a sufficient velocity of flow is about 0.09–1.22 m per second. This is quite enough to carry solid matter with the effluent.

A rule of thumb method of calculating the fall in a 100 or 150 mm diameter drain is by using the following gradients: a 100 mm drain may have a fall of 1 in 40, and a 150 mm drain 1 in 60. But it is important that these figures should only be used as a guide. This rule should normally be disregarded for 225 mm pipes and above.

The fall in a trench may be checked by using a set of three boning rods (Figure 338). One rod is either fixed or held at each end of the trench and the third placed on pegs which are driven at inter-

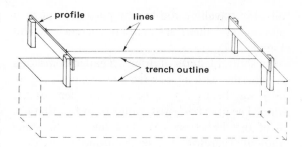

Figure 336 *Setting out the outline of a trench with a line stretched between profiles*

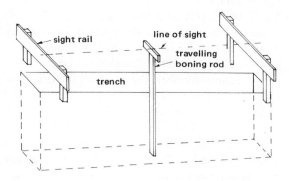

Figure 337 *Setting out a gradient with a traveller sighted through from sight rails*

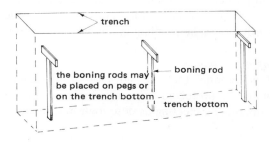

Figure 338 *Setting out a gradient with the aid of a set of boning rods*

vals along the trench, and then sighted through from the other two. The pegs are then checked for correct height. If sight rails are fixed at set levels above the inverts at the lower and upper ends of the drain, all that is needed is one long boning rod equal in length from the invert to the height of the sight rail. Thus by sighting through from the sight rails, the travelling rod can be placed on pegs at intervals and these set at their correct gradient (Figure 337).

On shorter lengths of drains, a gauge board or a straightedge with a block fixed at one end (Figure 339) may be used to check the gradient of the drain. The drawback with gauge boards is that not all of the drains on a site are laid at the same gradient. Therefore, the small amount of use does not always warrant the setting out and cutting of such a board.

The invert levels

The invert levels of a drain are quite simple to gauge. For example, if a short length of tributary drain is to be laid from a yard gully to a line of newly laid drain and the junction is to be made in an inspection chamber, the levels of the drain are fixed at the outlet of the gully at the upper end and the edge of the half-section channel. A trench may be marked out, dug and checked for evenness of gradient with a straightedge. On the other hand, if a long length of drain is to be laid, it may well be necessary to determine levels from the site data and set them up on sight rails, as previously shown. If a new drain is to be connected to an existing one, the invert levels are predetermined, and particular care must be taken to ensure that there is no *back fall* in the new work or, in other words, no gradient falling in the wrong direction.

Safety precautions

It is essential that the sides of drain trenches should be protected against possible collapse by timbering or sheeting as described in Chapter 1.

Methods of laying vitrified stoneware drains

There are several different ways of laying vitrified stoneware drains, each having certain advantages.

Method 1

1   When the trench has been excavated, it should be *bottomed-up*, or the bottom brought to an even surface and uniform gradient for the fall of the drain.
2   Pegs are driven into the trench bottom at intervals to mark the required depth of the

concrete bed. These pegs may be checked for accuracy in height by using boning rods or a straightedge.

3   The concrete bed is laid to the height of the pegs and finished off with a spade or shovel finish, and allowed to harden (Figure 340).

4   A line is fixed at the top of pipes situated at each end of the pipe run, and pulled tightly. Each pipe is laid to this line and the joint caulked with gaskin or tarred rope (Figure 306). The purposes of this gaskin are:

(a)   To assist in holding each pipe in place.
(b)   To prevent any mortar from being forced into the internal barrel of the pipe when the pipe is jointed.

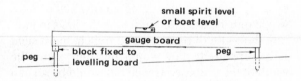

Figure 339   *The use of a gauge board*

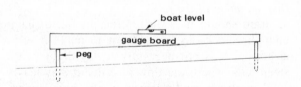

Figure 340   *Setting out a gradient with the aid of a gauge board*

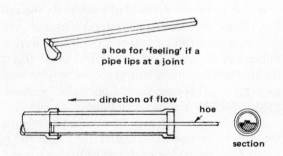

Figure 341   *Application of a hoe*

(c) To maintain an even invert inside the pipe and prevent *lipping* at the joints. Each pipe is checked for accurate setting by a *hoe* or tool with a half-round piece of timber at the end of a handle. By *feeling* inside the pipe at the joint, it is possible to see if the pipes are not forming an even invert (Figure 341). Each pipe is packed up to the line by mortar pats, pieces of slate or tile placed underneath the socket.

(d) The pipes are laid with their sockets laid facing upstream or against the flow of the drain. Any short length of pipe that is needed can be cut to length with a masonry saw or by filling the pipe solidly with sand and tapping around the mark on the pipe where it is to be cut with a hammer and a *sharp* chisel.

(e) The line is transferred to the side of the pipe to check the alignment of the drain.

(f) The joints are either made with patent flexible joints such as a Hepsleve joint (Figure 304), or by using a neat cement mortar or a 2:1 cement and clean-washed sand. The mortar is mixed to a stiff consistency, packed tightly into the joints, and smoothed and chamfered off with a pointing trowel.

(g) The joints should be covered over with damp hessian or cement bags to prevent them from drying out too quickly, which would cause shrinking in the joints with the possibility of their cracking as a result.

(h) Although the Building Regulations state that haunching and backfilling should be completed before the drain needs to be tested for leakages, it is generally wiser to test the drain before placing the concrete haunching; then, if there should be a leak, it will be much easier to locate and rectify than it would if the haunching and backfilling had been in position.

(i) After testing, the drain can then be haunched with concrete for protection, the backfilling of the trench completed, and the drain again tested for any leakage.

Advantages
The drain has a good bed underneath it while it is being laid, and, provided that the concrete has been laid evenly, the pipes will need only a little adjustment for height and alignment.

Disadvantages
Unless particular care is taken when placing the haunching, the barrel of the pipe will be acting as a beam. There is, thus, a possibility that the weight of the haunching and earth may cause a fracture in the pipe. It is also difficult to finish off the joints at the bottom because the small space between the concrete and the pipe does not allow ease of access for the hands or a pointing trowel. Therefore, it is difficult to guarantee that there are no leaks in the joints at their lowest extremities.

Method 2
1 The trench is excavated and bottomed-up.
2 Pegs are driven in at intervals to indicate the depth of the concrete bed as described in Method 1.
3 The concrete bed is laid to the height of the pegs.
4 At a distance equal to the length of each pipe a small amount of concrete is removed from the bed.
5 The pipes are laid with dry joints from the lower end with their barrels resting on the concrete bed.
6 The pipes are lined in, caulked and jointed as previously described.
7 The drain is then tested, haunched and backfilled (Figure 342).

Advantages
There is a solid bed below the pipe run and the barrels of the pipes are well supported throughout their lengths. There is less likelihood of the pipe being broken when the concrete haunching is being placed.

Disadvantages
There is only a small amount of room at each joint so that it may be difficult to make the joints watertight except when patent flexible joints are

used. Special care has to be taken to ensure that the hollows in the concrete bed are made in the correct places.

Method 3

1 When the trench has been dug and bottomed-up, the pipes are placed into position resting on bricks on edge and with dry joints.

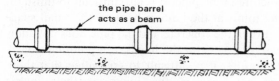

method of laying pipes on a concrete bed

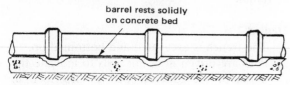

method of laying pipes with sockets let into pockets in concrete bed

Figure 342 *Laying pipes on and in a concrete bed*

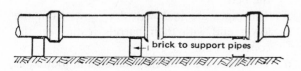

brick to support pipes

Figure 343 *Method of laying pipes on bricks and laying concrete bed after pipes have been jointed*

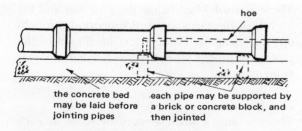

the concrete bed may be laid before jointing pipes

each pipe may be supported by a brick or concrete block, and then jointed

Figure 344 *Method of laying pipes and jointing as the drain proceeds*

2 A line is stretched from end-to-end at the top of the pipes and the pipes packed up with pieces of slate or tile to touch the line.

3 Each joint is caulked with gaskin or tarred rope and checked with a hoe.

4 The line is transferred to the side of the pipe run and the pipes adjusted to suit.

5 The joints are then filled and pointed as described in Method 1.

6 The pipes are tested for leakages.

7 The joints being satisfactory, the concrete is poured underneath the drain and also haunched up the sides in one operation.

8 The trench is backfilled.

9 The drains are again tested for leaks.

Advantages

Pegging the height of the concrete bed is not necessary. The joints can be made much more easily as there is plenty of room to get the hands and a trowel underneath the pipes and, therefore, there is less chance of leakages occurring. The concrete bed and haunching can be laid in one operation (Figure 343).

Slight disadvantage

The bricks which support the pipes are left in the concrete bed. A little more care has to be taken when supporting the pipes initially, and when pointing the joints to ensure that the pipes do not move. Otherwise there is a possibility of damaging the joints.

Method 4

1 A line is stretched from end-to-end of the drain at the top of the pipes.

2 Starting at the lower end of the pipe run, each pipe is placed into position on bricks on edge or precast concrete blocks (or the concrete bed is laid) and then caulked with gaskin or tarred rope, and jointed. The *hoe* is used to ensure that there is no surplus mortar inside the barrel of the pipe at each joint.

3 The pipes are tested for any leakages

4 The concrete bed and haunching are carefully placed around the pipes and finally the trench is refilled (Figure 344).

5 The drain is again tested for watertightness.

Laying a drain under a building

A drain is allowed to run under a building if it is protected by at least 100 mm of granular material or other flexible material around the pipe (Figure 345).

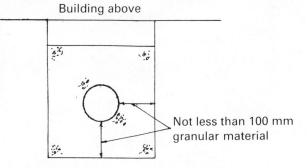

Figure 345 *Laying a drain under a building*

Where a pipe passes through a wall there is always a possibility of the pipe being damaged through differential settlement. To meet this situation there should be an opening in the wall to allow not less than 50 mm clear all round the pipe. To preserve the cavity and to prevent the ingress of vermin, cover plates should be placed each side of the wall (Figure 346).

An alternative method of protecting a pipe where it passes through a wall is to build a short length of pipe into the wall with its joints not more than 150 mm away from each wall face. Rocker pipes not exceeding 600 mm in length are connected to each side and these in turn are connected to flexible joints (Figure 347).

Testing drains

A hydraulic test is carried out by inserting a stopper, which is composed of two plates connected together by a screw-thread and wing-nut with a rubber band in between, at the lower end of the drain. A cap is provided so that the water in the pipe may be released after the test is completed (Figure 348). When the wing-nut is tightened the rubber band is compressed and forms a seal which prevents the water from escaping from the drain. Alternatively, an air bag which is supplied with a length of hose and brass lock may be used (Figure 349). The drain is filled with water which is allowed to remain. An allowance is always made for a small absorption in the pipes and joints by adding a small quantity of water. The drain should then be completely watertight. Any leaks

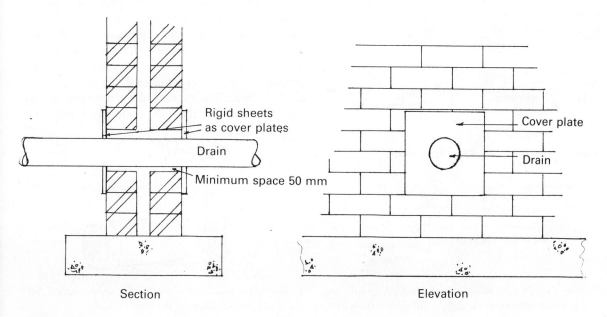

Section   Elevation

Figure 346

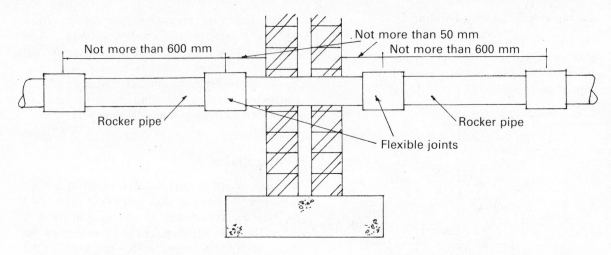

Figure 347   *An alternative method of passing a drain through a wall*

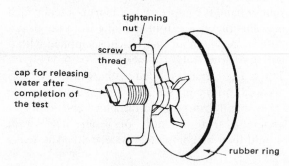

Figure 348   *Expanding drain stopper placed at the lower end of the drain when testing*

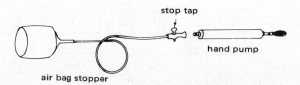

Figure 349   *Apparatus for carrying out an air test*

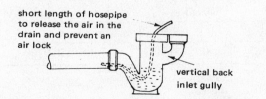

Figure 350   *A method of carrying out a hydraulic test when a trap is fitted at the upper end of the drain*

can be repaired by cutting out the joint and re-setting it. When filling a drain with a gully at the upper end, or any fitting which has a trap, a short length of hose pipe should be pushed around the trap (Figure 350). This will allow the air to escape from the drain and prevent an airlock from forming inside the pipes which would prevent an adequate test. The head of water in a drain under test may be increased by fixing a test bend at the upper end of the pipe (Figure 351). Extra pipes may be added on the top of the bend, if necessary.

An air test is a much more severe test than a hydraulic test. The drain is plugged at both ends with drain stoppers. To one stopper is connected a rubber tube with a bellow or air pump. The air pressure in the drain is pumped to approximately 0.021 N/mm^2. The rubber tube is then pinched to hold the pressure, the bellows or pump removed

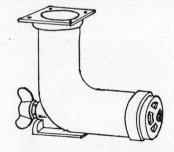

Figure 351   *Test bend placed at the upper end of the drain in order to increase the head of water*

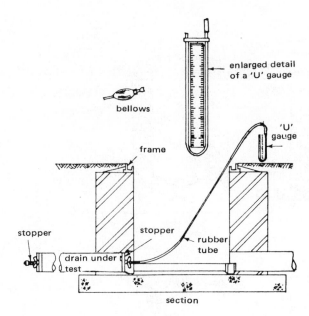

Figure 352   *A method of applying a low pressure air test to a drain*

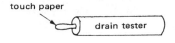

Figure 353   *Drain-testing bomb*

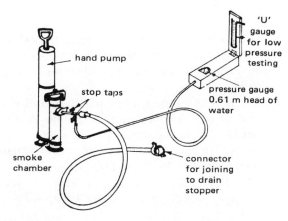

Figure 354   *Apparatus for applying a high pressure test*

and the end of the rubber tube fitted over a 'U' gauge. The pressure should not drop more than 25 mm in 5 minutes (Figure 352).

A *smoke test* is made by putting a stopper at one end of the drain, placing a drain testing bomb inside and then sealing the other end. If smoke

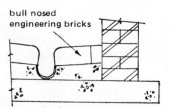

Figure 355   *An alternative method of forming the benching*

escapes, the drain leaks. One smoke drain tester will test up to 895 m of 100 mm drain; 457 m of 150 mm drain and 228 m of 225 mm drain (Figure 353).

Another method is to use smoke paper with an air pump (Figure 354). This type of apparatus can be used for testing all types of pipes and will indicate pressure up to 6.1 m head of water. The usual pressures are 0.6–1.52 m head of water for vitrified clay pipes and 3 m when testing iron or bitumen sewers.

Ball test. A ball can be passed through the bore of a drain by running it from the upper end to the lower end. This will show whether there is adequate fall on the drain, or if there is any blockage within the bore.

Mirror test. The underside of the joints may be inspected by holding a mirror underneath the joint.

Torch test. The straightness of the bore of a drain may be checked by having an electric torch held at one end of the drain and inspecting it from the opposite end. Any defects will be easily seen.

Inspection chambers

These are generally constructed of 1-brick thick walls which can be built of engineering bricks in chambers which are under roadways, or of hard-burnt bricks rendered with cement mortar for normal domestic drainage systems.

The method of constructing normal chambers is as follows:

1   The main half-channel is laid at the same time as the main run of pipes with an inlet and outlet drain chute if necessary. The length of the half-channel is equal to the length of the inspection chamber.

2   The three-quarter section channels are bed-

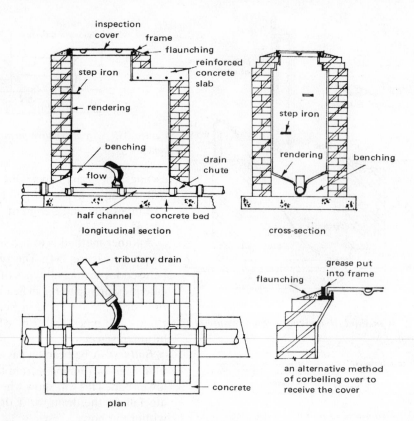

Figure 356   *A typical inspection chamber*

ded and the tributary drains laid into position. (In some cases it may be necessary to lay tributary drains with level inverts to the main drain, but these are generally the exception to the rule.)

3   The brickwork is set out for the chamber and built up to a height of about six courses. The pipes at their inlet and outlet are protected from wall damage by simple arches built over them to take the mass.

4   The benching is then built up on each side of the channels by using either:
   (a)   bullnosed engineering bricks (Figure 355); or
   (b)   stiff concrete rounded off at the front edge and trowelled to a smooth finish (Figure 356). Concrete benchings may be rendered with a strong mix of cement mortar to make them impervious to water.

5   Once the benching has hardened, the brickwork is built up to a height of any corbelling which may be necessary to reduce the walling to the size of the cover.

6   The walling should not be corbelled out on the side of the chamber which is on the downstream end of the drain. If a drain becomes blocked, it should be rodded upstream rather than downstream. Therefore, if there is no corbel on the downstream end of the chamber, it will allow a better sweep for the rods.

7   If the inspection is deep, step-irons should be built into the wall in a staggered pattern to allow easy access into the chamber (Figure 357).

8   The frame should be bedded solidly in a stiff mortar at the correct height.

9   The final operation is to grease the frame before the cover is placed within it.

Figure 357   *A typical step iron for an inspection chamber*

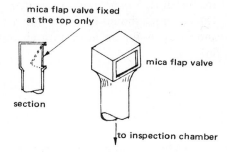

Figure 358   *A means of providing ventilation to a drain*

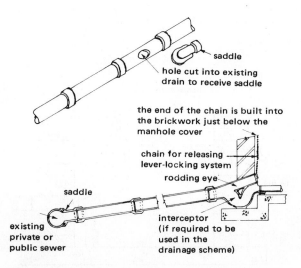

Figure 359   *A method of connecting a new drain to an existing private or public sewer*

Intercepting chambers

These are similar to normal inspection chambers except that they are usually built just within the boundary of a site, and an interceptor is fixed at the lower end of the channel inside the chamber. When the chamber is finished, the trap in the interceptor should be thoroughly cleaned out and the plug in the rodding eye fixed into position. If the interceptor has a lever locking system, the chain should be built in the brickwork just below the cover, so that the chain can be pulled in the event of a blockage and any water in the intercepting chamber can escape down the rodding eye. Inspecting chambers are generally finished off with a cement rendering. Before applying this rendering, the joints should be raked out to provide a suitable key to the brickwork.

Ventilation

All drains and inspection chambers should be well ventilated to avoid an accumulation of sewer gases. Ventilation should be provided at the lower end and at the highest point of the system to create a current of air circulating throughout the drain. Inspection chambers should be well-ventilated. Soil pipes may be used as ventilating pipes because they are not trapped before they enter the drainage system. In other cases, short lengths of pipes are taken from the chambers or drainage system to convenient walls or boundary fences, and these pipes should be fitted with a ventilator which has a light flap at its entrance. This allows the air to enter the drain but prevents a large volume of the sewer gas from escaping and causing a nuisance (Figure 358).

Connecting a new drain to an existing drain

1   The alignment of the drain is determined.
2   The trench is dug and bottomed as described previously.
3   When the existing drain is exposed, the hole for the new drain is marked out. (Remember that a hole for a circular drain will be elliptical when that drain meets the new drain at an angle.)

4   The hole is cut out of the existing drain with a
    light hammer and a *sharp* chisel. This must be
    done with great care otherwise the drain may
    be seriously damaged.
5   A saddle is bedded on to the existing drain
    over the hole which has been cut, using either
    neat cement or 2:1 cement and clean washed
    sand.
6   The saddle is then covered over with concrete.
7   The connections for the new drain are made
    using any of the methods described previously
    (Figure 359).

Clearing a blocked drain

When a drain is blocked it is generally better to
rod upstream rather than downstream because
the cause of the blockage can be reached more
directly. If the rodding is done from the downstream side, the blockage may be further compressed.

Subsoil drains

These drains are used to provide drainage to a site
so that:

1   A constant soil condition is maintained as far
    as possible. This stabilizes the bearing capac-
    ity of the soil and prevents wide variations
    within it.
2   It reduces the level of the water table and the
    site is kept drier and in some cases healthier.

The pipes used for this work are porous so
water may pass through the pipe material quite
freely. They are butt-jointed to each other, therefore, no jointing material is necessary. They may
be laid with the natural fall of the ground, in
which case a great deal of unnecessary excavating
may be saved. On the other hand, if it is not possible to lay them along the natural contours, the
trenches should be laid with slight falls. The bottom of the trench for such a drain may have about
75 or 100 mm of shingle or hoggin, or other similar granular material laid, on which the pipes are
placed butt-jointed. Granular material is placed
over the top of the pipes to a depth of about
300–375 mm (Figure 360). These drains should

not be normally connected to soil drains, but discharged into a ditch or stream. In urban areas,
this is not always possible and they are often connected to a waste-water drain. Before the connection is made, however, a catch pit is constructed
to collect any silt and mud which may be in the
subsoil drain. A typical method of building such a
catch pit is shown in Figure 361.

Each catch pit should be cleaned out at frequent intervals to prevent any silt from being carried into the waste-water drain. The catch pit
need not be rendered on the sides and the bottom
does not have any channels. The inlet and outlet
are about 225 mm above the catch pit bottom.
The catch pit should be fitted with a cover in the
same way as for an inspection chamber (Figure
361).

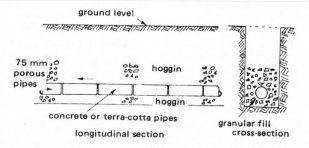

Figure 360   *A typical subsoil drain*

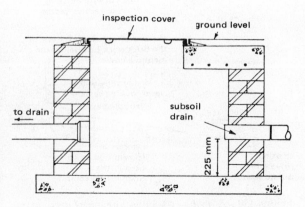

Figure 361   *Longitudinal section through a catch pit*

Soakaways

These are often provided underneath a rainwater pipe for disposal of the rainwater, instead of discharging into the drainage system. A hole about 0.9 or 1.2 m cube should be dug and filled with clean hardcore up to within about 300 mm from the top. Turves are laid grass side down on the top of this fill, to reduce the amount of soil being washed into the hardcore-fill as much as possible. The rainwater pipe is taken down to the level of the hardcore, and the fill above the turves is filled in with soil. Soakaways should be excavated in a soil which is fairly well drained as far as possible. If this is not possible (for example, when digging in a heavy type of clay), a subsoil drain should be provided from the catch pit to link up with the other subsoil system on the site. This will help to prevent flooding in the soakaway.

Self-assessment questions

1   A private sewer is a length of pipe serving
(a)   one householder and owned by him
(b)   two or more householders and owned by them
(c)   two or more householders and owned by the local authority

2   If there is no inspection chamber at a junction between two drains then the length of drain from the junction to an inspection chamber must not exceed
(a)   12.5 m
(b)   13.5 m
(c)   14.5 m

3   The maximum distance between inspection chambers must not exceed
(a)   35 m
(b)   40 m
(c)   45 m

4   When making connections between drains or drains and private sewers the tributary drain should discharge its contents
(a)   at right angles to the flow
(b)   obliquely with the flow
(c)   obliquely against the flow

5   A soil pipe must be capable of withstanding a smoke or air test for a minimum of three minutes at an equivalent head of water of
(a)   38 mm
(b)   40 mm
(c)   45 mm

6   The Hepseal joint is designed to withstand a pressure of
(a)   130 kN/m^2
(b)   135 kN/m^2
(c)   140 kN/m^2

7   A 'U gauge' is used to measure the
(a)   total fall in a drain or private sewer
(b)   pressure in a drain test
(c)   the height of the benching in an intercepting chamber

8   Ventilation should be provided in a drain or private sewer at the
(a)   highest point
(b)   lowest point
(c)   lowest and highest points

9   Describe how a broken drain may be repaired.

10   Describe a method of setting out and laying a length of drains.

11   Describe how drains may be laid under buildings.

12   Describe two methods of passing a drain through a wall to avoid the possibility of damage through settlement.

Chapter 14

Drainage: pitch fibre pipes

After reading this chapter you should be able to:

1 Have a good understanding of the use of pitch fibre pipes.
2 Have a good knowledge of the properties of pitch fibre pipes.
3 Appreciate the advantages of using these pipes.
4 Know how to store pitch fibre pipes.
5 Know the general requirements for the laying of pitch fibre pipes.
6 Know how to lay subsoil drains.

Pitch fibre pipes

Although pitch fibre pipes have only been in production in Britain since 1953, they have been used for sewers and gas mains in New York since the end of the nineteenth century. There has, however, been much development since then, and new manufacturing techniques have made pitch fibre products into excellent materials for drainage work, being light, flexible and tough, and with a high resistance to acids and soil corrosives.

The British Standard Specification BS 2760 relates to pitch-impregnated fibre drain and sewer pipes and includes minimum standards for:

Materials
Joints
Dimensions of pipes and tapered couplings
5 degree angle couplings
Tests: strength, resistance to acid, alkali, salt and kerosene, heat, boiling water and flattening, water absorption, joint tightness under water pressure, and all types of fittings

Properties of pitch fibre pipes

1 They have a low water absorption, usually not more than 1 per cent by weight.
2 They are resistant to hot water; they must withstand immersion in boiling water for 6 hours without disintegration or delamination.
3 They have a high crushing strength, ranging from 16.3 kN/m length for 50 mm pipes to 19.2 kN/m for 150 mm. (Dry and wet crushing strengths.)
4 They have a good resistance to paraffin; there must be no reduction in their crushing strength after ten days immersion in paraffin.
5 They have a very smooth bore.
6 They have a high beam strength; the minimum requirements are shown in Table 16.

Advantages of using pitch fibre pipes for drainage

1 They may be laid without any concrete bed or haunching, except in abnormal soil conditions.
2 They may be laid in bad weather.
3 In some cases drains may be prefabricated outside the trench, and testing and backfilling may be carried out immediately after laying the pipes.

Table 16

	50 mm	75 mm	100 mm	125 mm	150 mm
Length	508 mm	762 mm	762 mm	762 mm	1.07 m
Span	304 mm	608 mm	608 mm	608 mm	914 mm
Breaking load	4.45 kN	4.45 kN	9.96 kN	18.86 kN	19.75 kN

4 They are very resistant to breakages which may occur with normal handling.

Pitch pipes can be used in gradients as low as 1 in 85 for 100 mm pipes and 1 in 145 for 150 mm pipes, with a consequent saving in the amount of excavation and backfill required (Figure 362).

Storing pitch fibre pipes
The pipes should be stacked on site on level ground parallel to each other to a maximum height of 1.5 m. In cold weather the couplings should be kept frost-free.

Laying pitch fibre pipes

1 The trenches must be excavated with firm, evenly boned bottoms. Soft spots must be filled and rammed to grade.
2 Pipe ends and couplings should be wiped clean.
3 A coupling is fitted hand tight to each pipe.
4 A second coupling is fitted on to the leading end of the first length.
5 Pipes and couplings are laid out along the trench or trench side.
6 A firm backstop is constructed in the trench if no firm abutment is available (Figure 363). This is to protect and support the first pipe while further pipes are driven home. A coupling must be used on the pipe end against the back stop.
7 Pipes are driven into the couplings one at a time with a 2 kg hammer and a 50 mm thick wooden dolly (Figure 363). Pipe-ends must be protected by a coupling before driving.

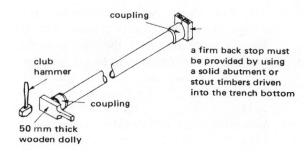

Figure 363   *Method of driving a pipe home*

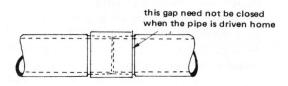

Figure 364   *Detail of a pitch fibre coupling*

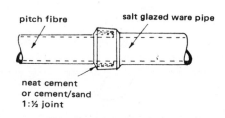

Figure 365   *A method of jointing a pitch fibre pipe to a vitrified clay pipe*

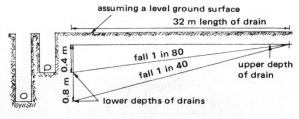

Figure 362   *How a saving may be made with both excavation and backfill by laying a drain at a low gradient*

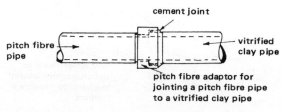

Figure 366   *An adaptor for connecting a pitch fibre pipe*

8   The drive should be approximately 6 mm irrespective of the gap at firm initial contact. There is no need to drive the pipe up to the shoulder of the coupling. In fact it is important not to over drive beyond the point where a good joint has been made (Figure 364).

9   Where connections are made to other materials such as stoneware, concrete or cast iron, the jointing compound for the particular material should be used (Figure 365), and a special pitch fibre adaptor fitted (Figure 366).

10   When driving on to it, a bend should be supported along its back (Figure 367).

11   Similarly, when driving on to a branch, support should be given (Figure 367).

12   In stone free soils, selected fill or imported material must be hand-packed and tamped in 75–150 mm layers along the sides of the pipes up to crown level. Above this, 300 mm of selected material, which should range in size from 18 to 2 mm with not more than one-third of fines mixed with it, must be lightly tamped by hand in 150 mm layers. Thereafter normal backfill can be consolidated as required.

13   In rocky or stony soils, the trenches should be over-excavated to a mimimum of 100 mm in depth and filled to grade with a selected material which must be well-tamped. The backfilling is then carried out as in (12).

14   Figure 368 shows a tool for tightening couplings in a run of pipes.

Cutting and tapering

The pipes may be cut with an ordinary coarse tooth handsaw. Water or paraffin may be used as a lubricant to make the sawing easier. A simple hand lathe may be used for tapering the pipe after it has been cut. The pipe should be held in a clamping vice when cutting and tapering to ensure accuracy of working.

Range of drainage pipes and fittings

Pipes are available in sizes of 50, 75, 100, 125 and 150 mm diameters, in lengths of 1.67, 2.44 and 3.05 m, both ends tooled to fit couplings.

Couplings are available in two types: straight; and 5 degree angled, which may be used for skirting obstructions. Both types are supplied in sizes up to 150 mm in diameter (Figures 369 and 370).

Junctions. These are supplied as equal or unequal, and are available in all sizes and with male or female tapers (Figure 371).

Bends are available as short-radius bends or long-radius bends. The former are made in 50 and

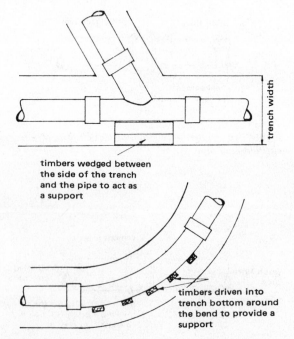

trench width

timbers wedged between the side of the trench and the pipe to act as a support

timbers driven into trench bottom around the bend to provide a support

Figure 367   *Supporting a junction and a bend when laying pitch fibre pipes*

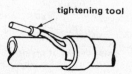

tightening tool

Figure 368   *Special tool for tightening couplings in a run of pipes*

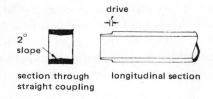

Figure 369   *Standard pipe*

Figure 370   *5 degree angle coupling*

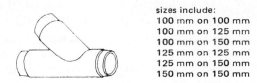

sizes include:
100 mm on 100 mm
100 mm on 125 mm
100 mm on 150 mm
125 mm on 125 mm
125 mm on 150 mm
150 mm on 150 mm

Figure 371   *Junction – these are available with male or female tapers*

Figure 372   *Ordinary and level invert tapers*

150 mm diameter sizes only, whereas the latter are available in most sizes.

Adaptors for jointing pitch fibre pipes to stoneware or cast-iron spigots. For stoneware sizes from 75 to 150 mm in diameter are available, and for cast iron 50 to 150 mm diameter.

Tapers are supplied as level invert or as ordinary tapers (Figure 372).

Channels and channel bends. These may, often, be sawn from normal pipes on the site and should be bedded and benched up in concrete in the

same way as described for inspection chambers in Chapter 13 (Figure 373).

Slipper bends are similar to three-quarter section bends in vitrified clay-ware and are used for the same purpose. These may be supplied to order or may be cut from pipes on site.

End caps. These are for blanking off a junction and are available in all sizes from 50 to 150 mm in diameter.

Jointing sleeves are available for joining either two untooled pipes or an untooled pipe to a cast iron pipe, and are made in all sizes from 50 to 150 mm in diameter.

Saddles. These are made to suit all pipe sizes up to 150 mm and are used for connecting a new drain to an existing one.

General requirements for laying pitch fibre pipes

1 The pipes should be uniformly bedded. To ensure this, the trench bottom must be of uniform gradient with no projections or hollows or soft spots.

2 No large stones or other hard objects should be within the trench bottom or in the backfill.

3 Packing pieces, such as brick tiles or slates, should *not* be used to raise the coupling of a pipe length, as this may well lead to uneven loading along the pipe barrel.

4 When a trench is overdug the soil which is used for replacing the excavated soil should pass a 18 mm sieve. This will provide a suitable bed for the pipes.

5 The backfill must be carefully rammed solid around the pipes. Otherwise, if hollows should be left, the pipes are liable to adopt an oval shape, due to the weight acting downwards and forcing the pipe into the hollow or soft backfilling.

6 Frozen soil should not be used for backfilling.

7 Before laying the pipes, boning pegs and other pieces of wood should be removed from the trench bottom.

8 Trenches for drainage should be as narrow as is conveniently possible to work in them.

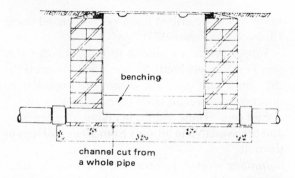

Figure 373 *Longitudinal section of an inspection chamber*

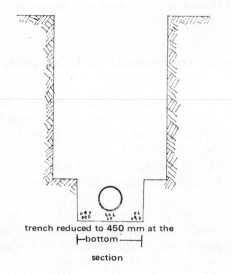

Figure 374 *Reducing a trench width at the bottom to receive the pitch fibre pipe*

Those which are intended for pitch fibre pipes generally need only be about 450 mm wide. Where for some reason the trench has had to be dug wider, it is a good practice to dig the bottom section to a depth equal to the diameter of the pipe, at 450 mm wide (Figure 374).

9 All drain trenches should not be excavated too far in advance of drainlaying and should be backfilled as soon as the work is completed. This is to reduce the possibility of the trench sides collapsing.

10 Where pipes are laid at less than 450 mm below the ground surface, concrete slabs may be laid over the top of the backfill immediately above the pipes. This is to protect the pipes against possible damage from stakes.

11 Pitch fibre pipes will withstand the impact of loading quite well, even at shallow depths, and are, therefore, very suitable for use in pipe runs under drives or roadways.

12 When driving the pipe home into the coupling, there is no need to use unnecessary force to make the joint.

Subsoil drains

Pitch fibre perforated pipes are available for draining subsoils. These pipes should be laid with their perforations on the underside, and should be surrounded with 150 mm of clean free-draining granular material not exceeding 18 mm. Jointing may be made by:

1 Normal coupling;
2 Split coupling; or
3 Spigot and socket pipe ends.

Self-assessment questions

1 Pitch fibre pipes usually have a water absorption by weight of not more than
  (a)   1 per cent
  (b)   2 per cent
  (c)   3 per cent

2 The minimum requirements for beam strength for 100 mm pitch fibre pipes is
  (a)   9.96 kN
  (b)   10.46 kN
  (c)   10.96 kN

3 When storing pitch fibre pipes they should not be stacked higher than
  (a)   1 m
  (b)   1.25 m
  (c)   1.5 m

4 When laying pitch fibre perforated pipes for subsoil drains they should be laid with their perforations at the
(a) top of the pipes
(b) side of the pipes
(c) bottom of the pipes

5 The recommended width of trench for laying pitch fibre pipes in is
(a) 400 mm
(b) 450 mm
(c) 500 mm

6 100 mm pitch fibre pipes may be laid in gradients of
(a) 1 in 75
(b) 1 in 85
(c) 1 in 100

7 State the properties of pitch fibre pipes.

8 State the advantages of using pitch fibre pipes for drainage.

9 Describe the method of driving a pipe into a coupling.

10 Describe how channels may be prepared on site.

11 Explain why the trench bottom must be uniformly graded when pitch fibre pipes are to be laid in it.

12 Describe the method of backfilling a trench after the pitch fibre pipes have been laid in it.

Chapter 15

Scaffolding

After reading this chapter you should be able to:

1 Understand the need to take all precautions against accidents occurring on site.

2 Know the basic requirements for a scaffold.

3 Have a good knowledge of trestle scaffolds and their uses.

4 Know the requirements for working platforms and gangways.

5 Appreciate the difficulties encountered when working on sloping roofs and how these may be overcome.

Accidents are far too common in the construction industry. These are often caused by people taking unnecessary risks, for example:

'Making do' with unsuitable or unsafe platforms.
Not waiting for proper platforms to be erected.
Using unstable scaffolds.
Using inferior materials for scaffolds.
Interfering with scaffolds without authority.
Generally ignoring the requirements of the law.

It has been stated that there is no such thing as an *accident*. Some degree of human failing is always concerned somewhere and this either causes or assists it. Therefore, if proper care is taken the accident might very well be prevented. While you may try to think of all the exceptions to this statement, in the main it is very true. The number of accidents will not be reduced until everyone on site is alert to all the dangers which exist and refuses to take unnecessary risks.

Health and Safety at Work etc. Act

The purpose of the Health and Safety at Work etc. Act is to provide the legislative framework to promote, stimulate and encourage high standards of health and safety at work.

The aim of the Act is to secure the health, safety and welfare of persons at work and also to protect persons other than those at work against all risks to health and safety arising out of, or in connection with, the activities of persons at work.

It shall be the duty of every employer:

1 To ensure, so far as is reasonably practicable, the health, safety and welfare at work of all his employees.

2 The provision and maintenance of plant and systems of work that are, so far as is reasonably practicable, safe and without risks to health.

It shall be the duty of all employees, while at work, to take reasonable care for the health and safety of themselves and of other persons who may be affected by their acts or omissions at work.

Section 8 of the Act places a duty on *all* persons, whether they be employers, employees or self-employed, and states: 'No person shall intentionally, or recklessly, interfere with, or misuse, anything provided in the interest of health, safety or welfare in pursuance of any of the relevant statutory provisions'.

The Construction (Working Places) Regulations No. 94

These are the statutory instruments concerning scaffolding and working places. In other words, they are the law of the land, and, as such, must be obeyed by *everyone* engaged in building operations or engineering construction.

The purpose of these Regulations is to try to make all construction personnel realize their responsibilities and to reduce the number of serious accidents. Apart from the actual pain caused, an accident is costly to:

1 *The victim and his family*, since it will very likely result in loss of earnings. This may have a serious effect on family life, from which it may be very difficult to recover.

2 *The employer* who not only loses the services of an employee, but has the running of the site interrupted and the organization of the team disrupted. Time must also be spent in investigating the cause of the accident and this will depend upon how serious its consequences are.

3 *The industry* which suffers the loss of an operative. Accidents also have an influence on recruitment into the industry because of the criticism expressed by those outside it. Production is also affected because of the demolralizing effect that an accident has on the victim's workmates.

4 *The nation*, because collectively the total number of accidents means a tremendous loss of working days and, consequently, of production. Money may also have to be spent in assisting families of victims, because of the hardships which are created due to loss of wages.

It is, therefore, obvious that nobody gains anything from accidents. Take every possible precaution against them, and ignore the foolhardy types who think that it is clever to take risks.

Scaffolds

The basic requirements of a scaffold are to ensure that:

1 It is strong enough to carry all the loads that will be placed upon it. Standards should not be placed too far apart, and a single tube should not carry too much weight.

2 It is stable and will not bend or move in any direction. It is most important that sufficient bracing is provided both across the scaffold and along its elevation.

3 Platforms are safe to work on and no traps are left in the boarding. Precautions should be taken against the accidental dislodgement of boards by wheelbarrows, etc.

4 Materials or tools do not fall off working platforms.

5 The safety of all personnel on site is safeguarded by taking safety precautions at every point where an accident is liable to happen.

The Construction Regulations are intended to cover all of the foregoing points, and their main requirements are outlined below:

1 All materials used shall be of good quality and in sound condition.

2 Every scaffold shall be of good construction.

3 Every scaffold shall be properly maintained.

4 No scaffold shall be partly dismantled unless it complies with these regulations or a notice is prominently displayed, warning that the scaffold is not to be used, and any access is effectively blocked.

5 Standards shall be either vertical or slightly leaning towards the building, and fixed sufficiently close together to secure the stability of the scaffold.

6 The foot of a standard shall be on a firm base.

7 Ledgers shall be as horizontal as possible and securely fastened to the uprights.

8 Putlogs shall be securely fastened to the ledgers or to the standards. Where they are supported by the wall they shall extend into the wall sufficiently to provide an adequate support.

9 The distance between putlogs shall not as a general rule exceed:
(a) 1 m for 31 mm planking
(b) 1.5 m for 38 mm planking
(c) 2.59 m for 50 mm planking

10 Scaffolds shall be securely supported and properly strutted and braced or rigidly connected to the building to ensure stability.

11 Loose bricks, drainpipes, chimney pots or other unsuitable material shall not be used for the construction of scaffolds.
12 Bricks or blocks, however, may, if they provide a firm support, be used to support a platform not more than 600 mm above the ground or floor.
13 No part of a building shall be used to support a scaffold unless that structure is of sound material and good construction.

Trestle scaffolds

These are varied in type and pattern, but they are normally extremely useful in confined spaces, or where a platform has to be quickly erected and dismantled and where great heights do not have to be reached. Safety precautions must, however, be taken and handrails should be fitted at all platforms of 2 m or more in height.

Some types of trestles are used only for small lifts of about 1.2 or 1.5 m high. A simple, but very effective, type of such trestle is shown in Figure 375. This is called a *Tres-Leg* and is made by the Acrow (Engineers) company and is particularly useful where there is limited headroom, for example, when building internal partitions. They are assembled quickly and efficiently, the weight of each leg being about 8.6 kg, and platform heights of 685 mm, 914 mm and 1.22 m are provided.

Split-head trestles may be either fixed leg (Figure 376), or folding leg (Figure 377). These are also used for platforms where great heights are not needed. These will extend to a working height of 2.44 m.

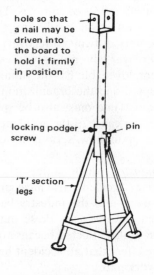

Figure 376   *Fixed leg split head trestle*

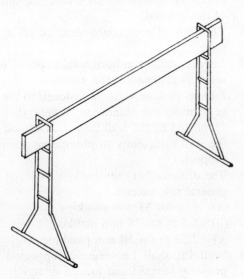

Figure 375   *Acrow Tres-Leg scaffold*

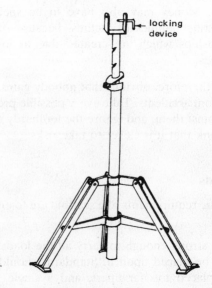

Figure 377   *Folding leg trestle*

Double folding trestles are very suitable for a working platform of five boards in width at a working height of 2.44 m. This would enable a wall of about 3.96 m in height to be built with this type of trestle scaffold (Figure 378).

A putlog trestle scaffold is illustrated in Figure 379. This type will provide a platform up to 4.57 m high, which will allow a 6.1 m high wall to be built. The Construction Regulations include the following requirements for trestle scaffolds:

1 All trestles must be of good material and construction.
2 A trestle shall not be used if the person using it is liable to fall from its platform for a distance of more than 4.57 m, or if it is constructed with more than one tier where folding supports are used.
3 No trestle scaffold shall be erected on top of a scaffold unless the width of the platform allows sufficient clear space for the transport of materials along it.
4 The trestles must be firmly attached to the platform and firmly braced.

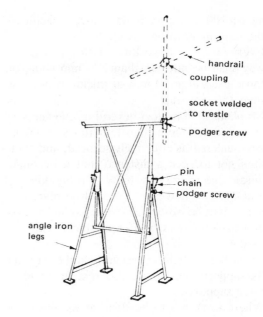

Figure 378 *Double folding trestle*

Working platforms and gangways

It is often necessary to provide an access to a platform by means of a gangway. These must be constructed so as to prevent accidents by people falling off them. They should never be too steep. If two or more boards are used, they should be braced together so that there is no uneven sagging between the boards. Precautions should also be taken to prevent accidents occurring during frosty or rainy weather. The Construction Regulations include the following requirements:

1 All working platforms and gangways shall be closely boarded, planked or plated. (Among the exceptions to this rule are occasions when open mesh metal plates are used.)
2 No gangway shall be used the slope of which exceeds 1 vertical to 1.5 horizontal.
3 Where the slope is more than 1 vertical to 4 horizontal, then stepping laths must be fixed at suitable intervals. Such laths must be the full width of the gangway except that they may

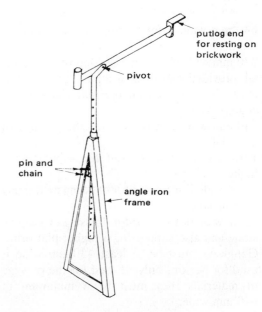

Figure 379 *Putlog trestle scaffold*

have a 100 mm space in the centre to facilitate the movement of barrows.

4   Every board in a working platform or gangway shall be not less than 200 mm wide, or those exceeding 50 mm in thickness not less than 150 mm wide.

5   No plank shall project beyond its end support by a distance more than four times its thickness, unless it is effectively secured; and even then not to such a distance that it becomes unsafe due to the possibility of it breaking.

6   Suitable bevelled pieces should be placed at the ends of boards which overlap other boards or where boards of different thicknesses are used.

7   Every board shall rest securely and evenly on its supports, and shall also rest on at least three supports.

8   Where work has to be done at the end of a wall the platform shall extend at least 610 mm beyond the end of the wall.

Widths of working platforms

Platforms must be of sufficient width. This depends on the particular use for which they are intended. For platforms from which a person is liable to fall a distance of more than 2 m the following widths shall apply:

1   640 mm wide if for footing only and not for the deposit of material.

2   870 mm wide if used for the deposit of material, provided that there is a passage way of at least 430 mm between the material and the edge.

3   640 mm wide if it is used for the passage of material.

4   1.07 m wide if it is used for supporting a higher platform.

5   1.3 m wide if it is used for dressing or roughly shaping stone.

6   1.5 m wide if it is used for dressing or shaping stone and also supporting a higher platform.

7   Gangways must be at least 430 mm wide if used for persons only. If used for the passage of materials they must be a minimum of 640 mm wide.

8   If a platform or gangway becomes slippery,

then, as soon as is reasonably practical, steps shall be taken to remedy the condition by sanding or cleaning. All platforms and gangways shall be kept free from rubbish, unnecessary obstruction or material, and any projecting nails.

Guard rails and toeboards

To prevent anyone from falling off a platform guard rails should be securely fixed on the inside of standards. Toeboards should also be secured to prevent materials from being pushed over the edge (Figure 380). The following regulations apply for any platform from which a person is liable to fall a distance of more than 2 m.

1   A guard rail shall be fixed at a height of between 900 mm and 1.15 m above the platform.

2   A toeboard of not less than 155 mm in height shall be fixed.

3   Guard rails and toeboards shall be fixed on the inside of the uprights.

4   The distance between the toeboards, or other barrier, and the guard rail shall not exceed 762 mm.

Ladders and folding step-ladders

All ladders and step-ladders must be of good construction and of adequate strength for the purpose for which they are to be used. They must be properly maintained. The Regulations include the following requirements:

1   No ladder shall be used in which there is a rung missing.

2   Every rung shall be properly fixed to the stiles or sides.

3   No ladder shall be used in which a rung depends for its support solely on nails, spikes or other similar fixing.

4   Every ladder shall have a firm and level footing.

5   A ladder shall not stand on loose bricks or other loose packing.

6   A ladder must be secured where necessary to prevent undue sagging or swaying.

7   A ladder shall be securely fixed at its upper resting place, and shall extend to a height of at least 1.15 m above the platform.

8 Ladders rising to a vertical height of more than 9.14 m shall be provided with an intermediate landing place. These must be provided with guard rails and toeboards.

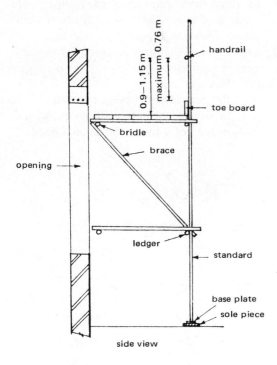

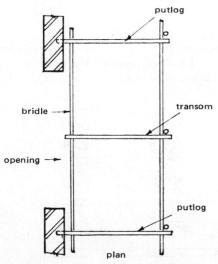

Figure 380 *A method of supporting a scaffold adjacent to an opening*

Loads on scaffolds

A scaffold must not be overloaded, and as far as possible the load must be evenly distributed and generally should not exceed 275 kg/m^2.

Any loads which are transferred on, or to a scaffold, shall be deposited without any violent shock. Materials shall not be kept upon a scaffold unless needed for working within a reasonable length of time.

Inspection of scaffolds

1 Before a scaffold is used, it must be inspected by a competent person within the immediately preceding seven days.
2 It must also be inspected if the scaffold has been subjected to adverse weather conditions which are likely to affect its stability.
3 Reports must be made in the prescribed register which shall show the following information:
   (a) The location and description of the scaffold or equipment.
   (b) The date of the inspection.
   (c) The result of this inspection. (If the scaffold is in good order then this must be stated.)
   (d) The signature of the person making the inspection.
4 These registers must be kept on site unless the works are not likely to last for more than six weeks. In this case, they may be kept at the office and the reports of the inspections must be sent there within seven days after they have been carried out by a competent person.

British Standard Specifications

The British Standards Institution also lays down certain minimum standards for scaffolding and equipment:

BS 1139 Metal scaffolding includes requirements for both steel and alloy scaffolding; types of fittings and methods of testing; steel trestle scaffolds; suspended steel scaffolds.

BS 2482 Timber scaffold boards includes

requirements for the quality of the timber; construction and methods of testing.

BS 1129 Timber ladders, steps and trestles includes requirements for all types of ladders; quality of timber; construction and methods of testing.

Scaffolding tubes and fittings

These should be of a minimum standard and may be listed as follows:

1   *Tubes* for scaffolding should be of 38 mm nominal bore, and for steel tubes, out of 8 s.w.g. (steel wire gauge) and for alloy 7 s.w.g.
2   *All fittings* should be of good quality and capable of taking a load without slipping.
3   *Putlog ends* should have an even bearing surface at least 75 mm long and 50 mm wide.
4   *Base plates* should have a level surface not less than 150 mm² in area, and be not less than 5 mm in thickness. The shank should be a loose fit inside the tube and should be not less than 50 mm long. They should also have two holes at distances of not less than 50 mm from the centre of the plate. If adjustable plates are used, these must be capable of carrying a load of not less than 6.096 tonnes f.
5   *Scaffold boards* should be 225 mm wide and 38, 50 or 75 mm thick. The minimum length of boards should be:
    (a)   2.74 m for 38 mm thickness
    (b)   3.35 m for 50 mm thickness
    (c)   3.96 m for 75 mm thickness
    with increments of 300 mm up to a maximum of 4.88 m. They should have a sawn finish and their ends should be bound with 25 mm hoop iron, extending for a minimum distance of 150 mm along each edge, and the ends so finished that injury through sharp ends is avoided.
6   *Toeboards* should be secured with toeboard clips to prevent accidental displacement.
7   *Builder's ladders* should not normally be painted, but if this is required they should be either varnished or coated with a protective treatment which neither conceals nor raises the grain of the timber.

8   *Bridles* will be used where it is not possible to support a putlog in a dependent scaffold; for example at a window or door opening, and may be erected as shown in Figure 380.
9   *Stair couplers* may be used by bolting them to scaffold tubes, if a flight of steps is required to pass from one level to another. The method of fixing the stair treads to the coupler is shown in Figures 381 and 382.
10 Two types of *spanners* are used for the erection of scaffolds:
    (a)   Box spanners,
    (b)   Podgers. These have a tapered end for tightening up bolts with an eyelet hole instead of a nut or hexagonal head.

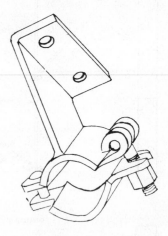

Figure 381   *Acrow Scaffold Stair Coupler*
For incorporating a stairway, complete with landings, in the body of a scaffold, thereby reducing accident risk and providing easy access to all stages

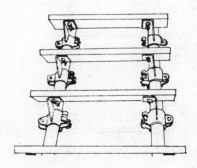

Figure 382   *The method of bolting the treads to the couplers*

Faults in scaffolding

The following is a list of some of the more common faults which may be found in scaffolds. A careful watch should be kept at all times to see that they do not occur on site.

1 Standards not truly plumb in elevation.
2 Base plates not placed underneath standards.
3 Base plates not resting upon adequate soleplates.
4 Ledgers not truly horizontal.
5 Sleeve couplers not used for jointing ledgers and not staggered.
6 Insufficient ties used (these should be placed at intervals of 3.6 m vertically and 6.1 m horizontally).
7 Excavations being carried out near scaffolds without adequate precautions being taken against possible collapse.
8 Insufficient ledger bracing being fixed.
9 Traps being left in the platform.
10 The distance between putlogs being greater than the safe span according to the thickness of boards being used.
11 Poor quality boards being used for platforms.
12 No handrails at all, or handrails placed at the wrong height.
13 Too great a space between the toeboard and the handrail.
14 Toeboards not used or improperly secured.
15 Ladders being used which:
   (a) Have rungs missing;
   (b) Are not securely tied;
   (c) Do not rise at least 1.15 m above the platform; or
   (d) Do not rest upon a firm base.
16 Untidy scaffold platforms, or gangways.
17 Insufficient warning notices being displayed when a scaffold is partially dismantled.
18 Insufficient care being taken with the erection of scaffolds when working near electric overhead cables.
19 People interfering with scaffolding without authority.
20 Craftsmen working on makeshift platforms, especially bricklayers on *hop ups*.

Work on roof areas

When work is to be done on a pitched roof, special provisions are necessary to reduce the risk of falling. On very small works it is permissible to use a secured ladder and a crawling board which must also be securely held in place – usually over the ridge of the roof.

Where substantial repair works are to be carried out a scaffold should be erected and adapted at eaves height as shown in Figure 383.

Hoisting materials

Gin wheel

This is a simple method of hoisting materials to a platform, but care must be taken when fixing the apparatus to ensure that it is securely fixed and capable of taking the load without creating too much stress on the poles or fittings. It should never be suspended from just one horizontal tube which is connected to the upright by a coupler, but always be securely braced (Figure 384). When a gin wheel is used on an independent scaffold, the supporting pole may be fixed to two standards on opposite sides of the platform. The gin wheel itself must be secured to the supporting pole by a wire lashing which should be a figure of eight, lashing at least five times round the hook. The hook must be suspended about 75–100 mm below the pole. Any spare wire on the lashing is to be used for as many frapping turns as possible to prevent the lashing from spreading.

If the gin wheel is suspended directly by its hook, this hook must have a safety catch and should be prevented from moving sideways by either a wire bond, or coupler fixed each side of it.

A coupler should also be fitted at the end of the horizontal pole to prevent the possibility of the gin wheel sliding off the pole (Figure 384).

Scaffold cranes

When this type of crane is used, it is important that the scaffolding is strengthened at the point of operation. This may be carried out by:

1 Coupling a second tube alongside the main standard, thus adding extra strength.
2 Being rigidly tied back, above the crane, with

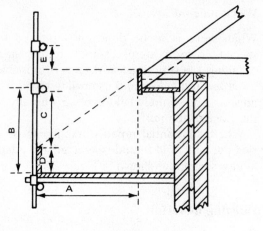

Key

A   minimum width of scaffold

B   guard rail between 0.920 and 1.15 m

C   maximum gap between toe board
and handrail 0.760 m

D   the toe board rises to the line
of the roof slope and is not less
than 0.155 m high

E   this distance does not exceed
0.440 m and the distance between the
guard rails does not exceed 0.760 m

Figure 383   *Scaffolding for working on a roof*

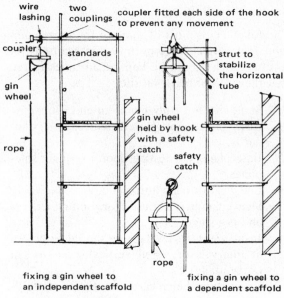

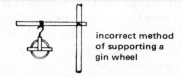

Figure 384   *Fixing a gin wheel to an independent and
dependent scaffold*

two-way ties, either to the scaffold or preferably to the building if possible.
3   Having plan bracing on the lift immediately
below the platform on which the crane stands.

A typical scaffold crane is illustrated in
Figure 385.

Hoists

Figure 386 shows two typical types of barrow
hoist. One shows a 508 kg two barrow hoist and
the other a 305 kg single barrow hoist. These
types of hoist must be fitted with the following
safety equipment:

1   Safety gates at each landing.
2   A notice on the machine stating clearly its safe
working load.

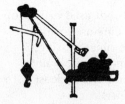

Figure 385   *150 kg scaffold crane*

3   A notice on the machine stating that no person must ride on the hoist platform.
4   A safety device to prevent the platform over-
running and jamming underneath the top of
the mast.
5   An automatic brake to prevent the platform
from falling in the event of a rope breaking.

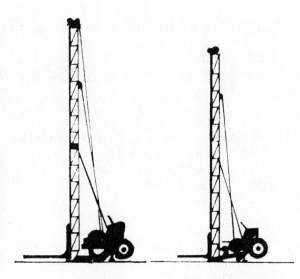

(a) two barrow diesel hoist, 508 kg capacity

(b) single barrow diesel hoist, 305 kg capacity

Figure 386 *Barrow diesels*

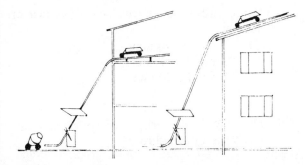

Figure 387 *A modern method of lifting materials into a building or on to a roof by means of a 'Clymall' (developed by Road Machines Ltd)*

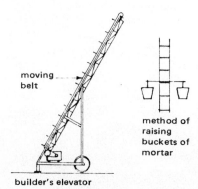

moving belt

builder's elevator

method of raising buckets of mortar

Figure 388 *Builder's elevator*

The Clymall

This has been developed by the Road Machines Company and is particularly useful for transporting materials both vertically and horizontally by a small bogie which travels on rails. This is very useful when working on a chimney stack or transporting materials to the inside of a building for alteration work or partitioning. 294 and 802 kg capacity models are available and can be used up to a height of about 10 m (Figure 387).

Builder's elevator

This is particularly useful on housing sites or low rise dwellings where an easily portable machine is needed for hoisting material to an upper level. The machine consists of a series of stops around an endless belt. Bricks are placed against the stops and raised to an upper platform. Buckets of mortar or water may be lifted two at a time by supporting them on each side of a rod placed across a stop (Figure 388).

Self-assessment questions

1 The Health and Safety at Work etc. Act is applicable to
(a) the employer
(b) the employee
(c) all persons employed on site

2 When using 38 mm planking the distance between putlogs should not exceed
(a) 1.00 m
(b) 1.50 m
(c) 2.00 m

3 Blocks may provide a secure support for a platform provided that it does not exceed
(a) 600 mm in height
(b) 700 mm in height
(c) 800 mm in height

4 Guard rails must be fitted to trestle scaffolds if they are higher than
(a) 1.50 m
(b) 2.00 m
(c) 2.50 m

5 Gangways must not be used if the slope exceeds
   (a) 1 vertical to 1.5 horizontal
   (b) 1.5 vertical to 1 horizontal
   (c) 1 vertical to 2 horizontal

6 No plank shall overlap its support by more than
   (a) four times its thickness
   (b) five times its thickness
   (c) six times its thickness

7 Platforms which are used for working also the deposit of materials shall be not less than
   (a) 640 mm wide
   (b) 870 mm wide
   (c) 1.07 m wide

8 The maximum height of a guard rail above the platform is
   (a) 900 m
   (b) 1.15 m
   (c) 1.45 m

9 The height of a toeboard must not be less than
   (a) 125 mm
   (b) 135 mm
   (c) 155 mm

10 The distance between toeboard and guard rail must not exceed
    (a) 762 mm
    (b) 812 mm
    (c) 862 mm

11 A ladder must be securely held and project above the platform at least
    (a) 1.00 m
    (b) 1.15 m
    (c) 1.45 m

12 Generally loads on a normal working platform should not exceed
    (a) 225 kg/m^2
    (b) 275 kg/m^2
    (c) 325 kg/m^2

13 Putlog ends should have a bearing surface of at least
    (a) 60 mm by 40 mm
    (b) 75 mm by 40 mm
    (c) 75 mm by 50 mm

14 Describe how works may be carried out safely on a pitched roof.

Chapter 16

Concrete

After reading this chapter you should be able to:

1 Understand the necessity for good concrete mix design and how such mix designs are obtained.

2 Understand the importance of workability of concrete.

3 Know how to carry out a slump test.

4 Understand the method of carrying out a compacting factor test.

5 Know how to carry out a Vebe test.

6 Appreciate the importance of having the correct water/cement ratio in a concrete mix and its effect upon the strength of a concrete.

7 Understand the effect of cement/aggregate ratio upon the strength of a concrete.

8 Have a sound knowledge of the grading of aggregates and how samples may be taken and tested.

9 Have a sound understanding of the characteristics of various types of aggregates.

10 Know how to prepare and test concrete cubes.

11 Have a sound understanding of the necessity for good quality control for concrete on site.

12 Appreciate the importance of good mixing and compacting of concrete.

13 Know why concrete is cured and how this may be done.

14 Appreciate the importance of accurate placing of steel in reinforced concrete.

15 Have a knowledge of the fire-resistance of concretes.

The need for concrete mix design

Concrete is one of the most versatile materials used in modern structures and will produce a material of great strength and durability provided good control is maintained through all the stages of production.

Concrete is composed of cement, fine and coarse aggregates, and water and, of course, a wide variety of ratios of mixes may be obtained from these ingredients.

Concretes are particularly affected by:

1 The wide variety of aggregates that may be

used, including gravels, non-porous stones, slags, manufactured types.
2 The surface textures of these stones.
3 The particle shapes.

Each mix of concrete has its own particular characteristics and should be designed to suit the requirements for which it is intended.

Once a particular type of concrete has been selected, it is important to maintain it throughout the series of operations, otherwise a weakness may be created in a structural member by the introduction of an inferior concrete. Constant checks are required, therefore, on the quality of the concrete mixes throughout the progress of the structure.

The elements of concrete mix design

This is the process of deciding the most economical proportions in which to combine the available aggregates, cement and water, to obtain concrete which has the required properties in both its fresh and hardened state. Hardened concrete must have, among other properties, durability and adequate compressive strength. The latter is usually taken as the criterion of quality because it is convenient to measure and lends itself to a better control of the quality of concrete as a whole.

Fresh concrete must have *workability*, which will enable it to spread easily and form a dense mass when dry and good *mixing* which will ensure even strength and a smooth surface.

Workability

Fresh concrete must be sufficiently workable so that it can be fully compacted so that its density prevents air bubbles. The factors affecting workability are:

1 Increase in the water/cement ratio (the amount of water in relation to the cement by weight).
2 Increase in the richness of the concrete mix while a constant water/cement ratio is maintained.
3 Increase in the cement/aggregate ratio.
4 Use of an aggregate of larger size combined

with a correct grading of coarse and fine aggregate.
5 Use of an aggregate with a rounded shape or with a smooth surface.
6 Reduction of the proportion of fine aggregate (subject to the limits imposed by the requirements of the surface finish).
7 The specific surface area of the aggregate (the amount of surface area of an aggregate per unit of weight). For example, a rounded aggregate will have less surface area per unit of weight than an irregular aggregate. Therefore, the more the surface area contained by an aggregate, then the more the cement necessary to cover it. If insufficient cement is used, the strength of the concrete will be reduced.

Workability may be measured by *the slump test* or *the compacting factor apparatus*.

The slump test

This has rather a limited scope, but is useful on sites where quick checks on control are necessary and it provides a comparison of workability between similar mixes. The apparatus for this test consists of a hollow frustum of a cone which has a diameter at the top of 100 mm and at the bottom of 200 mm and a vertical height of 300 mm (Figure 389). The cone is fitted with two handles on

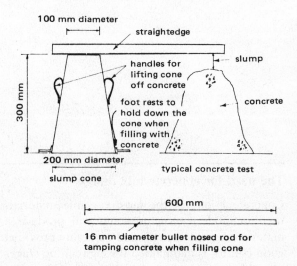

Figure 389   *Slump test*

the side for lifting and two small lugs on the bottom on which the feet are placed to prevent the cone from lifting while it is being filled.

This equipment is also available in a more elaborate design. This has the same basic conic shape which is held in a steel frame and allowed to slide freely up and down. The whole of the apparatus rests on a steel base plate (Figure 390). The tamping bar is a 16 mm diameter rod 600 mm long, with a bullet nosed end.

The slump test is carried out by placing the cone on a level surface. It is held down by placing the feet on the lugs (or, if the more elaborate equipment is used, by locking the cone into position). The cone is then filled with the concrete in four distinct layers, each layer being tamped with the rod 25 times. When the cone is filled, the top is *smoothed off* with the rod and the cone lifted, with a clean upward sweep. The cone is then placed alongside the concrete and the reduction in height may be measured by placing a straightedge or the rod across the cone and measuring the amount that the concrete has dropped in height or *slumped* (Figure 389).

The compacting factor apparatus

This is of a more precise design and tests made with it on concretes are usually carried out within a site hut or laboratory. The apparatus consists of two inverted hollow frusta of cones, one above the other, each with a hinged flap and a cylindrical container 300 mm high and 100 mm in diameter at the bottom of the apparatus (Figure 391). The method of using this apparatus:

· 1 It is placed on a level base.
2 Two laying-on trowels are placed side-by-side on the top of the bottom cylinder to prevent any concrete from inadvertently falling into it.
3 A sample of concrete is placed in the top hopper.
4 When the hopper is filled, the hinged flap is opened and the concrete is allowed to pour into the lower hopper.
5 The laying-on trowels are removed from the top of the cylinder.
6 The hinged flap on the lower hopper is

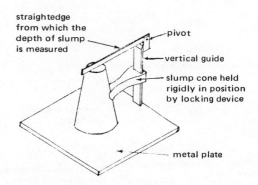

Figure 390 *Slump test apparatus*

opened and the concrete poured into the cylinder.
7 The concrete will be of greater volume than the cylinder can hold, so the surplus has to be cut off carefully from the top with the two trowels, cutting in from each side of the cylinder.
8 The cylinder is then carefully cleaned.
9 It is then weighed.
10 The mass of the cylinder itself is deducted from the total mass and the result indicates how much concrete, by mass, has filled the cylinder.

It will be easily seen that the more workable or wet the concrete the more will fall into the cylinder. If the concrete is dry, there will be a smaller amount in the cylinder because of the number of voids present. The compacting factor is calculated by:

$$\frac{\text{mass of tested sample in cylinder}}{\text{mass of fully compacted sample}}$$

Thus, the compacting factor must always be less than 1 and is usually given to two decimal points, for example 0.85, 0.90, 0.92, and so on.

The lower figures indicate dry, not-so-workable, concrete, and the higher figures indicate very workable concretes. Typical ranges would be in the region of 0.75–0.92, but it would be the aim to achieve figures in the middle of this range. Excessively dry or wet concretes would extend outside these limits, but these would only be used for special purposes which are not within the scope of this book.

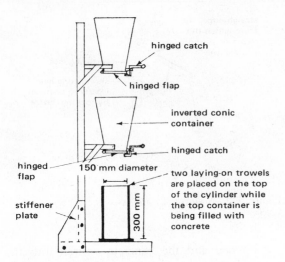

Figure 391   *Compacting factor apparatus*

hinged catch

hinged flap

inverted conic container

hinged catch

hinged flap

150 mm diameter

stiffener plate

two laying-on trowels are placed on the top of the cylinder while the top container is being filled with concrete

300 mm

The Vebe consistometer test

This is a test for measuring the workability of concrete, and is especially useful for those concretes which are so stiff that compaction by vibration is always necessary.

The test consists of two parts. Firstly a slump test is carried out inside a hollow cylinder on the top of a vibrating table (which at this stage is not switched on). The slump is usually very small or zero.

Secondly, a transparent plate which fits just inside the cylinder and which can drop vertically under its own weight is placed gently on the top of the slumped concrete. The vibrating table is then switched on and, under the action of the vibration, its own weight and the weight of the transparent plate, the concrete remoulds itself into the shape of the cylinder. As soon as the concrete is completely remoulded, as can be seen through the transparent plate, the power is switched off. The time taken in seconds for the concrete to be remoulded, known as Vebe degrees, is a measure of the workability of the concrete. A longer time indicates a lower workability.

Table 17 shows the workability of concretes for different purposes. It will be seen that the different methods of test do not necessarily correlate and the figures should be taken as approximations only.

Table 17

Purposes	Compacting factor	Slump in mm	Vebe degrees
Very high strength concrete for pre-stressed concrete sections compacted by heavy vibration	0.70–0.78	0	over 20
High strength concrete sections, paving and mass concrete compacted by vibration	0.78–0.85	0–25	7–20
Reinforced concrete sections compacted by vibration Hand compacted mass concrete	0.85–0.92	25–50	3–7
Heavily reinforced concrete sections compacted by vibration Hand compacted concrete in normally reinforced slabs, beams, columns and walls	0.92–0.95	50–100	1–3
Heavily reinforced concrete sections compacted without vibration. Work where compaction is particularly difficult Cast *in situ* piling	over 0.95	100–150	0–1

The water/cement ratio

This is the proportion of water, by weight, to the proportion of cement, by weight, that is added to a concrete mix.

(*Note:* 5 litres of water weigh 5 kg.)

Normally the strength of concrete at a given age depends upon the water/cement ratio. For example, with equal values of water/cement ratio a lean mix will give as high a strength as a richer mix *provided that they are both fully compacted*. But, of course, it must not be forgotten that the leaner mix will be more difficult to compact fully. This is illustrated in Figure 392, which shows the difference in strengths at twenty-eight days of concrete having various water/cement ratios.

When rounded aggregates are used, it is generally possible to reduce the amount of water needed in the mix because of the lack of friction caused by the aggregate when the concrete is being compacted. Therefore a low water/cement ratio, resulting in higher strengths, can be used. If angular aggregates, such as crushed stone, are required in concretes, more water must be used to achieve a good workability. Therefore the cement content must be increased if the same water/cement ratio is required.

The amount of water in a mix must be carefully controlled if high quality concretes with uniform strength are to be produced. For this reason the amount of water contained in the aggregates before they are mixed must also be carefully determined before adding the extra water required for mixing.

Types of cement

Ordinary Portland cement develops strength sufficiently rapidly for most concrete work. Its rate of hardening, however, may be accelerated by warmth and retarded by cold. Its resistance to attack by sulphates is generally low.

Rapid-hardening Portland cement does not set any faster than ordinary Portland cement but, after setting, develops strength more rapidly. Formwork can, therefore, be removed more quickly and is more useful for working in cold weather.

Sulphate-resisting Portland cement has a modified chemical composition to provide resistance to attack by sulphate solutions which are found in some soils.

Ultra-high early strength cement. This has a higher proportion of gypsum than ordinary Portland cement and its initial development of strength is much more rapid. There is, however,

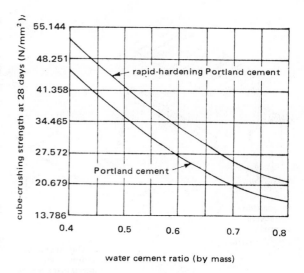

Figure 392 *Graph showing the relationship between the strength of concrete and water/cement ratios*

little increase in strength after twenty-eight days. It generates quite a lot of heat at the early stages.

Low heat Portland cement is intended for use in large masses of concrete to reduce the temperature rise during setting and thereby reduce the possibility of subsequent cracking. It develops strength more slowly than ordinary Portland cement but its final strength is not lower.

Cement/aggregate ratio

This is the weight of cement compared with the weight of aggregate in a concrete mix and will vary according to the compressive strength required in the finished concrete.

Grading of aggregates

The specific surface area of a single-sized aggregate decreases as the size increases. Thus, if the proportion of fine particles is decreased, there will be less surface area for the cement paste to coat. But, there is a limit to the reduction of a fine aggregate due to the effect on cohesion and the difficulty in filling its voids to produce a compact and even finish.

There are also certain limiting factors, which govern the *maximum* size of aggregates, such as:

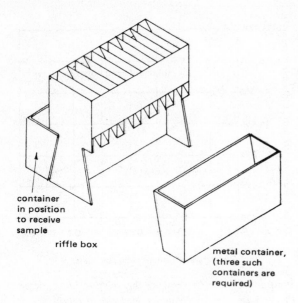

container
in position
to receive
sample

riffle box

metal container,
(three such
containers are
required)

Figure 393   *A method of quartering an aggregate*

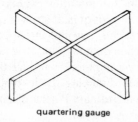

quartering gauge

Figure 394   *Quartering an aggregate with the aid of a quartering gauge*

1   The dimension of the concrete members being cast.
2   The spacing between, or the required cover to, the reinforcing bars.
3   The general economics of handling aggregates above 38 mm.

A combination of fine and coarse aggregates is, therefore, suitable for well-compacted and strong concretes. To check such a mix, the aggregates are tested for grading. A representative sample must first be taken. This is most important, otherwise the result will be incorrect. There is a tendency for the particles to become separated when they are in the stockpile, either by rain washing out fines from its outer surfaces, or

because larger stones roll down it. So the sample should be taken from several practical points in the pile at both the top and bottom. This sample is then placed on a clean floor and thoroughly mixed together. It is then *quartered* by the use of either:

A *riffle box*. This is a box with chutes sloping in alternate directions (Figure 393)
A *quartering gauge* (Figure 394)
A *shovel*

The riffle box

Three metal containers are used together with the riffle box. Two of these are placed underneath it, one on each side. The third is filled with the aggregate which has been thoroughly mixed together. The sample is poured into the top of the riffle box and separated into the two containers underneath. One of the containers is then removed and replaced by the empty one. The aggregate in the container which was removed is then poured through the riffle box, thus the sample which is collected in the replacement container is quartered. If this sample is too large for sieving purposes, the operation may be repeated by placing the empty container underneath the riffle box and pouring the quartered aggregate through the riffle box as before, and repeating until sufficient aggregate is obtained for testing.

The quartering gauge (Figure 394)

This is used by pressing it down into the heap of aggregate which has been carefully mixed together. Two of the quarters are rejected and the other two are once again thoroughly mixed together. The gauge is then pressed down into the aggregate and again two opposite quarters are rejected and the remainder mixed together. This is repeated until there is sufficient aggregate for testing purposes.

A shovel

This is used by simply pulling it across the heap of aggregate in two directions at right angles to each other. Two opposite quarters are then rejected and the remaining two are mixed together as with the quartering gauge. This operation is repeated until the required sample is obtained (Figure 395).

The quartered sample is thoroughly dried in a drying oven and allowed to cool. Then it is passed through sieves. The sizes of these, for concreting purposes, are: 75–37.5–20–10–5 mm and numbers: 2.36–1.18 mm–600 µm–300 µm–150 µm.

The amount of aggregate retained on each sieve is carefully weighed and recorded. A suitable chart for recording the grading is shown in Figures 396

and 397. The upper and lower limits of grading are also shown. The areas between these limits are called zones, and the result of the test on the sample should pass through a grading zone. If it is outside the zone on the left-hand side, the sample is too fine; if on the right-hand side, it is too coarse.

Aggregates

These should conform to the British Standard Specification 882 which, in addition to stating the grading zones for aggregates for various purposes, also lists the types of aggregates and their shapes. These include:

Rounded
Irregular
Angular
Flaky

Surface textures include:

Glassy
Smooth
Granular
Rough
Crystalline
Honeycomb or porous

Aggregates should be durable and hard. If the aggregate is soft, it is impossible to achieve a high strength concrete no matter how carefully mix design is used. The methods of testing aggregates are described in BS 812.

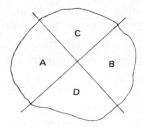

the concrete is thoroughly mixed and lines marked on the heap at right angles to each other; sections A and B are discarded and C and D are remixed and again quartered

Figure 395   *Method of quartering when using either a gauge or shovel*

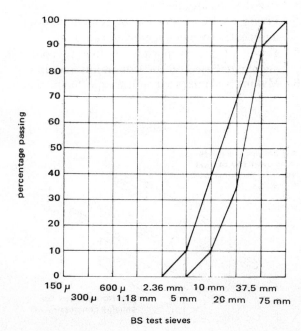

Figure 396   *BS grading limits for a nominal size of graded coarse aggregate 40 mm to 5 mm*

Crushing strength of concrete

This is usually taken as a criterion of the concrete's quality because it is a convenient property to measure. The method of tamping, compacting, curing and crushing cubes of concrete are described in BS 1881.

Cubes may be taken at either the mixer or the place of deposit. A steel mould should be used which will stand up to the compaction process. If a 150 mm cube is needed, it is made in three layers each compacted with a steel rod 25 mm square in cross-section, 375 mm long and weighing 2 kg. Each layer should be rammed *at least 35 times* or vibration may be used. The cubes should be smoothed off at the top when they are cast, and then stored under damp sacks for twenty-four hours in a place which is free from vibration, and at a temperature not lower than 10°C. The cubes should be carefully removed from the steel moulds and stored preferably in water until ready for testing within seven or twenty-eight days. If a suitable tank is not available, the cubes may be stored under wet sand or sacks for the hardening period.

Each cube is tested for strength in compression in a special testing machine, by placing it on a smooth face on the bed of the machine, and applying the load to the opposite face of the cube which must also be smooth. The rough face which was the top of the cube when it was being cast lies on its side when the cube is placed in the machine for crushing. The load is applied gradually until the cube fails, and recorded and expressed in N/mm^2 by dividing the load (in N) by 150 mm^2, which is the size of the face of the cube. (If 100 mm cubes are used, the load will be divided by 100 mm^2.) The cube strength is an indication of the strength the concrete will achieve, and also of its quality. It does not necessarily indicate the actual strength of the concrete when it is in place, since the degree of compaction in the cube may be different to that at the actual place of deposit. The process of selecting mix proportions for a site is essentially as follows:

1   Selection of the strength required.
2   Determining the degree of control. There are three classifications: 'A' is where a site has good control and observes all the correct methods to obtain a consistently high quality concrete; with 'B', control is reasonable and good concrete is mixed; with 'C' the degree of control is not so rigid and medium grades of concrete with a wider range of strengths are obtained.
3   Selection of the degree of workability required to obtain full compaction.
4   Determination of the water/cement ratio based on the strength required.
5   Selection of the aggregates. Local material is usually used for economic reasons, but, if a selection is available, trial mixes and alternative designs are made.
6   Fixing of the proportion of cement to total aggregates (cement/aggregate ratio).
7   Fixing of the proportion of fine to coarse aggregate based on the workability required.
8   Making trial mixes to confirm expected results.

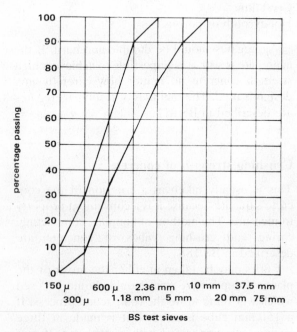

Figure 397   *BS grading limits for a Zone 2 fine aggregate*

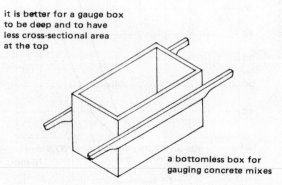

it is better for a gauge box to be deep and to have less cross-sectional area at the top

a bottomless box for gauging concrete mixes

Figure 398   *A typical gauge box for mixing concrete by volume*

These may be carried out first in a concrete laboratory, but eventually they should be done with the actual plant and materials on site. Any adjustments, if necessary, should then be made.

The average strength of the trial mix cubes should be higher than the minimum site requirements. This allows for site variations in materials and mix proportions. These averages will range from 30 per cent higher for a site with an 'A' degree of control, to 40 per cent to 50 per cent higher for a site with a 'B' degree of control, up to 60 per cent higher for a site with a 'C' degree of control.

Admixtures

Admixtures are materials added in small quantities to the concrete batch, usually with the mixing water, to modify particular properties of the plastic or hardened concrete. Although some patent products may carry out all that is claimed of them, nevertheless they may have other side effects on the properties of the concrete and it is always wise to carry out site trials to establish appropriate mix proportions and to ensure that the admixture to be used provides the required performance without adverse secondary effects.

Accelerating admixtures increases the rate of heat evolution and accelerates the setting and early strength development of concretes. They are useful when working in low temperatures or when high early strength is required.

Retarding admixtures reduce the rate of setting of concrete and are useful when working in high temperatures or when long ready-mixed hauls are unavoidable.

Plasticizing admixtures increase the workability of concrete at a given water/cement ratio. These may also be used to reduce the water content of a concrete, thereby producing an increase in strength while at the same time maintaining the same degree of workability.

Air entraining admixtures promote the formation and entrapping of very small air bubbles during mixing. This improves the workability and finishing qualities of the concrete. It may also enhance its durability particularly in relation to resistance to freezing and thawing actions under wet conditions. The air bubbles may reduce the strength of the concrete, but this may be offset by using less water in the mix because of the increase in workability which will offset the loss of strength.

Quality control

The purpose of quality control is to ensure that the materials used, and the proportions of every batch made are consistent and produce a good strong concrete economically. Control may roughly be divided into three stages:

1 *Control of materials.* Aggregates are kept in separate bays on hard standings. Cement is well stored. Constant checks are made on gradings and quality. Similar aggregates are used throughout the work.
2 *Control of batching.* If this is by volume, gauge boxes are used and allowance is made for bulking. If by weight, the correct weighing of aggregates must be ensured. Strict control must be maintained with the amount of water used in each batch. Correct mixing time must be observed.
3 *Testing and checking.* Careful checks made at frequent intervals to ensure the quality of the aggregate, water and cement.

All these controls need site supervision.

Concrete mixers

These may be of the tilt or non-tilt drum type and classified with a capital T or NT respectively. They are also identified by a number indicating the amount of wet concrete that the mixer produces. For example, a 0.1 T is a mixer with a tilting drum and will produce 0.1 m^3 at each mix.

Mixers may also have reversing drums. When revolving in one direction they will mix the concrete and will discharge it when reversed. These mixers are very efficient.

A paddle mixer is another type, consisting of a rotating drum, with revolving paddles inside it, thus ensuring efficient mixing of the ingredients. The mixing time for a concrete batch is usually from 1.5 to 2 minutes.

Batching

Before the concrete can be mixed together, the ingredients have to be measured in their correct proportions. This can be done either by volume or by weight.

In the case of the cement, the measuring is quite easy if the mix is being gauged to one bag because the volume is 0.035 m^3, or the weight is 50.8 kg. In other cases, where fractions of a bag are used, it is generally more convenient to have a gauge box made that will just hold enough cement for each mix if it is being batched by volume (Figure 398). If the batching is by weight, it may be supplied direct into the mixer from a silo holding a bulk supply of cement.

The aggregate can be measured by volume

1 By using gauge boxes with four sides and no bottom. One is normally required for the fine aggregate and another for the coarse. The aggregate is filled into the box and levelled off at the top. The box is then lifted off and the aggregate is shovelled into the hopper of the mixer. But, of course, this method requires two loading operations.
2 By dividing the hopper of the mixer into two compartments, one for the fine aggregate and the other for the coarse. The aggregate is loaded directly into the hopper to the pre-determined height and the required amount of cement is added. The whole is then raised mechanically and poured into the mixing drum.

The aggregates may be measured by weight with scales

1 By attaching scales to the mixer hopper so that the weight of the aggregates is recorded as they are shovelled into the hopper.
2 By placing a separate piece of apparatus next to the mixer consisting of two containers each connected to a scale. The fine aggregate is loaded into the first container until the required weight is reached and the coarse aggregate is similarly loaded into the opposite container. In both cases, the scales register the quantities loaded. By having two containers,

they may be loaded simultaneously, reducing the waiting time at the mixer.

The scales have an adjustable indicator on their face, which is positioned by the supervisor responsible for determining the weight of aggregates required. The operator on the mixer then loads the scales until the hand reaches the indicator on the dial.

Weigh-batching is much more accurate than volume-batching because fine aggregates usually *bulk* when they are damp, and this prevents their true volume from being measured. This is because a slight film of water around the aggregate will keep the individual stones apart, and the bulk may increase up to 25–30 per cent, particularly in fine aggregates. The finer the particles, the more will be the bulking. The amount of bulking is negligible with coarse aggregates because the film of water is thin and the stones large.

The increase in bulk makes no difference at all with weigh-batching and the increase in the weight of water would be very small. With fine aggregates, the weight of water would rarely exceed about 5 per cent and would generally be only in the region of about 3 per cent. (This may, however, create a bulking of anything up to about 30 per cent.) The degree of error is, therefore, much less as weigh-batching provides a more accurate proportioning of the aggregates. It is emphasized, however, that the amount of water contained in the aggregates must be taken into account when calculating the water/cement ratio.

Yield of concrete mixes

If the cement and aggregates are measured by volume then when they are mixed together to form the concrete mix there will be quite a reduction in the overall bulk of the ingredients to their separate volumes.

For example, if a mix consists of;

0.1 cubic metre of cement
0.2 cubic metre of fine aggregate
0.4 cubic metre of coarse aggregate
this will produce approximately 0.5 cubic metre of concrete.

Similarly, if a mix consists of:

0.15 cubic metre of cement
0.3 cubic metre of fine aggregate
0.6 cubic metre of coarse aggregate
this will produce approximately 0.7 cubic metre
of concrete.

On the other hand, when measuring the ingredients by weight, then the total weight will not vary.

For example, if a mix consists of 50 kg cement, 100 kg fine aggregate, and 200 kg coarse aggregate, this will produce 350 kg of mixed concrete.

Note: The weight of water has been disregarded in this example.

Transporting the concrete

For reasons of economy, the batch of concrete should be taken in one operation from the mixer. If only single barrowfuls are taken, the mixer does not operate efficiently. Time is, also, wasted while waiting for the barrow to return and complete the unloading of the mixer. It is, therefore, preferable to use a dumper, mechanical barrow, skip or monorail of sufficient size to empty the mixer in one discharge. The barrow run should be of a fairly even surface so that the concrete is not vibrated too much, as this is likely to cause segregation of the materials in the concrete.

Compacting the concrete

This may be carried out by using a tamping rod if the concrete is being used in a wall or column; or a tamping board if it is being laid in a slab. Unless special care is taken, it is difficult to ensure that the concrete is fully compacted when it is being done by hand. Therefore, it is much more satisfactory to use machines. These are called vibrators, and, as their name suggests, they vibrate very rapidly and settle the concrete with a high degree of compaction.

Vibrators may be of the internal type consisting of a *poker* at the end of a flexible drive and operated from either an electric, diesel or petrol motor. The poker is immersed in the concrete at intervals, and once the air bubbles cease to rise, vibration should stop at that place.

Another type of vibrator is clamped to the formwork and the vibration is operated from the outside of the concrete. This is very efficient, but the formwork must be strong enough to resist the vibration.

The electric hammer is a simple type of vibrator which is also used on the outside of the formwork. This type is not, however, quite so efficient as the two previously mentioned.

Curing the concrete

This is a most important operation espcially when producing high quality concretes. After the concrete has been placed, the surface should be kept damp so that it can achieve its maximum strength and not shrink too much due to drying out too quickly, which may result in cracks. The concrete should also be protected against the wind or sun, which will also cause surface cracking, and from cold weather which will delay the setting rate of the concrete and may affect its ultimate strength. The curing can be done by:

1 Spraying the concrete with a patent sealer. This seals the surface and traps the moisture within the concrete. These sealers are usually coloured, so that it is possible to see where the sealer has been sprayed. This ensures that the whole surface area has been coated.
2 Covering the concrete with hessian, sacking or plastic sheeting or other similar material. If hessian or sacking is used, it should be kept sprayed with water.
3 Covering the concrete with sand which is kept wet. This method, while quite satisfactory, is rather messy as the sand has to be cleared away after the concrete has been cured. This can be wasteful in both labour and materials.

The properties of concrete

In its fresh state it should:

1 Be composed of the correct proportions of fine to coarse aggregates.
2 Have the correct cement/aggregate ratio.
3 Have the water/cement ratio appropriate to the strength required.

4   Be well mixed.
5   Be fully compacted.
6   Be well cured.

In its hardened state it should:

1   Be durable.
2   Have sufficient strength.
3   Be fully compacted so that it is a dense mass.
4   Be impermeable to water.
5   Be resistant to friction.

Reinforcement

While concrete may be strong enough to resist high compressive stresses, it is comparatively weak in tension. Therefore, another material must be used to take the tensile stresses.

In the case of reinforced concrete, this is usually mild steel. The correct placing of this steel is most important, otherwise it may mean a failure in the concrete unit.

In the case of a simply supported beam where the compressive stress is at the top and the tensile stress at the bottom, the steel should be placed at the lower part of the beam (Figure 399).

In continuous beams the steel should be cranked over the supports, because the compressive and tensile stresses change (Figure 400).

In cantilever or beam slabs, the steel should be placed at the upper part of each concrete unit (Figure 401). This is because the tensile stresses are at the top of the beam or slab.

Steel may also be placed to resist shear stresses. The bars are cranked (Figure 402) or stirrups introduced at intervals along the beam.

The steel must be prevented from shearing away from the concrete, caused by the bond stress. This is done by forming hooks in the steel bars, which may be round (Figure 403), or square (Figure 404). Distributing rods are used in slabs to spread the stress from a load over a wider area and over a greater number of mild steel reinforcing bars. These rods are usually placed at right angles to the main reinforcement (Figure 405).

In columns, the reinforcement must be placed on both sides because of the tendency to bend (Figure 406). These rods are further strengthened by the use of links, which serve a purpose similar

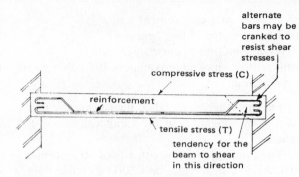

Figure 399   *A simply supported beam*

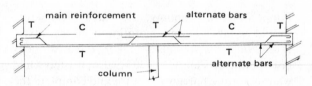

Figure 400   *A continuous beam*

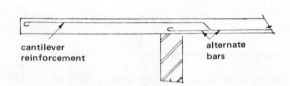

Figure 401   *A cantilevered slab*

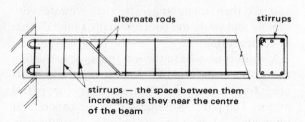

Figure 402   *The use of stirrups to resist shear stresses*

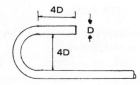

Figure 403 *Detail of a round hook for reinforcement*

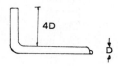

Figure 404 *Detail of a square hook for reinforcement*

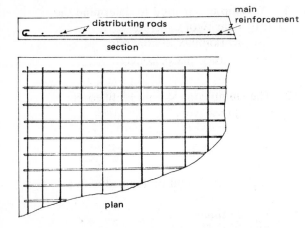

Figure 405 *A detail showing the use of distributing rods in a reinforced concrete slab*

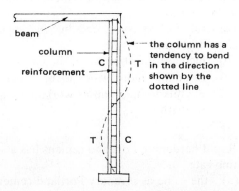

Figure 406 *Reinforcement rods should be placed on both sides of the column to prevent bending*

to the stirrups in the beams. Figure 407 shows methods of placing links in square, rectangular and circular columns.

Reinforcement bars

These must be clean, free from mill scale, rust, grease and paint, all of which would reduce the *bond* between the steel and concrete. It is also important that the steel should be placed accurately and well secured by soft iron wire. Great care should be taken to ensure that the reinforcement is not displaced during the placing and compaction of the concrete. It is important that a sufficient cover of concrete is given to the reinforcement to protect it from the weather and fire. To ensure the correct amount of cover, spacing blocks of concrete can be wired or threaded on to the steel rods, or plastic spacers can be snapped over the rod. The spacers are then placed against the formwork, and the rods held at the correct distance from it.

Fire resistance

The Building Regulations lay down certain requirements for the fire resistance of buildings.

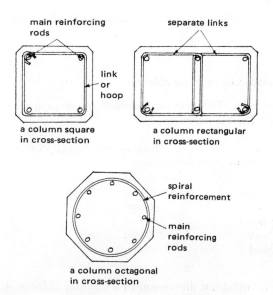

Figure 407 *Methods of reinforcing concrete columns*

Such periods of resistance range from half an hour to four hours, depending upon the size and type of structure, and the minimum thicknesses of concrete are listed in Table 18, where the minimum cover to reinforcement is 25 mm. Table 19 states the minimum dimensions of concrete columns for various fire resistance periods. Table 20 states the minimum cover required for main reinforcement for various fire resistance periods. For the purpose of fire resistance, aggregates are divided into two classes:

1 *Class 1 aggregate*. Foamed slag, pumice, blast furnace slag, pelleted fly ash, crushed brick and burnt clay products (including expanded clay), well-burnt clinker and crushed limestone.
2 *Class 2 aggregate*. Flint-gravel, granite and all crushed natural stones other than limestone.

Reinforced concrete for walls

Table 18 *Minimum concrete cover to main reinforcement of 25 mm*

Fire resistance period	Minimum thickness of concrete
4 hours	177 mm
2 hours	101 mm
1 hour	76 mm

Reinforced concrete columns

Table 19 *The minimum dimension of concrete column with finish in millimetres*

Fire resistance period	Minimum dimension of concrete column
4 hours	450 mm
2 hours	300 mm
1½ hours	250 mm
1 hour	200 mm
½ hour	150 mm

The minimum dimension of a circular column is the diameter.

Reinforced concrete beams

Table 20 *Minimum concrete cover with finish to main reinforcement in millimetres*

Fire resistance period	Minimum concrete cover to main reinforcement
4 hours	63 mm
2 hours	50 mm
1½ hours	38 mm
1 hours	25 mm
½ hours	12.7 mm

Self-assessment questions

1 A slump test is used to determine the
   (a) density of concrete
   (b) workability of concrete
   (c) correct mix of concrete

2 The slump cone should be filled in
   (a) three layers
   (b) four layers
   (c) five layers

3 Each layer should be tamped with a rod
   (a) 20 times
   (b) 25 times
   (c) 30 times

4 When using angular instead of rounded aggregates, the amount of cement should be increased to
   (a) fill the voids created by the angular aggregate
   (b) increase the strength of the concrete
   (c) to enable more water to be added to the mix to maintain its workability and strength

5 Rapid hardening Portland cement has a setting rate
   (a) the same as ordinary Portland cement
   (b) faster than ordinary Portland cement
   (c) slower than ordinary Portland cement

6   A riffle box is used to
    (a)   ensure correct proportions of aggre-
          gates in a concrete mix
    (b)   sieve aggregates
    (c)   obtain a representative sample of
          aggregate for grading.

7   Bulking of fine aggregate occurs when they
    are
    (a)   dry
    (b)   damp
    (c)   wet

8   Curing of concrete is carried out by keeping
    it
    (a)   dry
    (b)   warm
    (c)   wet

9   In a simply supported beam the main rein-
    forcement should be placed at the
    (a)   bottom
    (b)   middle
    (c)   top

10 An accelerating admixture in concrete
    (a)   helps to lay the concrete more quickly
    (b)   forms air bubbles during mixing
    (c)   speeds up the setting and early strength
          development of the concrete

Index